Raising Kain

"The adventurous life of Conrad Kain,
Canada's greatest mountaineer"

A historical novel by
Keith G. Powell

Wild Horse Creek Press

Raising Kain

*"The adventurous life of Conrad Kain,
Canada's greatest mountaineer"*

Published by
Wild Horse Creek Press
3212 - 6th Street South
Cranbrook, British Columbia V1C 6L9
Canada
250.417.4711
keithp57@gmail.com

Printed by
Rocky Mountain Printers
42 - 8th Avenue South
Cranbrook, British Columbia V1C 2K3
Canada

ISBN 978-0-9812146-2-7

This book is a work of fiction based on historical characters, events and occurrences.
Wherever possible dialogue was based on historical sources, though some
of the dialogue is based on my imagination.

Most characters appearing in this book are real, though some are
composites of several characters, while others are again
based on my imagination.

FRONT COVER PHOTO OF MOUNT ROBSON: ©iStockphoto.com/LightShow
FRONT COVER INSET PHOTO: Used by permission - V58-na66-408
Whyte Museum Archives

The Mountaineer

The sullen mountain bleak and grim
Confronts the mountaineer;
Who starts to climb with rhythmic ease,
His muscles stretched and steeled,
Up face of cliff to jagged ledge
Where lesser men would freeze
In rigid fear of life and limb;
There flings his rope with skill,
Retrieves, loops, ties and tests for strain
And clambers higher still—
To where the conquered peaks concede
His art, his fame, his will.

—By Marjorie Berglow

Published in Kinbasket Country:
The Story of Golden and the Columbia Valley

Dedication

Dedicated to my wife Linda,
my daughters Kate & Megan
and my grandsons Caleb and Grayson

Conrad Kain—Canada's greatest mountaineer.

Table of Contents

Chapter 1 ~ The Grave Robbers.. 5

Chapter 2 ~ Austria: Vienna and Nasswald—A History.................... 11

Chapter 3 ~ Meeting Amelia 23

Chapter 4 ~ The Anschluss.. 37

Chapter 5 ~ St. Eugene Hospital, Cranbrook, B.C. 43

Chapter 6 ~ The Fall on Mt. Lefroy | August 1896 49

Chapter 7 ~ Van Horne's Swiss Solution.. 55

Chapter 8 ~ A.B. Rogers and his Pass 59

Chapter 9 ~ The Building of Glacier House.. 69

Chapter 10 ~ A.O. Wheeler, Tyrant of the Rockies.............................. 75

Chapter 11 ~ Smithsonian Expedition | Summer 1911........................ 81

Chapter 12 ~ Siberia and a Return to Austria...................................... 91

Chapter 13 ~ The Mysteries and Legends of Mount Robson 101

Chapter 14 ~ The Debate 111

Chapter 15 ~ The Birth of Skiing in the Rockies 129

Chapter 16 ~ Sir Edward Whymper to the Rescue 133

Chapter 17 ~ Dear Conrad—Kain's Ladies 141

Chapter 18 ~ Albert (Mack) MacCarthy 151

Chapter 19 ~ Conrad Gets Married... 159

Chapter 20 ~ "Well, Lady, Here Is the Top" | July 1924 169

Chapter 21 ~ The Agony of Mrs. Stone... 179

Chapter 22 ~ A Kain Saves a Friend 187

Chapter 23 ~ Hetta's Pain | February 1933 191

Chapter 24 ~ Raising Kain 197

Chapter 25 ~ Death by Sleep 207

Epilogue 219

Author's Note 225

Chapter 1

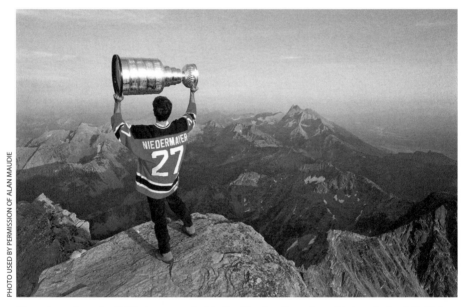

Hometown hero Scott Niedermayer hoists the Stanley Cup above his head atop Mt. Fisher, much to the chagrin of the NHL's Keeper of the Cup.

"One prominent snow-capped peak

glistened, head and shoulders above the

rest, as if standing on midnight sentinel

duty."

The Grave Robbers

"Grabe Mann, grabe! Wir müssen uns beeilen. Die Nacht ist so hell wie der Mittag."

"Dig man, dig!" shouted the tall thin man as he heard the sharp edge of the shovel scrape across something solid. "We must hurry. The night is as bright as midday."

"Ich grabe so schnell wie ich nur kann. Es würde viel schneller gehen wenn du nicht auf deiner Schaufel lehnen würdest. Höre auf mit deiner Angst vor dem Mondschein un komme runter und helf mir graben."

"I am digging as fast as I can," replied the shorter, more compact man who stood in the black rectangular hole almost to his shoulders. "This job would go a lot quicker if you quit leaning on your shovel. Now stop worrying about the moonlight and get down here and help me dig."

"Es ist leicht für dich zu sagen, bu bist ein Junggeselle. Du must dich um keine Familie sorgen, aber meine wartet auf mich. Wenn wir hier in Kanada erwischt werden, werden sie uns ins Gefängnis sperren und den Schlüssel wegwerfen."

"Fine for you to say—you are a single man," said the tall man, jumping back into the black pit. "You have no family to worry about, whereas I have a family awaiting at home. If we get caught here in Kanada, they will surely throw us in prison and toss away the key."

"Hör mal, ich wundere mich wie wir den Fund zuruck ins Rheinland schmuggeln können, bevor irgend jemand hier heraus finded wer wir sind."

"Listen, I'd be a lot more worried about how we are going to smuggle our find back to the Rhineland," said the stout fellow, "rather than someone stumbling across us out here."

"Die ganze Idee ist schlecht und das unheimliche Licht machts noch schlimmer."

"This whole idea gives me the creeps. This eerie light doesn't help."

"Wenn ich mich richtig erinnere wahrst du es der uns in diese Angelegenheit brachte. Je schneller wir hier fertig warden desto schneller können wir hier verschwinden."

"If I remember right, you were the one who volunteered us for this special assignment. The quicker we get the job done, the quicker we can be gone."

"Ich glaube, du hast recht."

"I guess you're right," said the tall man, as he furiously started to dig again.

The full moon hung over the Hughes Range of the Rocky Mountains, affectionately called the Steeples by the locals, emitting a luminescent glow and bathing everything in silvery shadows. The moonbeams shimmered across the craggy peaks, plunging down the rocky faces, oozing across the winding river below and pushing out into the valley beyond.

One prominent snow-capped peak glistened, head and shoulders above the rest, as if standing on midnight sentinel duty. The silvery rays crept down Wild Horse Creek, washed over the sleeping ghost town of Fort Steele and reflected off the tall metal lampposts that palely lit the main street of Cranbrook.

To the west, the brightly lit windows of the St. Eugene Hospital glowed in sharp contrast to the soft moonshine blanketing the entire Rocky Mountain Trench. Still farther west, the rock walls surrounding the small cemetery reflected the luminescent light away from the two sweating men though, to them, it felt as if they were working in the glare of a powerful torchlight.

"You are sure this is the right plot?" asked the short man for a second time.

"Why yes, man! We've been over and over this."

"We can't be too certain."

"That is true," replied the wispy man, stopping and pulling a crumpled piece of paper from his shirt pocket.

"What is that?"

"It is a page from the 1934 *Canadian Alpine Journal*," he said, pointing to a paragraph halfway down the page.

"What does it say? I can't read it in the dark."

"(He) was buried at Cranbrook beside his wife who predeceased him by less than a year," said the thin man, holding the page aloft to catch the light of the moon.

"Is that all?"

"No, it also says he became ill in December and, despite every care, he died after five weeks in the Cranbrook Hospital on February 2, 1934."

"That was more than five years ago."

A sharp metal-on-metal scraping sound, the kind that makes shivers run up and down your spine, drifted up from inside the ever-deepening chasm. Within another thirty minutes, the two men had completely uncovered the heavy, metal-reinforced wooden box, sprung open the lid with an edge of one of their shovels, carefully exhumed the dry, white bones and wrapped them carefully in several coarse military-grade blankets.

They slipped the mummified human skeleton into a soft-sided travel bag labelled ominously with two official-looking tags. One tag read: DO NOT TOUCH:

SCIENTIFIC SPECIMEN and the other tag, complete with a Canadian insignia, read: CLEARED FOR CUSTOMS DO NOT OPEN.

"That should keep prying eyes and nosy border guards away," smiled the more thickset of the pair, impressed at his own ability to generate such authentic-looking forgeries.

"Let's only hope!" sighed the tall man, as they started to refill the gaping hole.

Soon the nasty job was done. The two men carefully rolled back the grassed-over sod, so even the most suspicious searcher would have difficulty determining that the ground had ever been disturbed.

As they gathered up their tools and hoisted their duffel bags on their shoulders, the bright headlights of a car suddenly panned across the graveyard. The two men dove behind a large headstone and froze. Slowly the car drove around the perimeter of the rock fence and just as it appeared to be ready to leave, the bright red brake lights came on and the car ground to a halt.

"Who goes there?" shouted the city constable, climbing out of his car and peering over the rock fence into the shadowy cemetery.

Neither man dared to move. The tall, thin man could feel a cold trickle of sweat running down the back of his neck as he struggled to suppress a cough.

The constable reached back into his car and pulled out a large flashlight. He shone it back and forth across the cemetery, never quite reaching the spot where the two men lay motionless.

"Darn kids, always fooling around in the graveyard," the constable mumbled to himself as he switched off the light and climbed back into his car. He gunned the engine, took one more quick look back and forth across the rows and rows of headstones, and then cranked the steering wheel in the direction of town.

Still shaken by their close call, the two men slowly stood up and dusted the dirt and grass from their clothing. Then they cautiously worked their way to the gate and continued in the direction of downtown, sticking close to any dark shadows they could find.

But as they left, the short, stout man leaned forward and then went down on one knee. He closely examined the headstone of the grave next to the unmarked one they had just dug up.

It was exactly the woman's name they were looking for and the dates of 1884 to 1933 were correct. The stone was otherwise blank except for a bold inscription across the bottom that read . . . *At Peace.*

IN SEARCH OF A HOMETOWN HERO

Jake Renshaw stood at the edge of the rutted soccer field, spiral notebook in his hand and his camera poised to capture the action of the championship match at the All-Kootenay tournament. He was a tall, gangly young man, just two years out of journalism school, who took his assignment as sports editor of the *Cranbrook Daily Townsman* very seriously. He was a constant fixture at local hockey rinks, ball diamonds, soccer pitches, basketball courts and football fields, not to mention golf tournaments and award banquets in this small town tucked up against the Canadian Rockies in southeast British Columbia.

He was easily recognizable at whatever event he attended, as his gaunt 6'1" frame listed to one side, the result of a heavy camera bag slung over one shoulder. In addition to keeping tabs on the local sports scene, he was also an avid follower of major league football, baseball and, of course—like most Canadian boys—NHL hockey.

He had breathlessly reported all spring on the successful run for the Stanley Cup of the New Jersey Devils, captained by hometown favourite Scott Niedermayer. In the strike-shortened season of 1995 the New Jersey Devils had perfected a clampdown style of defensive hockey that had won them a lot of games. Fans around the league complained loudly that this brand of hockey may win games but it was terribly boring to watch. Despite losing some of their key players in trades and to free agency, the nucleus of the team was kept intact and the Devils once again won the coveted cup in 2000 and 2003.

With the capturing of the Stanley Cup comes the opportunity for each player to parade the championship cup through their respective hometowns, all under the watchful eye of the official NHL Keeper of the Cup.

It was Scott Niedermayer's chance to bring home the cup during the last week of August, 2000. After a brief ceremony and a photo op at the local hockey rink, Niedermayer, along with an entourage of ex-players, family and friends, high school buddies and some NHL front office personnel, paraded through town—stopping at local businesses and eventually ending up at a popular pizza restaurant. It was Scott Niedermayer's chance to bask in the glory of capturing the Holy Grail of hockey in front of his hometown fans.

As the Keeper of the Cup snacked on chicken wings and pasta, washing it down with a few pints of beer, he jawed away with the entourage of people coming and going—well-wishers, autograph seekers, fathers and sons. Suddenly Scott Niedermayer jumped up, and with the Keeper of the Cup in tow, he quickly whisked the Stanley Cup out the back door and onto a nearby waiting helicopter.

On board were the pilot, a couple of local photographers, the trembling Keeper of the Cup and, of course, Niedermayer himself. Their destination was Mt. Fisher, the 9,336-foot promontory which sits at the north end of the Steeples in the southern Rockies. Within minutes—and thanks to a bit of deft manoeuvring—the pilot dropped Scott Niedermayer off on the peak along with his precious cargo, Lord Stanley's Championship Cup.

Once aloft, the helicopter circled around the peak again and again. The two photographers on board snapped a variety of dramatic, panoramic images of the Stanley Cup hoisted high above the head of local champion Scott Niedermayer. Within thirty minutes the cup was back on the table of the local restaurant, much to the relief of the visibly shaken and somewhat airsick Keeper of the Cup.

"Reggie, Reggie, Niedermayer took the cup to the top of Mt. Fisher," shouted Jake Renshaw, as he burst into the busy newsroom of the *Cranbrook Daily Townsman.*

"What are you talking about?" grumbled Reggie Wilson, veteran newspaper reporter and general curmudgeon.

"Reggie, you won't believe it. Scott Niedermayer snuck the Stanley Cup out of the restaurant, hired a helicopter and did a photo shoot on the top of Mt. Fisher."

"Showboating. That's what I call it! Can't see Jean Beliveau or Gordie Howe ever doing that," said Wilson, seemingly unimpressed.

"It's got to be the front-page story in tomorrow's paper," said Jake excitedly. It wasn't too often one of his sports stories made the front page. "Just look at these pictures," he added.

"Talk to the editor but I can't see him bumping my court trial story off the front page for your Stanley Cup fantasy," stated Wilson emphatically. "Just showboating, I tell you. Wait until the NHL brass back in New York hears of this prank."

"Come on, Reggie. Niedermayer is the most famous person to ever come out of Cranbrook. He's a two-time Stanley Cup champion and a goodwill ambassador of the game. The NHL is not going to give him much more than a light slap on the wrist, if that."

"We'll see."

"Besides it's great publicity for the league—'Hometown boy takes Stanley Cup to new heights.' Reggie, these photos will be splashed across the sports pages of every major newspaper in the country tomorrow," said Jake, already contemplating a nice headline for tomorrow's story.

"I agree with you about Niedermayer being famous. He may be the most famous living Cranbrookite but if you venture over to the Cranbrook cemetery you will find a big granite stone marking the grave of the most famous person buried in Cranbrook," Wilson responded.

"Who's that, Colonel Sam Steele himself?" asked Jake sarcastically, as he peered over a contact sheet of photo proofs from atop Mt. Fisher.

"It wasn't Colonel James Baker either," Wilson retorted sharply.

"Then who was it?"

"He was an Austrian alpine guide who came to Canada in the early 1900s and eventually climbed just about every peak in the Canadian Rockies, including doing the first ascent of Mount Robson, the highest peak in the Rockies," Wilson smugly replied. "I believe he had over 50 or 60 first ascents."

"Who is he? Never heard of him," said Jake.

Jake's story and the accompanying dramatic photos of hometown hockey hero Scott Niedermayer standing proudly on top of Mt. Fisher did make the front page of the next day's edition of the *Cranbrook Daily Townsman*—much to Reggie Wilson's chagrin.

However, Jake Renshaw couldn't get Wilson's caustic remarks out of his brain. How could there be someone more famous than Scott Niedermayer? Someone buried in the Cranbrook cemetery and he, as sports editor of the newspaper, not know about it. From that point onward it became a personal obsession of Jake Renshaw's to piece together the story of Canada's greatest mountaineer.

Chapter 2

The Protestant parish church in Nasswald was built in 1826 by Georg Hubmer. The tower was built in 1910 with its three bells "Faith, Hope and Love." It also doubled as the local school, which Konrad Kain attended as a child.

"Georg Hubmer soon was known as the 'King of the Rax Mountain - Rax König' and in 1826 he helped build the village's first church. In addition to being a place of worship, it functioned as a school."

Austria: Vienna and Nasswald—A History

In the first week of January 1908 Vienna was inundated with an unusually deep blanket of snow. The normally picturesque streets were turned to rutted narrow paths—making it nearly impossible for trolleys or carriages to pass along. To make matters worse, once the heavy snowfall ceased, the sky turned crystal clear and the temperature plunged to a bone-chilling -20°.

A slightly built young man sporting a floppy felt hat shivered as he stepped off the train, which had arrived almost an hour late at the city's West Terminal. His worn boots and generously patched clothes went hand-in-hand with the fact that he only had a few spare kronen in his pockets. Despite receiving a small room at no charge from one of his former clients, he was unable to earn much more than three kronen a week by rustling up an odd job here and there.

Much to his chagrin, he was reduced to begging from his friends just to survive. His daily routine gravitated around English lessons in the morning, studying in the afternoon, then trudging off to one of Vienna's numerous "public kitchens" (the Viennese equivalent of a soup kitchen).

The public kitchen the young mountain guide most often frequented was located on Meldemannstrasse (Meldemann Street), only a few short blocks from the desolate-looking Mannerheim—Home for Men—that the municipal government had set up to keep "failures from becoming beggars."

As one writer noted, the Mannerheim "gave shelter to the black-sheep baron who had drunk away his last remittance, the evicted peddlar, the bit-actor too long between engagements, the free-lancer down on his luck, the day labourer always missing out on a steady job, the confused farm boy from the Alps, and the flotsam from the Empire's Balkan fringes. They were men without anchor, without family, without sustaining women. All of them were lost in the merciless glitter of the metropolis. For three kronen a week the Mannerheim gave them a last chance. That small sum provided a clean cubicle with a bed, a communal kitchen, a library with penny dreadfuls, a writing room for composing letters of application unlikely to be answered."

From his favourite chair at the end of a long oak table near the biggest window in the writing room, a tall, thin rake of a man with a ragged forelock of hair would spend most of his waking hours. With palette in one hand and paintbrush in the other, he would create dozens of vibrant watercolour postcards and portraits of the city's most famous landmarks—City Hall, the Hapsburgs' palaces, the Vienna skyline, the Danube, the Schönbrunn, the Opera House—all to be hawked on a street corner by a friend in hopes of earning a bit of extra cash.

"Konrad, take a few paintings and sell them on the street. Keep the money," the artist would say, flailing his arms wildly.

"No, I'm a mountain guide, not an art vendor," the young man would reply.

"Where did you say you were from again?"

"Nasswald, in the Rax Mountains to the west."

"So you are a famous mountain guide in the Rax?"

"Hardly famous and most certainly broke," he said with a smile and a sigh.

"Why, then, are you in Vienna?"

"I am here to learn English. I want to travel to North America and guide in the Rocky Mountains, but they will only hire guides who speak English."

"Then why are you here?"

"Simply to stay out of the cold and wait for my next language lesson. The warmth of the Mannerheim certainly beats the frigid temperature outside."

"Go take some pictures and postcards. You can sell them on the streets."

Every day the young climber would shake his head "No" and gracefully try to back out of any perceived commitment to sell the watercolours on the street corner. This would inevitably cause an eruption of emotion in the young artist. He would rise to his feet and pace about the room, his voice escalating to a fever pitch. He would launch into a harangue on morality, racial purity, the German mission, the Slav treachery, the despicable Jews, the reprehensible Jesuits and the baneful Freemasons.

He would just as suddenly stop, mop his sweat-beaded forehead, flick his stray forelock back on his head, return to his chair and stare out of the window at nothing.

"Konrad, here, you must take a painting," he said, rifling through the pile and pulling out a particularly colourful one. "Keep it for yourself if you won't sell it on the street."

"Thank you, I do like the mountain scenery. It reminds me of the Rax," he said, gently rolling up the picture and placing a soft elastic band around it.

The picture, bearing a crisp A.H. in the righthand corner, remained crumpled in the bottom of his duffel bag for many years to come.

NASSWALD, AUSTRIA

In 1853, according to the book *The Reluctant Empress: A Biography of Empress Elisabeth*, Austria was the largest state in Europe with, of course, the exception of Russia. It had roughly 40 million inhabitants, not including the country's 600,000 soldiers. Austria was a true melting pot of Europe, consisting of 8.5 million Germans, 16 million Slavs, 6 million Italians, 5 million Magyars, 2.7 million Romanians, about 1 million Jews and around 100,000 Roma (Gypsies).

The northernmost point of the far-reaching empire was Hilgersdorf in northern Bohemia (today's Czech Republic); the southernmost, Mount Ostrawiza in Dalmatia (today's Balkans); the westernmost, near Rocca d'Angera on Lake Maggiore in Lombardy (now Italy); and the farthest east, near Chilischeny in the Bukovina (now part of Russia).

Since the Revolution of 1848, when the 18-year-old Franz Joseph had ascended to the throne, the country had warmed up to the young emperor. Franz Joseph was an absolute monarch—he was commander-in-chief, and he governed without parliament or constitution, even without a prime minister. His government ministers were more advisors than decision makers.

Franz Joseph ably governed the land and its diversity by wielding the power of the army and the police, never hesitating to suppress any insurgence of democratic or nationalist forces. The old joke of the Metternich period was also applicable to the years of Franz Joseph's reign: The government of Austria was reinforced by a standing army of soldiers, a sitting army of bureaucrats, a kneeling army of priests, and a creeping army of informers.

Franz Joseph was an exceptionally good-looking, well-mannered young man, with blond hair, soft features, and a very delicate, slender build which was flattered by the close-fitting general's uniform he habitually decked himself out in. But for all his slight appearance, he was truly one of the most powerful men of his day.

Most of his subjects—some 40 million strong—made their living simply by means of agriculture, the country's primary source of income. Austria, at the time, was a world leader in the cultivation of flax and hemp and second only to France in wine growing.

Traditional occupations like farming, cattle raising, woodcutting and mining were still carried out in much the same way that they had been for centuries. Technical progress lagged far behind that of the western nations.

An uprising in Milan by Italian nationalists in 1853 saw an attack on Austrian soldiers—killing 10 and wounding 59. Some of the soldiers were skewered alive to house doors with long nails—an overt warning to the central government of the Hapsburgs in Vienna. Franz Joseph acted swiftly and viciously. The rebellion was suppressed within a few hours, 16 Italians were executed and another 48 were given long and harsh prison sentences "in irons."

At the time of the Milanese rebellion, a serious attempt was made on the life of the youthful emperor. As Franz Joseph was strolling along the Bastei—the original city fortification of Vienna—a disgruntled Hungarian journeyman tailor named Johann Libenyi approached the unsuspecting ruler and stabbed him through the neck with a dagger-like knife, seriously wounding the emperor. Even in this trying situation the brave emperor displayed his usual cool head. His first words to his mother were, "Now I am wounded along with my soldiers. I like that."

Libenyi, the attacker, was executed in short order. But his dastardly deed, coupled with the Milan revolt, was a vivid reminder to the Hapsburgs and Franz Joseph that their monarchy might not be as firmly founded as it once seemed.

Though the emperor and his monarchy lived in the luxury of their castles, the Austrian people were increasingly becoming an impoverished nation. So serious was the poverty of his subjects that Franz Joseph, on the occasion of his lavish wedding to the Duchess Elisabeth of Bavaria, gifted the people the generous sum of 200,000 guldens, with the intended purpose of "ease(ing) the existing emergency" and to "support the working class and the poor, who suffer most especially from the current rise in prices."

Some years later, the plight of the poor was made evident when Empress Elisabeth, affectionately known as Sisi by the people, welcomed a delegation from Erzgebirge. "But when the president movingly described the poverty of the mountain people, the beautiful eyes of the lovely sovereign filled with tears, and Her Majesty was hardly able to master her inner emotion," reported the local media.

The challenging economic times coupled with the social distortions of the era caused by industrialization and aggravated by the Depression after 1873, along with the threat of a growing Marxist labour movement, made for a difficult period of time.

In 1782, Georg Hubmer, a woodcutter from Gosau, Upper Austria, arrived in an area of Lower Austria that would soon be known as the village of Nasswald. Together with his brother and a number of other woodcutters, the enterprising Georg Hubmer soon had opened up a waterway from Nasswald to the thriving capital city of Vienna.

To this day, a memorial site in Nasswald gives visitors of the Hubmer Museum a glimpse into the life of the well-known Austrian pioneer and his fellow woodcutters. Georg Hubmer was also the first Protestant in the area. He helped found the local parish, which consisted of his family members, including his brother and many of his woodcutting colleagues.

Georg Hubmer soon was known as the "King of the Rax Mountain - Rax König" and in 1826 he helped build the village's first church. In addition to being a place of worship, it functioned as a school. Hubmer, rebelling against convention, installed round-arched windows in the building, something Protestants of the day were prohibited from doing. The all-powerful Catholic Church dictated that all non-Catholics were only allowed to use rectangular shapes for their church windows and never were they to have an entrance going directly to the roadside.

Defying a direct order from the emperor, the Protestant inhabitants of Nasswald, led by Georg Hubmer, remained firm and insisted, "Our windows shall remain as round as they are."

The school's wooden benches are pocked with indentations from where pupils placed their ink bottles. The first row of smaller benches was intended for the younger children, with the older, taller students taking up the rear.

On August 10, 1883, the daughter of the one of those woodcutters, who was married to a local miner, gave birth to her first son, the oldest of four children. Her name was Franziska (Fanny) Kain and the newborn baby boy's name was Konrad. He would eventually grow up to attend this simple village school from age seven to 14. The cramped quarters of the school housed more than 100 children, but it only had a single teacher, a teacher who had a deadly aim with a piece of chalk.

"Konrad Kain, pay attention to your lessons," scolded the teacher in a booming voice. "Must you always be staring out the windows at the mountains to the east?"

"Uh, what did you say?" stammered Konrad, flinching as a piece of chalk flung by the teacher caught him squarely on the side of the head.

"Konrad Kain, what is the sense of you even coming to school if you have no interest in learning what I am teaching," demanded the teacher, stalking down the aisle towards him.

"I'd rather be hiking and scrambling through the forest and mountains than sitting in this stuffy classroom," replied Konrad, his eyes watering from the sting of the chalk.

"Then come to the front of the class. Now explain your plight to the whole school, young man," said the teacher, grabbing Konrad by the scruff of the neck and hauling him before the rest of the school.

"I've got nothing to say," he mumbled, his head hanging down and his feet shuffling back and forth.

"Look, he's crying, Konrad's crying like a sissy," shouted a blond-haired heavyset boy with a squarish head and a large pimple on the side of his nose.

"I am not crying," said Konrad, rather unconvincingly.

"Then why are your eyes all red? You've even got tears running down your cheeks!" retorted the over-sized boy, leering at Konrad.

"Caught a piece of chalk on the side of my head," said Konrad in a muffled voice.

"Okay, okay. Boys, let's act civilized in the classroom," urged the teacher.

"Ah, Sir, he's just a big baby," continued the agitator.

"So tell the class what the problem is, Konrad. You don't pay attention, you haven't any interest in the subjects we are studying and you daydream all day," said the teacher.

"Can't say much more than that. Just don't like school. I'd rather be hiking out-side or cutting wood or anything but being trapped in here, especially with the likes of him here," said Konrad, shrugging, and pointing at his nemesis in the back row.

"Then, Konrad, why don't you just pack up your books and go home for the day," said the teacher. "I'll arrange for a meeting with your parents tomorrow."

"Yeah, Kain. Get lost!" his classmate hissed, as Konrad returned to his desk to gather up his books and belongings. "Why don't you just get out of here? You're stinking up the room."

Konrad struggled to keep his composure as he bent over to pick up his last text-book. As he set his books in a neat pile on his desk something inside him snapped. He whirled around and landed a punch squarely in the middle of the square-faced boy's nose. The swollen pimple on that nose burst, followed by a gush of bright red blood, and a bone-chilling howl emerged from the large boy.

He gasped, recoiled, caught his breath and then lunged back across his desk at Konrad. Soon the two boys were punching and flailing away like two tomcats in heat. Nervous girls tittered, some of the others boys cheered, whooped and hollered, and soon the entire schoolroom was bedlam.

"Boys, boys! Stop. You must stop this fighting now!" shouted the teacher, who struggled to separate them with the help of several of the older, more robust young male students.

"Konrad, you are suspended indefinitely," the teacher said in a trembling voice.

"And you too," said the teacher, pushing the bigger boy away from the fracas.

Konrad didn't hesitate for one more second. He grabbed his things and was out the door before the teacher could say another word. With his head down and his legs pumping as fast as they could, Konrad made a beeline for the forested hills and the craggy ridges of the mountains behind the school—in exactly the opposite direction of his home on the other side of the village.

"In Lower Austria, not far from Vienna, rises a little mountain called the Rax-alpe. More than 400 years ago Emperor Maximilian hunted chamois on its slopes. The inn below the Preiner wall is known to this day as the Kaiserhof and peasants still point out a spot on the cliff as the König's Schuss. Every corner of the district has its story. The village of Nasswald (lies) half hidden below the northern wall of the Rax. Far from the beaten tracks, it has remained a place of poverty, and its children more than once have gone hungry." So writes J. M. Thor-ington in his foreword to the book, *Where the Clouds Can Go.*

Konrad wandered the ridges, the cliffs and the trails of the Raxalpe for most of the day after being expelled from school. He felt comfortable and at home on the mountain. He stopped along the way to visit with a group of goatherds and they were kind enough to offer him a bite to eat. He didn't relish the idea of going home, for he knew that word had reached his mother, many hours before, concerning the brouhaha that had taken place in school. That could only mean one thing—if he was in trouble at school, he would be in trouble at home, many times over.

The Kains lived in a small—actually a tiny—house, which faced away from the core of the village in an area known locally as Hinternasswald. Located at the base of the Rax, it was difficult to imagine how a family of six could ever squeeze inside this little house. A postage stamp-sized yard was overgrown with flowers and bushes, obviously the work of someone who loved to garden but refused to acknowledge the lack of space.

As he trudged along the narrow, cobblestone streets of the Village of Nasswald, with its sharp, narrow buildings crammed together and hanging forbiddingly over the walkway, he finally turned toward Hinternasswald and sensed that something was wrong.

He knew that his father, a miner, was not well, but it was difficult for a nine-year-old boy to fully comprehend the seriousness of his father's ill health. The little alpine-style haus was dark and the blinds were pulled three-quarters shut, which struck him as odd as he pushed hard to open the heavy wooden front door.

"Shh. Konrad, where have you been?" said his mother, the strain of the situation creasing her face. "Your father has taken a turn for the worse. He may not survive."

"You mean he might die?" asked Konrad, in a state of disbelief.

"He wants to talk to you, Konrad. He has been crying out your name all day," she said, waving her arms in the direction of her bedridden husband, the other children cowering behind their flustered mother.

"Yes, mother, but what do I say?"

"Don't ask silly questions. Now go see him and then we will talk about your behaviour at school today."

"Konrad, Konrad is that you?" a weak voice seemed to trickle out of the cramped little bedroom.

"Yes, Father, it is me."

"Come here, I must speak with you."

"What is it, Father?" Konrad asked, kneeling beside the bed. He reached over and took hold of his father's bony, claw-like hand.

"Konrad, listen. The flood of things that come, and pass . . . beckon, and shine and fade away," whispered his father, his breath coming in short bursts.

Konrad felt his father's grip weaken, then he coughed weakly. His eyes fluttered and closed, and Konrad's father died without saying another word.

VIENNA

It has been written that during the grand old days of the Hapsburg dynasty, Austria was Europe's most powerful empire. Its royal court built a far-flung kingdom—the Osterreich or Eastern Kingdom—of more than 40 million people. It has also been said that this was accomplished by making love, not war—in other words, by having lots of children and marrying them into the other royal houses of Europe.

In a sense, Vienna, the glorious capital city, was like a head without a body. The city was for some 640 years the capital of the grand and widespread Hapsburg Empire. It was also the home of luminaries like Freud, Brahms, the Strausses and a dynasty of Holy Roman Emperors that rivalled the likes of Paris, London and Rome.

In Roman times, it was Vindobona, situated on the Danube River, facing down the Germanic barbarians. In the Middle Ages, Vienna was Europe's main bastion against the Ottoman Turks—a Christian breakwater of sorts—against the rising tide of Islam. It is reported that the city fended off up to 200,000 Turks in both 1529 and 1683. During this time Vienna lived in constant fear of invasion, even causing the ruling Hapsburg royal court to relocate to a safer Prague.

It is somewhat ironic that a true Viennese is not so much an Austrian, but a second-generation Hapsburg cocktail, with ancestors from the distant reaches of the old empire including Hungary, the Czech Republic, Slovakia, Poland, Slovenia, Croatia, Bosnia, Serbia, Romania and even Italy.

In 1900, Vienna's 2.2 million inhabitants made it the world's fifth-largest city (after Berlin, Paris, London and New York). The turn of the 20th century saw the rather hapless Hapsburgs clinging to power and trying to maintain unity throughout their enormous Austrian Empire. Under their influence the City of Vienna bathed itself in lavish high culture.

Vienna was home to Dr. Hofrat Erich Pistor, affectionately referred to by Konrad Kain as Dr. P. Dr. Pistor was a large, strong, somewhat bulky man. Though seemingly not suited to mountain climbing, he had a passion for the sport.

Erich Pistor first met Konrad Kain in the spring of 1904. Kain describes the meeting: "(It was) Pentecost week, with rain and mist, so that there was a bad outlook for holiday weather. But just at the right moment it changed. I was engaged by a gentleman for both days. About eight in the evening Dr. P. came to Kaiserbrunn. His first request was for a room. But unluckily it was in vain. We now went into the Weich Valley; there even the hayloft was taken. What was there to do? We must again return to Kaiserbrunn and at last secured a little room under a corner of the roof at the forester's. Naturally, if a gentleman gets a place with so much difficulty, what is to be done with a guide? For me it was, 'In the hay—if there isn't any room!'"

On the climb the next day up through the Hollenthal, Kain and the doctor scaled difficult ledges, roped and unroped, and dodged an avalanche of falling rocks, one of which smashed a bottle in Konrad's rucksack and another that glanced off Dr. Pistor's ice axe.

"Konrad, that was a close call," exclaimed Dr. Pistor, pausing to catch both his breath and his composure.

"Luckily, nothing serious occurred," replied Konrad. "We could really talk about luck."

"The way you climb it is more than good luck," said Dr. Pistor, admiring Konrad's mountaineering skills.

"Are you ready to continue on the Katzenkopf? It is after four."

"Yes, let's push on."

Just after five o'clock in the afternoon with the sun beginning to set, Konrad Kain and his client, Erich Pistor, arrived to tackle the 30-metre rock wall of the Katzenkopf.

"Konrad, don't you think it would be better if you took off your nailed boots? You might slip," shouted the doctor from the base of the wall.

"Don't be concerned, I won't fall off the Katzenkopf! I will set a secure position for you to follow."

"Should I follow now?" said the doctor, straining to see to the top of the rock wall.

"Now you can follow."

"Are you firm?"

"Like iron," Konrad shouted back down.

Within a few minutes the two climbers were on a beautiful lofty resting place. Here the provisions were taken out and quickly consumed. A bottle of Krondorfer and a cigar never tasted so good.

"Tell me, Konrad, how old are you?" asked the doctor, taking another swig of the Krondorfer.

"Twenty-one. Why do you ask?" replied Konrad.

"You climb like a man of many more years of experience."

"I left school in the spring of 1897 and I have spent most of my time endeavouring to become a mountain guide. I have climbed extensively with Daniel Innthaler—he is one of the best Austrian guides and a very good teacher."

"Innthaler. Yes, I have climbed with him myself."

"Daniel Innthaler says I will get my official mountain guiding certificate soon. I will be able to make this my full-time career. No more slaving away in the rock quarries."

"Does it pay? I mean can you make a living at guiding?"

"When I left school I could scarcely write but guiding on the Rax has taught me a lot. I've been a goatherd, cut wood like my father, worked in a stone quarry, been a poacher, but best of all I like guiding. And yes, I believe I can make a living at it. It is my dream to travel the world and guide tourists to the summits of any mountain I encounter," said Konrad, somewhat hesitantly, as if embarrassed about sharing his simple upbringing and his grandiose-sounding plans.

"You can read and write now?" asked the doctor.

"Yes, when I received my first pay and I could not figure out how much I made per day my eyebrows rose," he said. "I bought a writing pad and an account book and began to study by myself."

"That is good, but if you are to travel the world you need to learn English," said the doctor.

"Why do you say that?"

"The Kanadians are recruiting Swiss guides as we speak to escort the tourists up the great Rocky Mountains," Dr. Pistor explained, as they descended. "They not only want expert climbers, but they most of all want guides who can speak English, who can communicate with their visiting alpinists."

"The Rocky Mountains of Kanada. Daniel says they are soaring, majestic peaks; many of them never climbed before."

"That is right, Konrad! You can dream or you can reach out and grab the brass ring."

"Like on the merry-go-round?"

"Come to Vienna with me and learn English. Then your dream to climb in the Kanadian Rockies might become a reality."

"Thank you kindly for the offer. I would like to; however, I must earn some money now and obtain my guide's certificate as well," said Konrad.

"We must climb together again. I will write and request your services in the future," said Dr. Pistor, heartily shaking Konrad's hand, moments before he boarded the departing train back to Vienna.

Those couple of days in the Austrian Alps—the Kaiserbrunn, the Hollenthal and the Katzenkopf—were the beginning of a life-long client-guide relationship and friendship between Dr. Erich Pistor and Konrad Kain.

Soon Konrad was guiding Dr. Pistor and his fiancée on a regular basis as they set out to conquer some of Europe's most popular climbs—the Austrian Ennsthal, the Tyrol and the Italian Dolomites.

Within a year, Dr. Erich Pistor had made his Englishwoman fiancée his wife—a wife who shared his passion for mountaineering. It wasn't long before they contacted Konrad to have him guide them on their honeymoon excursion. The trip took Dr. Erich Pistor and his new wife on a whirlwind mountaineering tour of the Dolomites, Milan, Courmayeur, Chamonix (Mont Blanc, Aiguille de Grépon), Zermatt (the Matterhorn, Monte Rosa) and Interlaken.

The more they climbed together, the more Erich Pistor and his wife would plead with Konrad: "You must come to Vienna and learn English. There is a whole world of mountaineering that awaits you."

Chapter 3

PHOTO USED BY PERMISSION - ns22046 CPR ARCHIVES

Conrad Kain boarded the Empress of Britain in 1909 to embark on a new life and new adventures in the Canadian Rockies.

"Hundreds of people lined the dock to wave

farewell to friends and loved ones. He sadly

realized that not one of them waved to him."

Meeting Amelia

Not far from Konrad Kain's home was Gstatterboden, an area in the Austrian Alps which proved to be one of his most frequent climbing and guiding regions. The north wall of Planspitze, Innthaler Chimney, the Tamischbach Tower and Ennsthaler Hutte became some of his favourite haunts.

"The sun meant well," Kain exclaimed to a sweating group of climbers that had climbed from Gstatterboden. "One loses quite a few drops of sweat in going from the hut to the summit about midday."

"But it is a such wonderful view," replied one of the climbers as the group rested and gazed out at the surrounding peaks.

"Yes, but I do not like the looks of those black clouds to the north," said Konrad, pointing in the direction of a bank of heavy, swirling clouds.

Soon it was dark and the storm broke with a fury of lightning and thunder.

"What are we to do?" one of the climbers wailed.

"Come down here behind these overhanging rocks," shouted Konrad, beckoning the group to follow him.

"Will we be safe here?"

"Anyone who has not experienced such a storm in the mountains can scarcely imagine it," said Konrad in a quiet but reassuring voice. "But it will pass and soon the sun will return. We will continue our descent."

On his return to Gstatterboden, Konrad holed up at the local inn and impatiently waited for the swirling mass of storm clouds to pass.

The next day, he rose early with the intention of making his first ascent on the north wall of the Planspitze—an ascent he could call a "Kain" route. With caution he traversed the smooth walls, carefully picking each footfall, and soon he was back on the summit.

After a rapid descent to the Hotel Gesause, he made his way to the dining room and sat down for dinner.

"Good to see you return Konrad, so quickly," said the head waiter. "Didn't you have any clients to guide today?"

"No, the weather scared them all off. Yesterday's thunder and lightning storm quickly dampened the enthusiasm of my group of climbers, and most other groups, by the look of this empty dining room," replied Konrad, with a chuckle.

"If you look across to your left you will see two young ladies and their mother," said the waiter, pointing discreetly in their direction.

"Yes, I see them. Fine young women at that."

"It is my understanding they are seeking the services of an experienced mountain guide."

"Thank you for the tip. I will talk to them before I leave."

Konrad looked down self-consciously at his tattered attire—patched stockings, ill-fitting blue shirt, floppy broad-brimmed hat and well-worn hiking boots, with one of his toes almost protruding through the end.

"Hardly a way to make a good impression," Konrad thought to himself, as he rose to cross the room to introduce himself to the table of women.

But before he could formally introduce himself, the frail-looking mother of the two girls stood and greeted him. It was as if she was expecting his visit.

"So have you ever made such a climb as the Planspitze?" asked the mother of the two young girls.

"It would be better for you to use a rope than just an ice pick," interjected the younger of the two girls.

"That is very nice of you. Very well, I'll take a rope so that when I get to the cliff, I can use it next time," replied Konrad, taken aback by her forwardness.

"We were actually hoping to find Konrad Kain. We hear he is the finest guide in the region," stated the other older girl matter-of-factly. She looked to be eighteen or nineteen years of age.

"I have heard that myself," said Konrad, enjoying the joke and soaking up the adulation.

"Mother, I bet Konrad wouldn't need a rope to get us to the top," chimed in the younger sister.

"Oh, yes. I believe Kain would use a rope. He is a stickler for safety," replied Konrad. "I haven't seen Konrad in these parts for some days, but I can assure you that my guiding skills are on par with his."

"Okay, when will we leave?" said the mother, with an air of resignation in her voice.

"To make it to the top, I will pick you up at four o'clock tomorrow morning," said Konrad.

"Won't it still be dark?"

"Yes, the sun won't be out then; however, there will be enough early dawn light in the sky to get us off to a good start."

After several sharp raps on the door early the next morning, the mother answered, her hair still matted with sleep. She did not look like she was in any condition to go climbing or hiking.

"I did not sleep a wink. It must be the elevation," she complained.

"So the trip is off?" said Konrad, trying hard to hide his disappointment. A cancelled trip meant another day without any revenue.

"No, the girls are ready and raring to go," said the mother. "Will you still take them?"

"Yes, most certainly. I will have them back here safe and sound by dinnertime."

Konrad and the girls left the hotel shortly after four o'clock in the morning and quickly climbed the waterfall route, the Hess-Hutte and the Hochthor. Konrad soon discovered the girls had seldom been on similar mountain excursions, so he slowed his pace considerably.

"This is so exciting! Look at the view," exclaimed one of the girls.

"And look at all the alpine flowers and plants," said the older girl, as she busied herself collecting flowers.

"I must say I have hiked these paths many times, but I have never seen or noticed all the flowers you have," said Konrad, kneeling down close to the older sister to admire her botanical discoveries. After several hours on the trail the girls' energy began to flag.

"When will we stop for lunch?" they asked, as their pace ground to a virtual standstill.

"Another thirty minutes and we will take a break," replied Konrad.

With the bluest of skies above them, and a mountain torrent rushing through the rocks close to them, the three hikers finally stopped for lunch at a small, lush alpine meadow. While they unpacked their sandwiches, unwrapped cheese and generous chunks of chocolate and twisted open a thermos of tea, another group of climbers clamoured over the rocky terrain from the west.

"Yo, Kain. It is good to see you. How is your climb?" a young man shouted from the distance, following closely in the footsteps of his guide, Zettelmaier.

"May we join you for lunch, Konrad?" added the young man.

The ruse was up!

"You are Konrad Kain?" said the two girls in unison, turning to look at their guide with wide-eyed amazement and admiration.

"Yes, yes, I am," he stammered, now feeling somewhat silly about not owning up to it in the first place.

"Wait until we tell mother," one of the girls giggled. "I am sure she would have readied herself and came along, if she had only known we would be hiking with Konrad Kain."

"Finish up your lunch. We must be on our way if we are to make it to the summit and back again before dinner," Konrad urged, his face flushing with embarrassment.

The group of three bade the Zettelmaier hikers farewell. Once on the summit, they lingered only long enough to take in the spectacular view. They soon headed back down the Johnsbach and caught a carriage back to Gstatterboden.

"Mama, Mama. We climbed to the top with Konrad Kain," shouted the girls as they burst into the hotel's lobby.

"What are you talking about?" asked their mother, looking around as if confused.

"The guide you hired was Konrad Kain," they gushed.

Both girls and their mother were highly contented with the excursion. As they sat down for dinner—with Konrad seated somewhat uneasily across from them—they all enjoyed a hearty laugh over his hesitation to identify himself.

"Next time you need a mountain guide, be careful you are hiring the real Konrad Kain," he said, joining in their mirth.

The older of the two girls was tall, blonde and had the most bubbly of personalities.

After dinner, when the younger sister and her mother had left early for bed, the older sister remained behind to visit. Konrad was more than a bit smitten by her.

"Konrad, you must promise to keep in touch with me. Today was the best day of my life," she said cheerfully as she rose to return to her room.

"I plan to go to Vienna and learn English in the near future. It is my hope to travel the world and climb as many peaks as I can," he said.

"No matter where you go, Konrad, you must promise to write me. You must stay in touch, okay?" she pleaded, squeezing his hand softly and reaching over to peck him gently on the cheek. Then she quickly wheeled about and ran off down the long hallway which led to a steep flight of stairs to their loft.

It was his first meeting with Amelia Malek of Reichenau. It would not be his last. Amelia Malek was destined to become one of Konrad's closest lifelong friends.

A LETTER TO AMELIA

It was such a pleasure to guide you and your sister through the Alps. I once again returned to Gstatterboden last week to guide another party. The guide Zettelmaier informed me that a tourist had fallen to his death on the mountain. The fallen tourist was on my mind but the lust for climbing overcame all this, and I must admit that ambition had something to do with it as well.

When I was 30 to 40 metres up the wall I saw a piece of red paper, and another bit a little further along, and so the way was easy for me to find. From the start to the top I took two and a quarter hours. I rested, ate a little lunch and looked over the Hochthor to see whether I could discover anyone in the search for the unlucky tourist. But there was nothing to be seen or heard.

When I came to the high scree slope I noticed a black object; I thought it must be the unfortunate man, but it was only a dark bit of rock. A few steps farther along I found a hat, a few yards further a certificate of guarantee for a watch, and a tourist card of the "Naturfreunden" with the name of Franz Hahn. A little way along I saw still another paper, and I laid on my stomach to reach it. As I supported myself on my hands I saw to my right blood mixed with marrow and hair on a pointed stone.

At heart I was so afraid! I remained scarcely five minutes on the peak of the Hochthor and hurried down to the hut. When I arrived at the hut some people were assembled, and in their midst lay the dead tourist on a litter. It was Franz Hahn.

This kind of incident can only make the locals scoff ever so more at us for climbing. They often hurl nasty remarks in my direction: "I would like to know what they have lost up there," or "Such idiots ought to fall."

I mention this only because it was Franz Hahn we met with the guide Zettelmaier at the alpine meadow last week. It was Franz who blew my cover and revealed to you my true identity. I knew him well from my excursions on the Rax.

At about half past twelve the mourners of the unfortunate tourist Hahn arrived. There were only six: his brother, four friends and the tourist who had been with him at the time of the accident. His mother could not give him her last attendance, for she was a poor laundress and could not secure the money for the journey. It was indeed a sad case. Poor Hahn was carried from the vault to the church and then to his last resting place. Representing the "Naturfreunden" was a gentleman from Vienna who made a moving address at the grave. It was quite noticeable how it went to their hearts. I stood behind a gravestone and my tears ran down on the ground. I could not control myself. I cannot describe its true meaning to me. Hahn's brother said, among other things, "that rest may be granted him in the beautifully situated cemetery, as he was through and through a friend of nature and now had found his death in nature."

Amelia, of such men one can really say he is a "Friend of Nature." Yes, only those, who like poor Hahn, whom they have buried today, laying out his hard earned kronen in youth for Nature, and finding his joy in the mountains; only such, in the true sense of the words, can be called friends of nature. This is what I admired of you Amelia, your love of alpine flowers and plants. You, too, are truly a friend of nature.

I have received an invitation to take part in the course for guides to be held at Villach. We will have classes every day from nine to twelve and from one until four o'clock. The following things will be taught: map-reading, natural history, first-aid and the techniques of mountaineering. Mr. Aichinger, a most experienced climber, will instruct us in map-reading and technique. During the second week we will make an excursion to Tarvis under his leadership, and from there to Raibl and the Predil Pass to practise map-reading.

I hope this letter finds you well. I will write again after my course and tell of my success or failure.

With the warmest regards to you, your sister and your mother,

Konrad

In fall of 1907 Doctor Pistor wrote another long letter to Konrad, who had aspirations to learn a foreign language (English) and spend the winter in England. However, Doctor Pistor informed him that he was unable to find anything suitable for him in the British Isles but suggested he come to the Austrian capital.

He pleaded again, "Come to Vienna. My wife will give you free lessons in English and we will furnish the books. Mr. B., father of the young woman whom you have often guided, will furnish 20 kronen monthly, and Mr. G. will do the rest. Consider it well and let me know."

Konrad arrived in Vienna late in the year on December 8th. He visited his patrons and thanked them each for their kindness. Another doctor whom he had once guided offered him a room at no charge.

However, Konrad was uneasy with these arrangements, feeling that he was taking advantage of his client friends: "So everything went well, although it gave me no pleasant sensation to be kept by friends and acquaintances. But my few kronen were insufficient for a stay and the many expenses in the city."

So out of desperation, for the second time in his life, Konrad decided to go poaching once more: "I laid aside my resolutions, borrowed a rifle and tried my luck in the forest. But it was no use, for I didn't get a big buck with a fine beard. Nothing, nothing at all."

In the first week of 1908, Konrad began his studies. He started out with the same books and pictures that a six-year-old English boy receives on the first day of school. The first lesson was: the pencil, the book, the paper—everything seemed so difficult. The words were harder, there were words he could not sound out and words he could not even hope to pronounce like perceive, amphibion, quadruped, respiration and pleasure. Seemingly most difficult of all was the English article "the."

Though Konrad could see little progress in his learning English, his teacher, Erich Pistor's wife, seemed quite content with his advancement.

Yet to heap insult upon injury, his meager funds were quickly running out. Soon his money was gone and he was forced to return to his client friends to again ask for assistance. Konrad, much to his displeasure, was once more reduced to begging. He pawned off his watch, but could only scratch together a few kronen to buy it back, and within days he was forced to pawn it once again. To add to his helplessness and poverty, Konrad was overcome with homesickness and a strong desire to escape back to the mountains of Nasswald.

"Konrad, you must not give up," said Amelia, upon her arrival in Vienna, on a brief afternoon stopover. She could sense his frustration and despair.

"I know, I know, but it is so difficult to even survive in this city. I am reduced to begging from my friends," he complained, glancing around the small coffee house, hoping no one would overhear him.

"Konrad, Doctor Pistor is right, you need to learn English if you want to succeed as a guide in a foreign country," she said.

"Yes, it is true."

"You can always repay your friends once you obtain gainful employment as a guide," she added.

"Amelia, you have a power over me. I must learn to trust my fate to you," he replied.

"Oh Konrad, don't be silly. It is just common sense. Things in Austria are difficult and you have told me, more opportunities exist in other countries, right?"

"Your kindly words give me courage, and revive me to endure these unhappy days in Vienna."

"Konrad, my stay here is brief, and I promised to meet my mother and sister at the train station in an hour. I must be on my way," Amelia said, as she stood to leave.

"Are you sure you cannot stay longer?"

"No, we must be back home by tomorrow. Remember, Konrad you must promise to continue to write," she said, leaning over and giving Konrad a warm embrace.

"Yes, I will, and I must accompany you to the train station and see you off."

Konrad later confided in Doctor Pistor: "I do not know whether I shall ever have so much respect for anyone on earth—man or woman—as for this girl. And I know that she was not only kind to me but to everyone. She made a good impression everywhere, and was much loved in the places where she spent her summer vacations. I cannot thank her in words for all the good she did me. But I will hold her memory all my life. Thus I made the discovery what a woman can do for a man if she be kindhearted and upright."

At the end of February 1909, Konrad received news that bouyed his spirits. He received an invitation to take part in the course for guides held at nearby Villach. On his arrival he found 12 other guides there slated to take the same course. He only knew one of them, a Josef Stocker of Sexten—a guide he had met during the preceding summer at Dreizinnenhutte. Staying at the Hotel Lamm, Konrad and the other guides soon felt at home. Best of all, in addition to their food they each received a litre and a half of beer each day.

Konrad describes the experience in a letter back to Doctor Pistor . . .

"We had classes every day from nine to twelve and from one until four o'clock. The following things were taught: map-reading, natural history, first-aid and the technique of mountaineering. Mr. Aichinger, a most experienced climber, instructed us in map-reading and technique. During the second week we made an excursion to Tarvis under his leadership, and from there to Raibl and the Predil Pass to practise map-reading . . . On March 8th there were ski races and jumping. Examinations were held on March 15th. Several members of Section Villach were present, as well as some of the officers. The central committee of the German-Austrian Alpine Club was represented by Mr. Muller of Munich. My examination questions were as follows: Can you tell us from what place one makes the Katzekopf climb? To what river system do the streams of the Rax belong? Then I had to tell something about the origin of limestone and something on atmospheric pressure. The examining physician presented the question as to what I should do with a person dug out of an avalanche shortly after the accident. How does one give artificial respiration? Knee bandages? How one could make litter from articles of clothing, rope and ice axes? The following questions concerning foreign districts were given: How high is Mont Blanc? From whence does one ascend the Matterhorn? None of these questions were difficult for me. I passed the examination in the First Group. That evening we had supper and a dance with Section Villach. There were some speeches made, and I presented our thanks to the Alpine Club. In closing, could you now write to the CPR in Kanada and request that I might guide for them."

Doctor Pistor was quick to follow up on Konrad's request and soon drafted a letter to the Canadian Pacific Railway seeking a position for his friend as a mountain guide. He gave Konrad a glowing report and the highest of recommendations in his letter.

"Doctor Pistor, a letter from the Canadian Pacific Railway arrived today," shouted Konrad, as he burst into the doctor's office.

"Well, what does it say?" asked the doctor.

"I haven't opened it yet. Besides, it's in English. Will you read it for me?"

"Konrad, what is the sense of you taking English lessons if you want me to read your letters?" the doctor replied.

"Okay, okay. I'll read it myself," he said, picking up a long, thin silver letter opener from the doctor's desk and slitting the letter open in one fluid motion.

Immediately, his face fell.

"Well, what does it say?"

"Nothing but disillusionment and disappointment," Konrad exclaimed. "The representative of the railway says it is too late in the year and that the current Swiss guides have already been engaged and that there is no place vacant."

"Let me see that letter," said the doctor, reaching up to take it away from the young climbing guide. He quickly scanned through the tersely written letter.

"Konrad, not all is lost," said the doctor.

"What do you mean, I can read NO!"

"Yes, but the railway official states at the end of the letter that the Alpine Club of Canada might need a guide. True, it's a long shot, but I think it's worth a try, don't you?" said the doctor, doing his best to revive the young man's sagging spirits.

"Will you write the same kind of recommendation to the Alpine Club?"

"Yes, I'll sent it off before the day's end," said the doctor.

Doctor Pistor, who was on the Board of Trade of Vienna, now wrote to the president of the Alpine Club of Canada, stating: "Konrad Kain is a fine fellow. With ladies he is as gentle as a lamb, but with men he is like a lion." After several letters back and forth, Konrad Kain was finally accepted as a guide for the newly formed mountaineering club. The accepting letter stipulated that his employment was only for the summer months. He was guaranteed two dollars per day, two dollars for each mountain excursion, and board and lodging was free. Travel expenses were promised. Konrad was elated.

The only obstacle was the fact that he did not have the money to pay his passage to Canada. He approached his aged grandfather, who didn't really give him a straight answer, but just expressed amazement that his grandson wanted to go so far away, saying that it was not really necessary for him to go to America, as he had already seen half the world! A grandfatherly way of saying no.

As fate would have it, Konrad, who had pretty much given up on the idea of going to Canada, happened to come across a former client and friend, a Mr. A.G. (Albert Gerngross), who inquired about his North American journey. When the man heard that he lacked the money to go abroad, he promptly said, "If there is no other way, then I can help you. Why didn't you come to me when you knew that I was a good friend?"

That evening he returned to tell his grandfather the good news about his reversal of fortunes. His grandfather was not pleased and said, "A sea voyage is really most unsafe! If a strong wind comes up and throws the vessel topsy-turvy, then it's all over! And you can't swim a bit—no, my boy, there's nothing to it!"

It was hard for Konrad to see the dear old man so concerned about him. It broke his heart to see his grandfather weep the day he finally took leave. The last evening at home in Nasswald was a melancholy one for him: "I packed up my things, the younger children gathered about me, my mother was serious and contemplative. These were sad hours. Next morning I gave my weeping mother a kiss of farewell, comforting her with words that I would certainly come home again, perhaps in a couple of years. Once more I gazed back at the limestone walls, then went on."

Konrad enjoyed a brief stopover in London, England. He walked to the Houses of Parliament, strolled along the Strand, dined on English fare (he quickly agreed with the saying, "The food is tasteless and the beer is no good . . . that's why the English are as thin as a lath and built like a fiddle bow"), got lost on the Underground, needed the kind assistance of an Englishman to find his way back to the Hotel Cecil, and summed it all up by saying: "It is fine to have seen London, but for a mountain man it would be difficult or impossible to remain here."

After stowing away his luggage in his dingy third-class room buried deep in the hold of the steamliner, Konrad made his way back to one of the ship's outer decks. Hundreds of people lined the dock to wave farewell to friends and loved ones. He sadly realized that not one of them waved to him. As the sight of Liverpool faded in the distance, he thought of the craggy peaks of his beloved Raxalpe mountains in Austria. He thought of his crying mother, his weeping grandfather, his bewildered brothers and sisters, and he thought of his father's dying words, "The flood of things that come, and pass . . . beckon, and shine and fade away," But most of all he thought of Amelia.

EN ROUTE TO CANADA

The Empress of Britain was one of the flagships of the Canadian Pacific line. It was launched with much fanfare in 1906. She was 570 feet long and 65.7 feet wide. She could hold 310 first-class passengers, 500 second-class passengers, 500 third-class and 270 in steerage. Top speed was 19.8 knots which meant the Empress of Britain could cross the Atlantic Ocean in six days at full speed in good weather.

It was somewhat of an unsettling adventure for Konrad Kain to be stowed away in the cramped quarters of third-class. Though there was good food aboard, the many stormy seas caused a great deal of seasickness. After tossing and lurching across the Atlantic, the weary, motion-sick travellers finally got a glimpse of their new homeland.

A shout of excitement echoed over the boat late one afternoon as Konrad stood on an upper deck smoking his pipe and enjoying the brisk air. After many dreary days on the grey Atlantic, Newfoundland appeared on the horizon. This prompted the spontaneous outburst from the passengers. It was a welcome reminder to the passengers that their journey on the choppy sea would soon end.

However, unbeknownst to most passengers, this was not their first glimpse of

Canada, for Newfoundland would not be a part of Canada for many years to come. Skirting past Newfoundland, the Empress of Britain steamed past Nova Scotia and Prince Edward Island and on up through the Gulf of St. Lawrence. Despite the excitement of seeing dry land once again, it would be a few more days before the travellers would actually feel terra firma beneath their feet. Konrad, a man of mountains, of solid granite slabs, yearned to be back on solid ground.

"Look, look! It is a great big white fish," a young female passenger screamed through the howling wind, as she pointed over the starboard side of the ship.

There was a mad scramble of passengers to the ship's railing, all straining to look at the sea creature below.

"Belugas, a pod of beluga whales. They are the white whale of the St. Lawrence," said Konrad, tapping his pipe on the shiny steel railing.

"Are they dangerous?" asked the young woman.

"No," he laughed. "Whales, unlike sharks, are harmless. It's grizzly bears I am worried about when I reach the Rocky Mountains."

"Why would you go to mountains if there are grizzly bears there?" she asked, with a questioning look.

"I am an Austrian mountain guide. It is what I do for a living—I climb mountains and guide tourists to the top. Grizzly bears or not."

"You must be a brave man!"

"No, not brave, just stubborn and some say a little crazy."

Entering the Gulf of St. Lawrence, Konrad and the other thousand-plus passengers and crew onboard left the open ocean behind them. They collectively seemed to enjoy the relative security of once again having land on both sides. As the Empress of Britain slowly steamed up the St. Lawrence, passengers and staff alike began to scurry about to get ready for the ship's first stop, the Grosse Ile quarantine station. Konrad and everyone on board knew that their journey could be severely delayed if disease or sickness was discovered. It was important to present the immigration doctors with a picture of good health and cleanliness for both passengers and ship.

Finally, on June 11th, 1909, the ship docked in the harbour on the mighty St. Lawrence River at Quebec City, Quebec. The passengers were hustled off the boat and bustled onto the economy-class section of a waiting CPR train, which would take them further west on their Canadian journey. Mr. Arthur O. Wheeler, president of the Alpine Club of Canada, had sent a letter to dock officials with the specific request that they assist Konrad Kain. Wheeler presumed that Konrad knew little or no English at all.

The trans-continental train trip was as uncomfortable as it was dirty. When the windows were opened for fresh air, the steam and soot from the engine would blow into the passenger cars. As the train made many stops to take on more coal and water, vendors would board the train selling refreshments. This gave the weary travellers an opportunity to stretch their legs, but most didn't venture too far from the trains for fear of getting lost in this vast new land.

A LETTER TO AMELIA

We have finally arrived in Canada. It is truly a country too vast to describe or even imagine. About eight o'clock the train started off for the Wild West. The trains go perceptibly faster than in Europe. The noise is terrific. More bells than whistles and I have noticed, as well as often heard, that in the beginning it makes one very nervous. There are special cars for immigrants, practically furnished, as they must be on account of the long distances that one travels.

There are seats for groups of four persons, with a demountable table in the middle. Then there is a bed, a shelf to be pulled down and used for two people, and for the other two the seat is used. Good drinking water is at hand and, in the larger stations, ice is put in. There is a good stove in every car on which one can cook little things. The employees of the Canadian Pacific are very kindly and it does not at all agree with what I have heard of foreigners being handled like cattle. But it is true, all right, that in Austria outsiders are treated like animals—I believe you will agree.

On the first few days en route from Quebec to Winnipeg one doesn't see much of fertile Canada. Nothing but bushes and rocks and for half a day at a time there is not a house or human habitation. Before reaching Winnipeg, I hear it becomes more interesting, especially if one goes to Lake Winnipeg. Winnipeg is a large city and, for a long time, was the point of departure for the West. It is said that 18 languages are spoken here. We had three hours' stop in this city. I met several Germans.

The prairie begins at Winnipeg. As far as the eye can see there are nothing but fields, all the way through Manitoba. It is said to be the best province for wheat growing. The region was too flat for me and the broad plain hurt my eyes.

Farther along, in the province of Saskatchewan, I noticed that nearly everyone had a piece of brushwood in his hand and was beating about with it. I soon discovered why. Here begin those awful, annoying mosquitoes, of which naturally no land agent in Europe informs a person!

On the afternoon of June 16th I arrived in Calgary, where the Canadian Alpine Club has its headquarters. I gave my sack into the charge of the checkroom and went into town. First to a barber, who was also a German. He told me where to go. But I didn't find the avenue, and went into the post office, where the Club was located. A gentleman of friendly countenance advanced toward me. "You are Conrad Kain!" he said. "Yes, and you are Mr. Wheeler!" "No, the secretary." The president was not at home. Mr. Mitchell conducted me to the Queen's Hotel, where he introduced me and told them, on account of my poor English, to look after me.

Calgary is a sprouting city in western Alberta. All nationalities are to be found there, and Germans are well represented. I saw a Chinaman for the first time. Near the city there are even Indians—Stoneys. "Calgary" is an Indian word mean-ing "slow flowing water." The city is situated in the foothills, outliers of the Rockies. I looked at the snow-covered peak with longing! I will write again once I meet Mr. Wheeler and make my way to the mountains.

With the warmest regards,

Konrad Kain

Chapter 4

The Anschluss of 1938 saw the German army flood into Austria and seize control of the country. Here crowds of Austrians cheer as the Germans parade through Vienna.

"Without firing a single shot…the Fuehrer

had added seven million subjects to the

Reich, and gained a strategic position in

central Europe."

The Anschluss

GERMANY | JANUARY 30, 1933

Shortly before noon, a long shiny Mercedes-Benz disgorged a thin man with a Charlie Chaplin mustache at the steps of the German Chancellery. This lean-framed man, who had been a down-and-out tramp in Vienna in his youth, an unknown soldier of desperation in World War I, a derelict in Munich in the grim postwar days, and a somewhat comical leader of the famous Beer Hall Putsch, was not even German but rather Austrian. He was forty-three years old and had just been administered the oath as Chancellor of the German Reich.

Tens of thousands of storm troopers marched outside the open windows of the Chancellery, their high-polished jackboots filling the crisp air with a cacophony of rhythm on the pavement. The new Chancellor gazed out of the open window, beside himself with excitement and joy, dancing up and down, his arms continually jerking up in salute, smiling and laughing until his eyes were once again full of tears.

The Reich was born and its leader, its Fuehrer, Adolf Hitler, boasted it would endure for a thousand years—in the vernacular of the times it was referred to as the "Thousand-Year Reich."

AUSTRIA | FEBRUARY 12, 1938

Austrian Chancellor Kurt von Schuschnigg, forty-one years old, found himself alone with the German dictator in the spacious, second-floor study of his expansive villa. Hitler was wearing the brown tunic of a storm trooper, with smartly creased trousers and a sharp, peaked military hat.

The villa's grand picture windows looked upon the stately, snow-capped Alps and on Austria, the birthplace of both men. Schuschnigg, a man of impeccable Old World Austrian manners, offered a friendly but formal greeting.

Both men now gazed silently towards the mountain scenery, enhanced by a clear frosty winter morning and bright sunshine. Thin plumes of smoke rose from the chimneys of distant farmhouses.

"Magnificent view, wouldn't you say, Adolf?" said the Austrian Chancellor.

"Yes, reminds me of my youth growing up around Linz," replied the Fuehrer, casting his beady eyes back and forth across the mountainous panorama.

"Especially beautiful on a fine day like this—makes you proud to be an Austrian," added Schuschnigg.

"We did not gather here to speak of the fine weather," said Hitler curtly.

"Pardon me, I was only making small talk," said a somewhat rattled Schuschnigg.

"You have done everything to avoid a friendly policy. The whole history of Austria is just one uninterrupted act of high treason," Hitler fumed, the tone of the conversation suddenly shifting. "That was so in the past and it is no better today. This historical paradox must now reach its long-overdue end. And I can tell you right now, Herr Schuschnigg, that I am absolutely determined to make an end of all this."

"But how and why?" stammered the Austrian Chancellor.

"The German Reich is one of the great powers, and nobody will raise his voice if it settles Austria's border problems," screamed Hitler, sweat popping up on his brow.

"Border problems? What borders?" asked Schuschnigg, taken aback at Hitler's rancorous outburst. "Austria's contribution in this respect is considerable, wouldn't you say?"

"Absolutely zero."

"I beg to differ with you."

"I am telling you, absolutely zero."

"Zero? You must be joking!"

"I am telling you, absolutely zero."

"Why do you say this?"

"Every national idea was sabotaged by Austria throughout history; and indeed all this sabotage was the chief activity of the Hapsburgs and the Catholic Church," shouted Hitler, his high-pitched voice cracking.

"All the same, many an Austrian contribution cannot possibly be separated from the general picture of German culture. Take for instance a man like Beethoven," Schuschnigg pointed out in a slightly shaky voice.

"Oh, Beethoven? Let me tell you that Beethoven came from the lower Rhineland," Hitler roared, spittle flecking the face of the Austrian Chancellor.

"Yet Austria was the country of his choice, as it was for so many others. Like the men who climb our Alps and leave their legacy on our peaks," Schuschnigg shot back.

"That's as may be. I am telling you once more that things cannot go on in this way," said Hitler, softening his tone somewhat.

"What are you proposing?" asked Schuschnigg.

"The Austrian Alps, they are beautiful," Hitler said, choosing to ignore the question. "Climbers you say? When I stayed at the Mannerheim in Vienna, there was a young climber everyone seemed to love."

"There are many such climbers in Austria."

"No, this climber was from a poor family like my own. He told me he came from the Rax mountains. Kain was his name, Konrad Kain," said Hitler. "Chancellor, you must find this man and bring him back home."

"Yes. Kain you say? I believe he immigrated to Kanada many years ago. He's never been back to Austria, as far as I know."

"We must bring him back—now!" shouted Hitler, his voice again rising.

"I have heard rumours he may not even be alive," said the Austrian Chancellor.

"Bring him back, dead or alive," screamed Hitler. "The Austrian people will need a hero."

"Herr, you did not answer my original question. What are you proposing for Austria?" replied Schuschnigg, taking a step back. "We will do everything to remove obstacles to a better understanding, as far as it is possible."

"That is what you say, Herr Schuschnigg." Hitler's tirade continued. "But I am telling you that I am going to solve the so-called Austrian problem one way or the other."

The harried Austrian Chancellor, a chain smoker, looked worried and preoccupied as he broke away from Hitler's presence to snatch a smoke on the balcony of his villa.

There he was able to break the bad news to his Foreign Undersecretary, Guido Schmidt. Hitler's ultimatum, in effect, was calling on him as the Austrian Chancellor to turn his government over to the Nazis within one week, including the complete assimilation of the Austrian economic system into that of Germany.

"I fear this means the end of Austria's independence," said Schuschnigg sadly, turning away from Foreign Undersecretary Schmidt.

AUSTRIA | MARCH 10, 1938

It was a cold, gray, foggy night when Schuschnigg and Schmidt silently drove down the steep mountain road to Salzburg, after declining the Fuehrer's invitation to dinner. Unaware of or powerless to do anything about the situation, Dr. Kurt von Schuschnigg went to bed on the evening of March 10 firmly believing his proposed plebiscite would be endorsed by the Austrian people, thus thwarting the Nazis' aggressive plan against his state.

History recorded the rest: "At half past five on the morning of Friday, March 11, the Austrian Chancellor was wakened by the ringing of the telephone at his bedside. Dr. Skubl, the Austrian chief of police, was speaking. The Germans had closed the border at Salzburg, he said. Rail traffic between the two countries had been halted. German troops were reported to be concentrating on the Austrian border."

Without firing a single shot, and without interference from the powers of the day, including Great Britain, France, Russia or the United States of America, whose combined military forces could have easily overwhelmed Hitler's aggression, the Fuehrer had added seven million subjects to the Reich, and gained a strategic position in central Europe. The capital of the old Austro-Hungarian Empire, Vienna, had long stood as the centre of commerce and communications for Central and Southeast Europe. Now, the city that Hitler loved to hate was firmly in German hands.

Austrian Chancellor Schuschnigg was soon arrested and subjected to degrading treatment, treatment that many suspected was ordered directly by Hitler himself. He was kept under house arrest. The once genteel Chancellor was soon cleaning the wash basins, slop buckets and latrines of the S.S. guards and Gestapo.

Hitler ordered Dr. Wilhelm Stuckart, an undersecretary in the German Ministry of the Interior, to rush to Vienna and draft a law making the Fuehrer the President of Austria, and to further draft a law providing for a total Anschluss. The so-called Anschluss law was quickly drafted and transported to Linz, Hitler's hometown, and signed there by Hitler, Goering, Ribbentrop, Frick and Hess.

Hitler was giddy, and reportedly relished the first line of the document that read, "Austria is a province of the German Reich." The Fuehrer shed tears of joy.

Hitler was soon back in Vienna, awaiting the arrival of the ubiquitous and double-dealing Franz von Papen, who was rushing by plane from Berlin to Vienna to get in on the festivities. Papen found Hitler already standing at the reviewing stand opposite the Hofburg, the ancient palace of the Hapsburgs.

"I can only describe him (Hitler)," Papen later wrote, "as being in a state of ecstasy."

As Papen clambered onto the stage, he saw the Fuehrer lean over to Hermann Goering, his second in command, and whisper in a soft low voice, "I told Schnuschnigg the Austrian people will need a hero. Have your men get Kain, Konrad Kain the climber, back to Austria." Goering gave the Fuehrer a puzzled look and nodded his head, as if it was fait accompli, and then he turned his attention back to the screaming crowd of thousands of Nazi sympathizers now gathered in front of the stage.

After the tumult of this triumphant night had died down, Hitler returned to the Imperial Hotel and sat alone in his room. He thought back to his summers in Austria, when he often appeared in lederhosen, the shorts that most Bavarians donned in seasonable weather. He had fallen in love with the lovely mountain countryside; it was here that he would later build Berghof, his spacious villa in the Bavarian Alps. He was certain the return of Konrad Kain would help him capture the hearts of the Austrian people.

Chapter 5

Dr. F.W. Green, Cranbrook's first doctor, standing in front of the well-stocked lab of the St. Eugene Hospital in 1933.

"Dr. Frank William Green arrived in the East Kootenay in 1898 at twenty-two years of age…He was recruited and hired by the Canadian Pacific Railway (CPR) as a surgeon, a 'saw-bones' as the construction crews would come to call him."

St. Eugene Hospital, Cranbrook, B.C.

With the heavy, pleated window shades tightly drawn, the bright morning sunlight was completely cut off from the sparsely furnished hospital room. The dark and dingy ward emitted a feeling of impending doom. The pallor of death hung heavy through the narrow, crowded hallways.

The Catholic Sisters, as the nurses were known, quietly shuffled in and out of the blackened room. Its lone occupant lay motionless yet sweating profusely in a rigid steel-framed bed. His open but unseeing eyes belied his catatonic state, as they seemed to pierce the peeling paint on the ceiling directly above.

One Sister gently dabbed his feverish forehead with a cool washcloth, another nurse carefully spooned ice chips through the frail man's cracked, parched lips, while still another hovered at the head of the bed checking his vital signs.

Death hovered over the man.

The contingent of young nurses suddenly scattered as Doctor Green and Doctor Bell entered the room. The two doctors were immediately followed by a clearly annoyed, stern-looking Mother Superior.

"Sister Evelyn, why do you and your staff insist on keeping this room in perpetual darkness?" asked Doctor Green, looking perplexingly at the Mother Superior.

"I told you yesterday, Doctor, the light just agitates him. He starts thrashing about, crying out and shouting, sometimes in English but mostly in German," explained the Mother Superior. "His arms and legs flail uncontrollably. He constantly screams that he is falling. It's most unsettling for my young staff."

"I understand, you are doing the best you can, Sister," Doctor Green said in a consoling manner as he pulled back the bed covering to examine the patient.

"Let's face it, Doctor, the man is dying," said the Mother Superior, in a hushed but matter-of-fact tone.

"It is true, he probably won't pull through this but we don't need to encase him in a tomb of total darkness, now do we?" added Doctor Bell, as he reached over and smartly snapped the heavy window shades open.

The bright morning sunlight streamed into the room. The patient convulsed and almost sat straight up in the creaky hospital bed.

"The rock is bad, nothing but shale. There's nothing to hold on to, nothing to grasp. I'm slipping, my axe won't bite . . . the ledge . . . I'm going over the ledge," screamed the patient, in his thick Austrian accent.

"See what I mean? I told you he can't handle the light. It just tortures him," said the Mother Superior in an I-told-you-so manner, as she snapped the shades back shut again.

"My rope, it's snapped, I'm falling. For the love of God someone catch me," the patient shouted as he collapsed back on the sweat-soaked bedsheets.

"With all due respect, Sister Evelyn, I am the doctor. The problem is that we have a dying man here. It's not the light that is the problem, it's the shock of going from pitch black to bright sunlight," Doctor Green patiently explained. "It's a shock to his sensory system. Let's keep his shades pulled just halfway during the day and keep a low light on at night. It should be easier for him then."

"Well, if you insist," sighed the Mother Superior.

"Remember, this man has spent his entire life outdoors. His body craves natural light," added Doctor Green.

The Mother Superior reached over and adjusted the window shades ever so slightly downward. She then wheeled about and brusquely left the room.

"Look out, I say man, look out above. I hear an avalanche of rocks above us. They are crashing toward us. Take cover, man . . . take cover behind that boulder. Make yourself small . . . flat against the rock," the dying man struggled with his words as he tossed and turned in his bed.

The man was fighting death.

"I am tangled in my ropes. I can't get free. I am going to fall . . . I'm going to pull the climbing party into the crevasse . . . I'm falling," he said, in a desperate but barely audible tone.

The young nurses fidgeted about in the presence of the incoherent man and the concerned doctors.

"What do you think it is, Doctor?" asked one of the young Sisters hesitantly, as she straightened a pile of linen in the corner. "He suffers like this day and night. Nightmares, hallucinations, and he is always falling."

"He is a man of the mountains, no doubt," agreed the doctor.

"Or he pleads to go back to his birthplace to see his mother and friends, who he said he hasn't seen in 22 years," she added sadly.

"Will he get better?" asked the other young nurse, as she again dabbed her patient's burning brow.

"Unfortunately, it is unlikely he'll improve. I suspect he has sleeping sickness," said Doctor Green. "Though I haven't seen a case this severe since the major outbreak back in the 1920s. He might go tonight, he might go tomorrow, but then again he might hang on for a few more weeks, or even a month. Hard to say—just try to keep him comfortable the best you can."

"He's not that old, just turned 50, according to his medical records," said one of the young Sisters, as she drew back his sheets to begin to replace them with fresh ones.

The man's left arm lay exposed as his hospital gown slipped off his shoulder.

"That's a nasty-looking bruise on his upper arm," said Doctor Green. "He hasn't taken a fall since he's been in the hospital has he?"

"No, it was noted when he was admitted to hospital," said the nurse. "It's just been getting darker with each day. You might not have noticed it before when the room was so dark."

"Looks like a bite mark, a big bite mark, don't you think? A horse bite, maybe?" said Doctor Bell, as he touched the swollen flesh. "Keep an eye on it and try to let him get used to the light."

"That's as far as I can take you," shouted the patient, gripping the side of the bed, his body convulsing again.

DOCTOR GREEN AND ST. EUGENE HOSPITAL

Dr. Frank William Green arrived in the East Kootenay in 1898 at twenty-two years of age, freshly graduated with his medical degree from McGill University in Montreal. He was recruited and hired by the Canadian Pacific Railway (CPR) as a surgeon, a "saw-bones" as the construction crews would come to call him. The CPR subsequently dropped him off in the middle of the wilderness at the end of the rail line in a place called Goat River Crossing, near present-day Creston. Dr. Green was presented with a horse to use to make his rounds, an extensive kit of basic surgical instruments and a small variety of medicines. His direct instructions were simply to "go to work."

However, even his extensive McGill Medical School training would not have prepared him for some of the uncanny and medically challenging predicaments he would soon face.

M.J. Haney, superintendent of construction on the Crowsnest Pass Railway (the B.C. Southern), declared that it would be built in 15 months. Started in 1897, he pushed the project relentlessly to completion in 1898. It was difficult terrain, with high snow loads in the winter. The combination was devastating on both man and beast. Horses died by the hundreds and were not suitably disposed of. Typhoid fever developed and spread throughout the approximately 4,000 men on the workforce. Coupled with large numbers of industrial accidents, the project created a medical nightmare.

For example, during railway construction there were few women associated with the rough and tumble tent-cities. However, on one occasion, an adventurous nurse arrived to help out during an outbreak of the typhoid epidemic that swept the railway line construction camps. On one of Dr. Green's first visits to the Kuskanook camp, at the Kootenay Lake terminus, he found the workmen in hot pursuit of the terrified white nurse who had just arrived. One way or another he, along with a black nurse, managed to get the woman into a rowboat and row her through the choppy waters of Kootenay Lake around a jut of land to safety—a reflection of the typical unbridled rowdiness of camp life.

Dr. Green and his medical cohort Dr. King, who was working an eastern portion of the rail line between Cranbrook and Elko, were both paid about $100 a month. "Neither one of them could afford to pay their dues to the B.C. College of Physicians," said Bill Green, son of Dr. Frank Green, "and so they didn't have a provincial licence." For that reason they avoided each other for a long time, fearing that one might notify the College on the other.

Much needed medical supplies were distributed to the camps by these somewhat inexperienced doctors. Such things as liniment, dressings, bandages, adhesive tape, painkillers and cough mixtures were doled out to the men who were often racked with fevers, infections and heavy congestion.

Twice a month the Doctors Green and King would travel their assigned sections on horseback. Often this meant a ride of 30 miles or more a day, in every type of weather imaginable. As a rule, at the end of their long day of dressing wounds, setting fractures and handing out medicines, they found themselves without sleeping accommodation, and they were forced to provide for themselves, usually using their saddles as pillows.

To quote from *The Medical History of British Columbia* (1932): "In the summer of 1898, typhoid swept through the country. The old log hospital at Goat River Crossing was filled with typhoid cases, and the overflow had to be provided for in the town. At the height of the epidemic the hospital staff, which consisted of a cook and three male nurses, resigned and the doctors had to attend the patients, cook for them and bury the dead. The unfortunate doctors had to make all funeral arrangements and carry out the funeral service. In one case the men refused to carry a coffin and the doctor was obliged to pay each man $2 to have the coffin carried a few hundred feet. The doctors were young men who had just graduated and their method of treatment was somewhat crude. It is said that in their right-hand pocket they carried a quantity of lead and opium pills, and in their left-hand pockets, compound cathartics. The usual treatment was to administer either one kind of pill or the other according to the patient's condition, and evidently from the popularity of the doctors their system met with some success!"

Finally meeting in the Cranbrook Hotel in late 1899, with the southern line of the CPR work almost completed, Doctors Green and King decided to strike up a medical partnership. Recorded as Cranbrook's first doctors, they soon had contracts with the railroad and lumber companies which covered almost 1,500 people. The main industry at that time was lumbering, and within a short distance of Cranbrook at least four mills were operating. Not too far away large sawmilling operations were operating in Jaffray, Bull River, Yahk, Ryan, Wardner, Baker, Wattsburg, Waldo and Wycliffe. All had an agreement with the Cranbrook-based doctors and the St. Eugene Hospital for about $1.25 a month per man—covering medical and hospital care and drugs.

The Canadian Pacific Railway had established construction camp hospitals along the route of the Crowsnest Pass Railway. They quickly proved inadequate, taxed to the maximum and serviced only by the two travelling doctors in the employ of the CPR. Conditions were deplorable enough that two separate Royal Commissions were struck to investigate the living conditions along the railway construction route. Many of the findings indicated that more appropriate health care and better facilities were required.

A Catholic priest, Father Coccola, was approached to develop a better facility at St. Eugene Mission. The first development money came from his friend, miner James Cronin—in the amount of $1,000. This was quickly followed by a $5,000 pledge from M.J. Haney and the Canadian Pacific Railway. In a timely fashion, the first dedicated hospital building was constructed at the St. Eugene Mission. This facility grew to meet the demand and when railway construction was completed the facility served as a regional hospital.

By 1900 Cranbrook was growing as a divisional point for the Canadian Pacific Railway and development was occurring rapidly all along the railway route. A feeder line had been constructed into Kimberley, and the growing town of Moyie had a station, as did Fernie and Elko. It was decided that the main hospital should be located in closer proximity to the railway, and construction on a new St. Eugene Hospital was started in Cranbrook. The new Cranbrook St. Eugene Hospital opened in 1901.

Chapter 6

Professor Charles Fay and a group of rescuers on Mt. Lefroy in search of the body of Philip Abbot after his tragic fall in August 1896. This prompted the CPR to bring skilled Swiss guides to the Canadian Rockies.

"The imposing silence was shattered by a dull but unmistakable THUD!—the horrifying sound of the soft, forgiving mass of a human body shattering itself on the hard, unforgiving surface of the solid granite below."

The Fall on Mt. Lefroy | August 1896

If there is one thing a mountaineer will not accept it is failure. On Monday, August 3, 1895, three men—Charles E. Fay, Philip S. Abbot and Charles Sproull Thompson—had been turned back from the summit of Mt. Lefroy, a towering 11,000-foot peak that looms over the dark-green waters of Lake Louise in the Canadian Rockies.

"The failure of that endeavour, a failure fraught with possibilities of ultimate success, increased our desire. All winter we planned and plotted to overcome the difficulties of that mountain," Charles Sproull Thompson later wrote.

Exactly one year later to the day, with the mountain sky just starting to brighten, the three men, now accompanied by a fourth companion, Professor George T. Little, found themselves on the wooden platform that skirted the Canadian Pacific chalet at Lake Louise, staring upward at the lofty peak.

"We're going to do it this time, boys," exclaimed an excited Philip Abbot, pumping his fist in the air. "We've had all winter to lick our wounded pride and plan for this day. Today it will be our day. There will be no failure accepted."

"I like your confidence, Philip, but Mt. Lefroy is a tougher climb than it appears from here, as we found out the hard way last year," said Charles E. Fay. "Listen to the thunder of those icefalls. It's no wonder Mr. Allen calls this mountain the 'death trap.'"

"Don't forget, I've climbed the best mountains the world can throw at you, Charles. Popocatepetl—now that's a mountain. The Sierras, the ranges of Alaska, the peaks of Yellowstone and the ridges of Norway, now fellows, those were real mountains," boasted Philip Abbot, giving Mt. Lefroy a look of disdain before heading back into the chalet for another cup of coffee.

Charles Sproull Thompson wrote: "A magnificent sight opened southward as we swung rapidly around the corner of the farthest buttress of Mt. Lefroy. It came suddenly, almost in the twinkling of an eye—a glacier-filled gorge a mile and a half long, at its widest perhaps three hundred yards, rising in rounded terraces to the summit of the pass, over 2,000 feet above. The lower slope, deeply cut between Mt. Lefroy and Mt. Green, lay in heavy shadow; the higher neve glistening a dazzling white under the undimmed rays of an alpine sun...the ascent was neither difficult nor toilsome. Once, below the debris of an avalanche, which had swept far down the narrowing slope, we paused to photograph and lunch. As we ate, a block of ice broke from the overhanging glacier on a cliff near us and fell, pounding into dusty fragments, almost at our feet. At hand, overshadowing us, Mt. Lefroy. Never before was such a combination of the far and the near…the conquest of Mt. Lefroy seemed assured."

"What do you see from above?" shouted Professor George T. Little, straining his neck back to peer around the boulder to catch a glimpse of Philip Abbot in the lead.

"Three ice streams, or rather one stream broken into three parts, then a sheer limestone cliff weathered into a series of turrets and bastions," Philip Abbot yelled back.

"It looks like a block of grey rock beyond the ice slope—we should be at the summit within two hours," Charles E. Fay added from above.

"How about we take another quick break before the last push to the summit?" suggested Professor Little, who was starting to show signs of physical exhaustion.

"Stop again? We just finished lunch less than an hour ago. Let's push on before we lose the sunlight in the shadows," shouted an exasperated Philip Abbot.

"No, Philip, if the Professor needs a break, I think we should take one," said Thompson, feeling a bit tired himself. "The barometric altitude is at 10,000 feet, and if Abbot and Fay find a seat over there and Little and I remain here, we'll be in the District of Alberta while you others sit in British Columbia."

Charles Sproull Thompson further wrote: "The first blow of the axe upon the ice, heavy, dull, resistant, altered our plans, dashed our hopes of an easy success, and, little suspected, turned the fortune of the day. No longer an easy, rapid ascent along footholds carelessly taken, kicked in the snow; instead, a long, arduous scramble over intermittent ledges, changing to ice, and toilsome step cutting only as a last resort. Abbot, as ever, went first."

"Philip, stay to the right, stay on the whitened scree slope," yelled Charles Fay in the general direction of Philip Abbot. "Stay with the most northerly of the three ice streams—that one leads to the summit."

"Come on, Professor Little, we can cut our way up and over to the second ice stream and make our way to the second ledge and then pass across to the third ice stream just like Philip's done," said Thompson, coaxing the flagging Professor along.

"Where is Philip?" asked the Professor, stopping once again to catch his breath. "I've lost sight of him."

"He's pushed ahead, anxious to be the first to summit this peak, I suspect," said Fay, shaking his head in disapproval.

Charles Sproull Thompson again noted: "Nothing can surpass the supreme exultation of such a moment, the clear, exhilarating atmosphere, the great silence, the virgin peak almost won . . . All the visible mountains were even now beneath us—all save five. Perchance the coming conquest, perchance the quickened heartbeat enhanced the beauty of the view. Across the pleasure fell a deepening shadow. The day was passing; already it was half-past five. At such an hour our position on the slope became indeed critical. Pushed more and more by the general configuration of the ledges toward that end of cliffs farthest from the summit, we were now driven either to scale their face or to cut a traverse below them to the main ice stream; a line of perpendicular rock conveniently near us was manifestly impossible."

As Philip Abbot reached the base of the cliffs, his face brightened and with a tone of certainty in his voice he shouted back down the face, "There is a good crack here."

The three climbers below gathered together on a small bed of scree, some 200 feet below and a seemingly short 300 feet south of the summit. All three strained their necks back to track cocky young Philip Abbot, who was, of course, always considerably higher up the mountain.

Jutting from this narrow bed of scree, a knife-like knee of rock some four feet high offered a stepping stone of sorts. Above the knee, extending to the right and the left, was a broad stone face. The junction of the two rock faces offered a slight crevice, which a man might squeeze through.

A plan quickly formed in Philip Abbot's mind, the result of the determination of youth coupled with the arrogance of his conviction. Through the fading light he turned and yelled back down the line.

"I can see the top, boys! Drop the rope, fellows, and I will lead us on to the summit."

As Charles Sproull Thompson would later write: "Abbot bade us put off the rope. Thus released, dragging both our two ropes tied together behind him, he passed up on the knee, and immediately thence to the right-hand crevice. (Professor) Little followed. Both, entering the crevice, disappeared behind the rock face. Fay and I remained upon the scree awaiting the time when, with the aid of rock firmly fastened (by Abbot), we might easily and safely join our comrades on the top of the cliffs."

Abbot, leading the charge, hesitated for a moment and then chose a shallow groove, hopper-shaped, leading directly to the pinnacle. He entered the slender groove and quickly vanished from Little's view, the ropes now dragging behind him and scraping against the hard, cold granite.

Five, ten, fifteen minutes passed as the remaining three climbers awaited a signal from Philip Abbot that it was safe to ascend. Charles Fay, who stood under the safe protection of an imposing buttress, leaned outward and stared intently along the sharp spine leading to the top.

The imposing silence was shattered by a dull but unmistakable THUD!—the horrifying sound of the soft, forgiving mass of a human body shattering itself on the hard, unforgiving surface of the solid granite below.

Thompson wrote: "In the impressive silence came the dull thud of a falling body, faint and rattling at first, heavy and crashing as it came bounding nearer. Crying to Fay that a great stone was coming, I made two steps toward him, turned, saw Abbot pitch through the left-hand crevice, strike upon the top of the knee, turn completely over, and, clearing the scree, plunge headlong down the ice slope."

"Abbot has fallen, headfirst down the mountain," yelled a distraught Professor Little. "We must descend and rescue him."

As Little descended to the other two climbers, the three visibly shaken men peered below into the shroud of darkening sky. Their eyes strained to faintly make out the crumpled mass of Philip Abbot lying on the edge of an escarpment, the ropes he was lugging to the peak tangled about his broken body.

A heart-wrenching three hours later, the three remaining climbers reached the body of Philip Abbot. Charles Sproull Thompson bent over and examined the corpse. From the V-shaped wound in the back of young Philip Abbot's head, Thompson could only surmise that Abbot's tenuous hand-hold had given way and that he had fallen straight backward, receiving the fatal injury even before his body tumbled down the mountainside.

The news of Philip Abbot's death rumbled through the climbing community of North America like a rogue boulder plunging out of control down a mountain face. Soon his untimely demise was being reported in all the major newspapers of the day and public sentiment quickly began to turn against the brash, young climbing community.

It was as if the gates of Hades had broken loose at Windsor Station, headquarters of the mighty CPR, when the morning edition of the *Montreal Star* landed on the desk of William Cornelius Van Horne, 3,000 miles away, with a 48-point headline that screamed, "American climber plunges to his death in the Canadian Rockies. Public demands sport be banned."

Conrad Kain Campfire Tales

A hole in the bottom of the boat:

One of the funniest stories my old friend Jimmy Simpson ever told was the one about the Professor's folding boat. It seems that this craft belonged to Professor A.P. Coleman, an avid explorer of the Rockies.

The boat had been taken to Athabaska Pass in 1893 for the purpose of navigating the infamous Committee Punch Bowl (a small lake not more than 200 yards in length at the Height of Land—some of its waters flow to the Arctic Ocean and others to the Pacific). It was used on a return journey to carry one of Coleman's party down the Saskatchewan River from the Kootenay Plains to Edmonton. A canvas boat, presumably the same one, was again taken by Coleman's party in 1907, when travelling from Laggan to Mount Robson. It never arrived beyond the sources of the Athabaska again.

Coleman wrote, "As our loads were heavy and some of the horses had sore backs, we cached the folding boat and fifty pounds of supplies, enough to take us home from this point, in a thick spruce tree, fastening everything up tight in bags to keep out winged or four-footed marauders. We hope thus to make better time. This cache we were fated never to see again."

The cache near Athabaska Glacier remained untouched for several years. Then along came an outfit and camped beside it. An outfitter, waking suddenly in the night at the scratching of a small animal at the tent door, and with dreams of a grizzly still confusing him, fired his gun point-blank. The porcupine seems to have escaped unscathed, but a gaping hole was blown in the side of the folding boat.

Later in the season Jimmy Simpson took the boat down to the Saskatchewan Forks, repaired it and used it for several years at the ford. It was finally burned up by a couple of Indians who, for reasons unknown, bore Jim a grudge. Thus ends the strange maritime history of a craft whose lengthiest voyages were made on the back of a pack-horse through high mountain regions!

Chapter 7

Three Swiss guides including Edward Feuz (centre) and Rudolph Aemmer (right) lug heavy camera equipment along a towering ridgeline in the Rockies.

"That's what we need in the Rockies, some well-trained Swiss guides—men of the mountains who can babysit these excursionists safely up and down those rocky slopes."

Van Horne's Swiss Solution

In 1887 the Canadian Pacific Railway was just completing Canada's first transcontinental railway. It began building the imposing Windsor Station in the heart of Montreal. In an effort to impress both shareholders and the government of the day, the company wanted to have not only a suitably impressive station, but an equally impressive headquarters.

American architect Bruce Price was commissioned to design Windsor Station and chose to style it in what is commonly referred to as Romanesque Revival. It was Price's architectural design that soon became the CPR's signature chateau-style hotel, starting with the construction of Montreal's Windsor Station and reaching across the country to the likes of the mountain hotels of Banff and Lake Louise.

Windsor Station was completed in 1889, and substantially expanded again in 1900-1903 and 1910-1913 by Canadian architects.

The distinguishing feature of Windsor Station was its rugged appearance. As one source described it: "Windsor Station's rusticated arrangement of grey stone, in true Montreal tradition, contributes to its impression of strength, as do such Romanesque-inspired forms as the great arches rising three stories high. (Architect) Price was dissatisfied with the result, however, feeling it lacked character."

With the office of William Cornelius Van Horne housed inside, Windsor Station by no means suffered in that regard, though it emanated a character somewhat different from what the architect may have originally had in mind.

Van Horne was known for his bombastic speech, meticulous attention to detail and the onerous demands he placed on his underlings, as he controlled every nuance of the CPR from behind his massive roll-top desk.

It had been twenty-four hours since the gates of Hades had broken loose at Windsor Station, when an unsuspecting paperboy had tossed the morning edition of the *Montreal Star* onto the desk of William Cornelius Van Horne.

The young paperboy had planned to hang around, like he often did on Friday mornings, for he had come to learn that Mr. Van Horne would on occasion reach into his pocket and toss him a few coins as a tip.

"Good morning to you, Mr. Van Horne," said the young lad. "Looks like the weather will be fine over the weekend. Hope you enjoy the newspaper."

But by this time William Van Horne's eyes had scanned and absorbed the 48-point headline that screamed, "American climber plunges to his death in the Canadian Rockies. Public demands sport be banned."

"Be gone with you, boy," he shouted at the young fellow. "I have no time to waste upon childish chatter."

"I am sorry sir, I didn't mean to bother you. I just thought you might have a few spare pennies for a lad?" implored the paperboy.

"Here's a few pennies, all right," growled Van Horne, reaching in his vest pocket and throwing a handful of coins at the flabbergasted young paper carrier.

"I must be gone," said the boy, turning and dashing down the stairs, not even pausing to pick up any of the tossed coins.

"Don't you understand?" Van Horne continued to shout, somehow not fully comprehending the irony of his yelling at the now vanished newspaper boy. "A climber has died in the Rockies and that could have absolutely devastating consequences on our efforts to attract mountain excursionists."

The fuming Van Horne turned his attention to his assistant, a tall, pale man cowering in the far corner of the office.

"Clifford, why have I not been notified about this tragic death before now? Did you not hear of this climber's death before it hit the newspapers? It must have come over the telegraph," Van Horne roared, pounding the assistant's desk. "Don't you understand the implications of the accident? We are pinning our future hopes and plans, not to mention profits, on attracting alpinists from around the world to the Canadian Rockies."

"Yes sir. I heard about it the day before yesterday, but didn't think it was a matter that would overly concern you," replied Clifford, his nonchalant attitude indicating he had become more or less immune to these daily tirades. "Hundreds of men have died pushing the railroad through the mountains but that never seemed a real concern of yours."

"This is different, Clifford," barked Van Horne. "This has the potential of turning public sentiment against mountaineering. This article says the climber is a Yale graduate. If mountaineering loses its lustre, our opportunity to develop the Rockies into a tourism mecca will vanish like a desert mirage."

"How many times have you told me that the Canadian Rockies are like the Alps of Switzerland, only many times better," replied Clifford. "The Alps have survived many a tragic climbing accident over the years."

"That's it Clifford, that's bloody well it!" said Van Horne, starting to calm down and think a bit more rationally. "What do the Swiss have that we don't?

"Really old mountains?" asked Clifford.

"No, don't be daft man. Switzerland's got guides. Trained mountain guides!" mused Van Horne. "That's what we need in the Rockies, some well-trained Swiss guides—men of the mountains who can babysit these excursionists safely up and down those rocky slopes."

Before the start of the 1897 tourist season, according to historian E. J. Hart, a request had been sent directly from Van Horne's office to the CPR office in London to investigate the possibility of hiring Swiss guides. Someone in the office was acquainted with an English émigré named Clarke living in the town of Interlaken. Clarke soon had a letter on his desk from the CPR giving him the authority to hire two guides; through his son Charles, who could speak German and was himself a qualified guide, he approached Edward Feuz, the chief guide of the district. Feuz agreed to go and persuaded his friend and fellow guide Christian Hasler to accompany him.

E. J. Hart continues in his book, *The Selling of Canada*: "Their trip to Canada in the spring of 1899 was a publicity man's dream. The CPR put the guides, dressed in full climbing gear, on parade in public places in London. On their arrival in Montreal more public appearances were scheduled, including a climb staged in a local stone quarry. The great rush of free advertising reinforced the CPR's 'Swiss' theme and it continued after the guides' arrival at Glacier House. In fact, they may have done more promotional work than guiding in their first year, posing for pictures with delighted tourists. The climbers were pleased to have the guides, even at the rather steep price of $5 a day, and the guides were equally pleased to be able to show their worth."

American climber Charles Fay, who was one of the members of Philip Abbot's fateful party, was the first to hire the services of the Swiss guides to assist him on his ascent of Mt. Dawson. He found them to be eager and ready to go when he arrived at Glacier House on August 3rd, 1897. He wrote in his journal:

"I believe I may assert with no immodesty that my advent was a source of unmixed pleasure to at least two of the varied companies gathered on the platform (of Glacier House) to witness the event of the evening, the arrival of 'No.1,' as the west-bound overland train is commonly designated. I refer to the two unique-looking, bronze-faced men, who, religious in the performance of their duty, paced the platform during those important half-hours in hob-nailed shoes, pipe in mouth, and otherwise attired as the regulation Swiss guides. Glad they were, for they were longing for more entertaining labours than these promenades, and the hardly bolder ones that constituted the chief of their function, the guiding of tourists to the foot of the Illecillewaet Glacier, with the possible roping up for short trips on the ice-foot itself."

Chapter 8

Albert B. Rogers discovered the Rogers Pass, which opened the west to development and tourism, though some say he picked the wrong route.

A.B. Rogers and his Pass

The inner elbow of Cape Cod is known for its cold, late springs. The delayed spring of 1829 was no different. A wintry gale had blown in a few weeks earlier, leaving a few vestiges of snow in the shady corners behind the white clapboard house that was located not far off the main street of Orleans, Massachusetts.

It was in this house that the son of Zoar and Phebe Rogers was born on May 28th, 1829. As a young man Albert Bowman Rogers apprenticed to a ship's carpenter, but he only made one journey to sea. It seemed from a very early age the young lad was drawn more to the land than to the water.

At his father's prompting, young Albert entered the engineering faculty of Boston's Brown University in 1851 and soon transferred to Yale where he obtained his bachelor's degree in 1853. Upon graduation he gained employment on the Erie Canal in Upper New York State. He married Sarah Lawton, who died a year later. He headed on to Iowa, where he married Nellie Brush, and they soon moved on to Minnesota.

In 1862 he was commissioned to be a Major in the United States cavalry by the governor of Minnesota, Alexander Ramsey. Rogers undoubtedly played a pivotal role in suppressing the Dakota Sioux uprising. The bloody conflict reportedly saw some 400 settlers killed by the natives, before the cavalry crushed the rebellion and executed 30 Dakota Sioux in a mass hanging in December of 1862.

However, it was Rogers' engineering work for the Chicago, Milwaukee and St. Paul Railroad a year earlier that garnered the admiring attention of railroad magnate James Jerome Hill of St. Paul, Minnesota. Hill was a member of the executive committee of the Canadian Pacific Railway (CPR) and he was desperate to find a viable crossing through the formidable Rocky Mountains to the west. This was especially true since the CPR had abandoned the proposed, and already surveyed, northerly route through the Yellowhead Pass in favour of a rumoured pass through the southern Rockies. With each passing day, more and more track was being laid across Canada's vast prairies, bringing the railroad closer and closer to the yet undiscovered pass through the Rocky Mountains.

Having built his reputation on the construction of the Iowa and Minnesota division of the Chicago, Milwaukee and St. Paul Railway; the Minneapolis to St. Louis road; and the Hastings and Dakota Railway across Minnesota, Major A.B.

Rogers was a man in demand. With his sterling reputation as an outstanding locating engineer and his advanced ideas in railroad construction, it is little wonder that he attracted the attention of the famous American railroad builder, Mr.
James J. Hill, who was also one of the principals of the Canadian Pacific Railway
syndicate.

In 1881, Mr. Hill engaged Rogers to take charge of the Mountain division of the
Canadian Pacific Railway from Savona's Ferry, (now Savona) in British Columbia, to Moose Jaw, then in the Northwest Territories, with instructions to find the
shortest practicable routes between these points.

Obtaining from intrepid surveyor Walter Moberly as much information as possible regarding this section as his personal experience had given him, and analyzing the Hudson's Bay Company letters to its western posts, and last, but by no
means least, a most generous letter to the Jesuit missions and a photograph of
His Grace from Archbishop Tache, Albert Rogers left St. Paul with his nephew on
April 1st for Victoria by way of San Francisco, then the quickest route. Before
leaving St. Paul, he made arrangements with the company to forward up the Missouri River by boat to Fort Benton, thence by wagon to Bow River Gap on the east
side of the Rockies, five complete engineering outfits, 125 men with their equipment and a year's worth of supplies.

The spirit of the man is shown, according to the book *The Selkirk Range*, by the
boldness of his plans, his purpose being to make his way from the Pacific coast
across an unknown mountain region and meet his assistants by July 1st. By his
indomitable push he accomplished this purpose, only fifteen days later than the
time set, having covered all but about 100 miles of the mountainous route as finally accepted and having made a long detour into the United States for more
supplies.

Albert L. Rogers, A.B. Rogers' nephew, accompanied his uncle and vividly
recorded their harrowing experiences in his diary. He writes:

"Twenty-two days were consumed in our trip from St. Paul to Kamloops, B.C.,
the principal outfitting point of that country. The desire for information regarding the country into which we were to venture was ever uppermost in our minds,
and the art of asking questions was used to the limit. Eight days more of our time
was exhausted in estimating distances; trying to find out how far an Indian can
travel between suns with 100 pounds on his back and no trail, how little food he
would require to do it and what kind of food was best under such conditions;
what protection we should need from weather and the possibilities of supple-
menting our larder, for killing game. After a good deal of trouble which resulted
in subsidizing the Indian Chief Louie, and with the kind assistance of the priest in
charge of the mission, we enlisted 10 strapping young Indians on rather an iron-
clad contract—their services would be ours without grumbling until discharged,
and if any came back without a letter of good report, his wages were to go to the
church and the chief was to lay 100 lashes on the bare backs of the offender.

"From my orders of April 29th, 1881, I take the list of supplies bought at the Hudson's Bay post in Kamloops: two rifles, 200 rounds of ammunition, eight pairs blankets, two axes, 50 feet ³/₈" rope, 12 tin plates, one tin bucket, two fry-pans, 12 trump-lines or pack-straps and six dog tents, each of these tents being made of two strips of drilling nine feet long sewed together lengthwise and with a stout cord fastened to each corner, 800 lbs. of flour, 337 lbs. of bacon, 25 lbs. of baking powder, 25 lbs. of salt, 10 lbs. of teas, one tin of matches.

"On the 29th of April, we chartered a small steamer to take us to the mouth of the Eagle River on Shuswap Lake. On Sunday, 1st May, landing at the mouth of the Eagle, we bade farewell to the last sign of civilization.

"Finding an old canoe at the mouth of the river, we used it in transporting our outfit as far as possible. After caching the canoe and taking our packs on our backs, we discovered that though our commissary seemed meager, it was not possible to carry it all at one trip. The necessary cachings and returns made our trip across the Gold Range to the Columbia one of fourteen days of hard travel. On reaching the Columbia, we built a raft of cedar logs large enough to carry our supplies. Major Rogers and myself, the Indians swimming, with one hand push-ing the raft to make the crossing, landed a mile above the mouth of the Illecille-waet. Our provisions had now been so lightened that caching and return trips were unnecessary. Having learned by this time what a day's march through the average country was, as well as the capacity of the Indian appetite, we were obliged to make a strict ration. This caused much discontent among the Indians, as the work was extremely hard, but finding that no distinction was made be-tween them and ourselves they soon became reconciled.

"From now on we pushed them, making 20-minute runs, with five-minute rests, through the day. The travelling was exceedingly difficult and picking our way over mudfalls, scaling perpendicular rock-points, wading through beaver swamps dense with underbrush and the villainous devil's club, all the time bal-ancing 100 pounds on the back of the neck, made life anything but a pleasant dream, and I am convinced but for the fear of the penalty of returning without their letters of good report our Indians would have deserted us.

"Although at this season the days were very long and we travelled from early till late, we were five days making 16 miles and arrived at the forks of the Illecille-waet, which was the farthest point white men had ever reached. Our course was up the east fork and one mile and a half from its mouth, we came to a most won-derful box canyon or gorge, which three years later was named by Rev. George M. Grant—Albert Canyon—in honour of the writer.

"There must have been heavy snows in the mountains the preceding winter, for snow on the level was several feet in depth in shaded spots, and for the next five days our course was across avalanches, some of which had started from the very peaks and had left a clean path behind them, crushing the timber into match wood for several hundred feet on the opposite side of the mountains. We crossed several snow-bridges under which the river passed, which were 150 feet above the river's bed.

"On May 27th, we found the snow in the valley about five feet on the level and, it being too soft to hold us, we waded the river most of the day. At different times, we killed caribou, mountain goat and bear and restocked our larder.

"On the 28th May, we came to where the streams seemed to fork and in front of us appeared the backbone or main range of the Selkirks. The whole success of our trip and the possibilities of getting a direct route for this great national thoroughfare depended upon the gateways that might be at the head of either of these streams.

"At this altitude it was cold enough to freeze during the night and when the snow became hard enough to bear our weight, we broke camp in the night, keeping as much as possible in the shade of the mountains after sunrise. By nine o'clock in the morning we had to camp, the snow being too soft to carry us. At the forks we decided to cache everything that would have impeded travel and make a hurried trip up the north fork to the summit. The stream had now grown so small we could easily jump it. We took all the Indians with us, not daring to leave them with the supplies which were getting alarmingly low, and short rations had already begun to tell on us by the number of holes we had taken up on our belts. The terrible travelling with our heavy loads, soaked to the skin by rain and wet brush, wading in snow and ice-water and sleeping in but one-half pair of blankets to each man had begun to show on all our faces. With two days' rations we started as soon as the crust would hold us and, with easier travelling, we made fine time. Keeping in the lee of the great mountain which we called Syndicate Peak, we were in its shadow all day and were able to travel until four p.m., when we came to a large level opening which appeared to be the summit. We camped on the edge of the timber out of the possible path of the snowslides for we were beginning to have a wholesome respect for this great force of nature whose rumbling thunder we had heard for the past few days. The moment the sun's rays disappeared behind the mountains the crust began to form and in a short time we were able to make a hurried trip across the summit and convinced ourselves that the water divided here, running east and west.

"After checking up our barometric readings and mapping the course of the valleys, we decided to climb the mountains on the south side of the pass to get a better geographical idea of the country, as the timber in the valleys was very dense and obstructed our view.

"From the opening of the summit we had seen a strip of timber extending about halfway up the mountain between two snowslides, and decided to make ascent at that point. Cutting each a good, tough, dry, fir stick and adjusting our light packs, we began to climb. Being gaunt as greyhounds, with lungs and muscles of the best, we soon reached the timberline where the climbing became very difficult. We crawled along the ledges, getting a toe-hold here and a finger-hold there, keeping in the shade as much as possible and kicking toe-holds in the snow crust. When several hundred feet above the timberline, we followed a narrow ledge around a point that was exposed to the sun. Four of the Indians in the lead had tied their pack-straps to each other's belts in order to help over bad places. The leader had made several attempts to gain the ledge above by crawling on the soft snow, when by some awkward move he fell backward with such force as to miss the ledge upon which the other three stood, pulling them headlong after him. They fell some 30 feet straight down, striking upon a very steep incline. The snow being soft and their momentum so great, it was impossible to check their speed and they went rolling and tumbling, tangled up with their pack-straps, until they disappeared from view over another ledge. Our hearts were in our mouths, fearing the worst might have happened to them. Dead Indians were easily buried, but men with broken legs, to be carried out through such a country and with barely food enough to take us back to the Columbia River on a forced march, made a problem which even strong men dreaded to face. Anyone who has been a mountain climber knows that there are times when going down is a great deal more dangerous and difficult than going up. Slowly descending, we had nearly reached the timberline when one of the Indians with an exclamation pointed to four black specks moving across a snowslide far below. Our glasses were quickly turned on them. There they were and, to our great relief, all were on their pins making down the mountain as fast as possible. We had lost several hours of the best part of the day for climbing, but we had started for the top and what Major Rogers purposed he performed. It was late in the evening when we reached the summit, very much exhausted.

"Such a view! Never to be forgotten! Our eyesight caromed from one bold peak to another for miles in all directions. The wind blew fiercely across the ridge and scuddy clouds were whirled in the eddies behind the great towering peaks of bare rocks. Everything was covered with a shroud of white, giving the whole landscape the appearance of snow-clad desolation. Far beneath us was the timberline and in the valleys below the dense timber seemed but a narrow shadow which marked our course. We had no wood for fire, no boughs for beds. We were wet with perspiration and eating snow to quench our thirst—not a pleasant prospect for camp; but the grandeur of the view, sublime beyond conception, crowded out all thoughts of our discomforts.

"Standing upon a narrow ridge at that great elevation, mid nature crowned by solitude, where a single false move would land one in the great beyond, man feels his weakness and realizes how small is human effort when compared with the evidence of nature's forces.

"Crawling along this ridge, we came to a small ledge protected from the wind by a great perpendicular rock. Here we decided to wait until the crust again formed on the snow and the morning light enabled us to travel. At ten o'clock it was still twilight on the peaks, but the valleys below were filled with the deepest gloom. We wrapped ourselves in our blankets and nibbled on dry meat and bannock, stamping our feet in the snow to keep them from freezing and taking turns at whipping each other with our pack-straps to keep up circulation.

"Only four hours we waited, but it seemed as if those four hours outran all time. At two o'clock dawn began to glimmer in the east and as soon as we were able to distinguish objects, we were only too glad to crawl back to the ridge. Coming to the foot of the great triangular peak we had named Syndicate, we traced the valley to the upper south fork of the Illecillewaet and found that it extended but a short distance in a southerly direction and paralleled the valley on the opposite side of the dividing range, through which we concluded, ran the waters of the Beaver, which emptied into the Columbia on the east side of the Selkirks. But old Syndicate was in front of us and further progress south on the ridge was ended, for it would be a bolder climber than we who would attempt to scale this point. From here we started straight down the incline, the snow having crusted and settled sufficiently to bear our weight. So steep was the descent that we were forced to go down backwards, kicking toe-holds in the snow as we descended. After travelling in this manner for several hundred feet, one of the Indians missed his footing and fell, sliding five or six hundred feet and landing in a basin just above the snow line. The rest of us, seeing that he reached the bottom safely, promptly sat down and followed. Swinging to the left, we travelled for a mile or more through the timberline and came upon another great field of snow with a moderate incline to the bottom of the valley. Little did we dream that before us lay the great glacier, nor did we discover its nature till 'Little Alee,' who had ventured ahead, suddenly dropped out of sight. Hurrying to the spot we found him some thirty feet below the surface between two walls of blue ice. Splicing our pack-straps we lowered the line which, with difficulty, he fastened to his belt and we hauled him out. From here we proceeded with more caution, not knowing what pitfalls lay under the light snow. Reaching our cache without further trouble, we found our other four Indians smoking the meat of a caribou which they had killed the day before on their way down the mountain. With much regret we were forced to give up going further, as we had but a scant eight days' rations left and decided to retrace our steps to the Columbia, which we reached after seven days of hard travel, having lived entirely upon dried meat, saving our flour."

"The Columbia had risen some thirty feet since our crossing it 20 odd days before. Having made a raft of two cedar logs and sweeps also of cedar, we sent eight Indians home by the Eagle Pass and, taking the other two, we started down the river hoping to meet some Columbia River Indians of whom we might get canoes and a guide and so make our way to Fort Colville, Washington Territory.

"Pulling the raft through the Upper Arrow Lake, using our dog tents for sails, we finally found Indians from whom we obtained canoes and food. Hiring one as a guide, we proceeded down the lake and river and passed the boundary at old Fort Shepherd, Saturday, 11th June, at about 10 o'clock. We made portage at the Dalles and kept on to Marcus, where we hired a team and drove to Fort Colville. Here we discharged the last of our Indians, they to make their way back over the old Kettle River trail.

"Going from Fort Colville to Spokane, we bought saddle horses, pack train and supplies and hired two men and made our way through the Pend d'Oreille Pass in Northern Idaho, crossed the Kootenay River at Bonners Ferry and followed the old government trail up the Moyie River to Wild Horse mining camp. Here, Major Rogers hired two Indian guides and went alone up the Kootenay River and down the Columbia.

"Crossing the Bristow Range by Kananaskis Pass, he went down the Bow River, arriving at the Gap, where his engineers were camped, on the 15th of July. The writer (A.L. Rogers) followed with the pack train to the headwaters of the Columbia, where he hired Indians and canoes and went down the river to the mouth of the Kicking Horse. Leaving one Indian in charge of the supplies, with the other he followed the Kicking Horse to its source, where he met one of the engineering crews which was at work at the summit of the Rockies.

"The rest of the summer was spent exploring the different passes in the Rockies at the head of the Bow River and its tributaries. The next spring, having our base of supplies at the mouth of the Kicking Horse, Major Rogers with myself and six white men made the summit of the Selkirks by way of the Beaver on the east slope."

Major A.B. Rogers continued with the Canadian Pacific until the driving of the last spike, when he was again employed by Mr. Hill to prospect the route from Sun River, Montana, to the Puget Sound, over which now runs the Great Northern Railway.

The tiny village of Waterville, Minnesota, was like hundreds of other small villages scattered across the American Midwest. It had suddenly sprung up in the mid-1800s when the Great Northern Railroad, owned by business magnate J.J. Hill of St. Paul, had pushed its way through the frontier.

Its dusty main street was made up of a ragtag collection of clapboard buildings, all sporting false fronts. It consisted of several general stores, a hardware store, a bank, a couple of blacksmith shops/livery stables, a doctor's office/funeral parlour and a generous variety of saloons and drinking establishments.

A block off the main street sat the train station, now not much more than a glorified whistle stop since the railroad crews had moved on. Another block to the north lay a small residential area of compact wooden-framed houses.

On the morning of May 4, 1889, the blinds remained drawn in one of these houses, as first the local doctor and then the undertaker made their visits. Shortly after 11:00 a.m. a long narrow carriage pulled by a plodding old horse rounded the corner and stopped at the front door.

Within minutes the shrouded body of A.B. Rogers was placed on the hard cold floor of the carriage. The driver slammed the wooden gate shut and climbed on the front seat, he snapped the reins and the carriage slowly moved up the street and around the corner.

A.P. Rogers—Albert Bowman Rogers' brother—and son, Albert, stood on the porch, shielding their eyes against the bright morning sun, as they watched the carriage disappear. Both men fought back salty tears.

"Ornery old cuss, but I still loved him," said the son, as he leaned further out over the veranda to catch a last glimpse of the disappearing hearse. "I still remember the day when I finally showed up after being lost in the Selkirk Mountains for almost a month. The air was blue as Uncle Albert called me every name he could think of and then some. But when he finished cussing me out, he gave me a slap on the back and said he knew I would eventually show up."

"Yep, tough as nails, that brother of mine," agreed his father. "I told him he shouldn't take that job pushing the Great Northern through the mountains of Idaho. He was getting too old for that bushwhacking anymore."

"And to believe he died in those little mountains outside Coeur d'Alene, especially after all those years of exploring the Selkirks and Rockies looking for Van Horne's phantom pass," said the son. "The doctor said he actually died of cancer of the stomach. Probably brought on from the injuries he suffered when he was bucked on that cayuse he was riding. Landed on a jagged old stump, never did really recover from that."

"Like I said, he was too old to be traipsing through mountains. Well, at least J.J. Hill won't have my brother to kick around anymore," added the father. "Between Hill and Van Horne, they drove that poor man to distraction. He's gone now—I better get over to the undertaker's and finish up the funeral arrangements."

There are those who claimed Major Albert B. Rogers succumbed to the intense pressure of William Van Horne, J.J. Hill and the rest of the CPR syndicate, and chose the wrong pass through the Rockies.

In his book, *Carving the Western Path*, author R.G. Harvey states: "When J.J. Hill stormed out of a Canadian Pacific Railway boardroom in May 1883 over the decision to keep the railway entirely within Canada, the only remaining member of the hierarchy supportive of Hill's protegé, Major A.B. Rogers, was his fellow American, William Cornelius Van Horne. It might have been better for Canada if Rogers had left with Hill.

"Rogers chose Kicking Horse Pass as the railway's route through the Rockies, and he clung to this choice, even when he must have had doubts about it. Kicking Horse was the wrong pass—they should have used Howse Pass, as Walter Moberly had advocated. By May 1883, CPR track had only reached Medicine Hat from the east. There was still an opportunity to use another crossing of the Rockies.

"Rogers' line up the Kicking Horse Valley crossed the face of Mount Stephen over 200 feet above the river at the point where Field is today. It required a 1,600-foot-long tunnel through the nose of the mountain, and it also crossed two difficult avalanche paths. James Ross, the engineer in charge of construction, rejected the line when he first saw it late in 1883, and he never returned to it. He authorized a survey up the Bow Valley at the last minute with an eye to going through Howse Pass. This survey showed that they would have to cross Bow Pass, within the Rockies, at an elevation of 6,878 feet, and that was impossible. To use

Howse Pass properly they would have had to enter from the North Saskatchewan River Valley, but by this late date CPR trackage was in place for many miles up the Bow Valley past Calgary.

"To solve their problem in the Kicking Horse Valley going eastwards, CPR engineers had to reverse their gradient at a point below Mount Stephen, thereafter known as Muskeg Summit, and descend to Field, then climb at a gradient of 4.5 per cent (twice that recommended or allowed) to Kicking Horse Pass, on a section which was dubbed the Big Hill. The first train to go down it ran away and killed a crew member. The route was a financial drain on the CPR for years, as extra locomotives were needed to haul trains up the Big Hill and numerous runaway tracks were built in an attempt to make it safer. In 1902 they re-routed around Muskeg Summit for six miles, following the edge of the river. The CPR eventually replaced the four-mile climb up the Big Hill with the spiral tunnels in 1909. These tunnels involved a large amount of hand work with a huge crew—at one time said to be 10,000 men working around the clock for two years.

"This was not cheap, but it was a solution to the problem, one that few location engineers would have survived. Rogers blustered through, with the help of Van Horne, and he emerged as a hero."

It was as a direct result of Albert B. Rogers' "error" that Glacier House, the hub of the early alpine establishment, found itself at the base of the massive Illecillewaet Glacier. Glacier House was constructed in 1887. The CPR had specified that the grade through the mountains could not exceed 2.2 per cent. But in desperation Major Rogers recommended a route that was double that at 4.4 per cent. This meant that the CPR could not pull their heavy dining cars over the summit. So they needed a lunch stop for travellers somewhere near the halfway point between Banff and Farwell (later called Revelstoke). Thus the birth of Glacier House, tucked away amongst the soaring peaks of the Canadian Rockies.

It was from Glacier House that Conrad Kain began his first explorations into the Canadian Alps—as William Van Horne liked to call the Rockies.

Chapter 9

The famed Glacier House located deep in Rogers Pass was for many years the hub of mountaineering in the Canadian Rockies.

"The splendid and well-appointed hotel,

Glacier House, at the summit of Rogers Pass,

was built because trains...couldn't make it

up or down the Big Hill with a heavy dining

car attached."

The Building of Glacier House

On the far side of Rogers Pass, where the milky-blue waters of the Illecillewaet River plunged downhill between crevasses choked with ferns, skunk cabbage and the horrid devil's club, the CPR line made a gut-wrenching double loop. It then swung back across the valley to the tip of the massive Illecillewaet Glacier and future site of the famed Glacier House. The track then twisted back again in the shape of an inverted S, thus taking nine and a half miles to reach the level of the stream four miles from the summit. All this twisting and turning was meant to avoid the ever-present danger of snowslides—often deemed the "white killer of winter."

For future visitors or tourists swaying down this dramatic slope and gazing out from the comfort of the glassed-in observation car, the dramatic views would be breathtakingly spectacular.

The splendid and well-appointed hotel, Glacier House, at the summit of Rogers Pass, was built because trains, even those pulled by four or five heavy locomotives, couldn't make it up or down the Big Hill with a heavy dining car attached. The dining car was dropped on a siding at the foot of the ascent and the train still strained to reach the lofty summit, where eager passengers disembarked for refreshments and a snack.

In his book, *Diamond Hitch*, historian E.J. Hart writes: "When William Cornelius Van Horne, the general manager of the Canadian Pacific Railway, looked at the costs of construction for the Mountain Section of the line, it was apparent something had to be done. The numerous steep grades, the expensive blasting and tunnel work and the many wide chasms to be bridged had made the price of the section almost unbelievably high. Not only was it dear to build, but also looked to Van Horne's knowing eye as likely to be uneconomical to operate. The Mountain Section promised little sustained traffic, unlike the Prairie Section, which had agricultural colonists to bring west and the fruits of their labour to ship back east.

"Van Horne's carefully considered solution was to 'capitalize the scenery,' or, in other words, to invite the travelling public to partake of the area's myriad splendours by utilizing the company's transportation system. One of the first manifestations of the plan was the creation of a system of luxurious hotels to accommodate the expected tourists. These included Glacier House and Mount

Stephen House, opened at Glacier and Field respectively in 1886, and the Banff Springs Hotel, opened in Banff in the spring of 1888.

"Within a few years Van Horne's concept began to pay excellent dividends as an increasing flow of excursionists, attracted by a well-orchestrated international advertising campaign, travelled to and became enamoured with the Canadian Rockies and the Selkirks. However, it became apparent after the establishment of these hotels that the transportation system could not end at their doors. The attractions of the mountains—unexplored valleys, unclimbed peaks and plentiful fish and game—lured the more hardy visitors to venture beyond the confines of 'civilization,' requiring the provision of horses, equipment and guides."

E.J. Hart continues: "...the company (CPR) continued to expand its program of attracting tourists to its hotels in the Rockies and Selkirks. (William) Van Horne's policy of importing the tourist to the scenery had resulted in the organization of group excursions, the opening of new trails and carriage drivers and even CPR and federal government co-operation in the development of Banff and its hot sulphur springs. These measures were, of course, good for the outfitting business, but perhaps one of the most significant and gratifying steps taken by the railway was the decision to supply Swiss climbing guides for prospective mountaineering parties. The lack of qualified climbing guides in the region had proved to be one of its drawbacks, as far as mountaineers were concerned, and in 1899 this situation was remedied when two Swiss guides, Edward Feuz and Christian Hasler, were brought from Interlaken and stationed at Glacier House for the summer. They proved so popular that soon (Swiss) guides were situated at the company's mountain hotels as well."

One early traveller, the Reverend William Spotswood Green, made this comment about making Glacier House his base of operation for further exploration into the Canadian Rockies: "It is admirably situated near the foot of the Great Illecillewaet Glacier and most comfortable in every way . . . Glacier House is built on exactly the same plan as the little inns at Field in the Rockies and at North Bend on the Fraser. It is somewhat in the Swiss chalet style and possesses, besides the large 'salle a manger' where dinner is served to passengers of the Atlantic and Pacific trains which meet here every day, six or seven small but snug bedrooms...The hospitable manager, Mr. Perley, his wife, and their little niece, Alice, about nine years of age; Mr. Hume, the secretary, the French cook and his assistant Chinaman, three capital waitresses and the 'boy' made up the staff. Another man, 'Charlie' belonged specifically to the railway, his chief business being to watch the white stones round the fountains, which played in front of the verandah. These white stones were nothing more than pieces of common vein quartz, broken up to trim the edges of the little ponds; but so impressed were the numerous emigrants who went westward with the idea that quartz meant gold, that whenever the trains stopped men, women and children pounced on these white stones and would have left not one but for the vigilance of 'Charlie.'"

A despondent and frustrated Conrad Kain soon realized that the guiding season in the Canadian Rockies was extremely short. This, of course, also meant that his earning potential was greatly limited as well.

"Mr. Wheeler, I have met no other tourists in the clubhouse and saw, to my astonishment, that the season is over," said Conrad Kain. "The men from Chicago have left and there are no others to guide."

"Are you not content?" asked Mr. Wheeler, president of the Alpine Club of Canada.

"Yes, so far," said Conrad, "but if there is nothing else to do from now on, it isn't really worth the trouble to come as guide for such a few weeks in Canada."

"Don't worry, Conrad," said Mr. Wheeler. "I have just secured an extension to my contract to survey the boundary between the provinces of British Columbia and Alberta. You can accompany me and the rest of the surveyors on the project."

"But what is the pay?"

"The pay? No need to worry about the pay, Conrad. I will be sure you earn as much on the survey crew as at the summer camp of the Club. But I won't need you for several weeks so why don't you make your way to Glacier House in the Selkirks and I will send for you when we are ready to head out."

"What will I do at Glacier House?"

"That's like asking what fish will do in the water, Conrad. You will, of course, climb. Glacier House is in the heart of some of the best peaks around," chuckled Mr. Wheeler, slapping Conrad on the shoulder and almost spinning him around to point him in the right direction.

So Conrad left Banff in better spirits and made his way west to the Selkirk Mountains of British Columbia. The hotel, Glacier House, was the centre of mountain excursions and during the summer there were always two Swiss guides on staff.

"Welcome to Glacier House," said one of the Swiss guides, somewhat coolly, upon Conrad Kain's arrival. "Are you here to guide or to climb?"

"Don't worry, I am not here to steal your business. I will only take an excursion if you cannot keep up with the demand," Conrad replied, somewhat cautiously. "I am here at the recommendation of my employer, Mr. A.O. Wheeler, president of the Alpine Club of Canada."

"We don't need an Austrian cutting in on our business," said the Swiss guide, his eyes flashing with anger. "We know the dangers of these mountains, having climbed the peaks of Switzerland."

"I know of all the dangers of the peaks of Switzerland too, having climbed them myself," replied Conrad.

"Oh, what do you know about Switzerland?" challenged the guide.

"I know Switzerland, your home, better than you do, and certainly have made more ascents there than you," said Conrad heatedly, taking out his guide's book and hurling it in the direction of the Swiss guide.

The irritated guide slowly paged through the thick little book and soon discovered the truth of Conrad's assertions.

"Don't be angry! You look much too young and one can hardly believe you have travelled so much," said the Swiss guide, reaching out to shake Conrad's hand.

In the eight days Conrad Kain stayed at Glacier House, he busied himself climbing the likes of Mt. Avalanche, Mt. Abbott, and Mt. Sir Donald, and scrambled on the great Illecillewaet Glacier several times. It was on the trails around Glacier House that Conrad Kain discovered the bane of all hikers—devil's club.

"The path leads at first through a very lovely forest of Douglas fir and beautiful cedars, where I also met with the attractive looking devil's club, which, however, is cursed by every explorer or hunter on account of its almost invisible little thorns which pierce the skin at once and often come out in another place. Horses suffer very much from this, and it sometimes happens that the beasts bite at their feet until they are bloody," Conrad noted in his journal.

It was on the verandah of Glacier House that Conrad Kain met packer Fred Stephens. They sat for the longest time smoking, Conrad his pipe and Stephens his long cigarettes, and told stories of their mountain adventures.

Stephens told Conrad the story of the German army officer who, one morning after breakfast, took a map and an ice axe, stood on a rock and gave orders for the day.

"Sounds typical. What did you do?" asked Conrad.

"Well, when his preaching and commanding came to an end, I simply said, 'Are you through, you goddamned silly fool? If not, I'm going to knock you clear off that rock you're standing on! Do you think you have soldiers or slaves in front of you? No, we are free Canadians and don't give us any more of your German sauerkraut stories, you damned fool!'"

Conrad laughed out loud, as he tapped his pipe on the ledge of the verandah. "I have guided many who reflected the same attitude, but it is good to hear someone else putting such a one in his place."

Mr. Wheeler arrived the next day to take measurements of the Great Glacier, which was receding at a rate of 30 feet a year. Then the survey troop, with Conrad Kain among them, made their way to Revelstoke and on to Kamloops.

Conrad Kain Campfire Tales

Bear on the roof:

After a tough day of crossing and re-crossing the Whirlpool River and watching one of our pack horses somersault off a low rock ledge into the river below, we camped near a small lumber camp where railroad ties are cut and floated down to Jasper.

Passing by the cookhouse of the lumbermen, we were just too late to witness a lively incident. The cook, preparing lunch, had heard some scratching noises on the roof of the house. Thinking it was a squirrel, he did not pay much attention to it, but, happening to look up suddenly through the little skylight above, found himself looking squarely into the face of large black bear. Both were immensely startled, the bear being much the more frightened of the two. The cook threw a frying pan full of hot grease straight up in the air; bruin made an unceremonious dive over the eaves and galloped off amid a shower of kettles and dishes. We arrived in time to help the cook gather up his scattered utensils, and to confirm his story by examining the muddy paw-marks on the cabin roof.

Chapter 10

Arthur O. Wheeler, the first president of the Alpine Club of Canada, was often called the "tyrant of the Rockies" because of his abrasive ways and demanding nature.

A.O. Wheeler, Tyrant of the Rockies

At the dawn of the twentieth century, most Canadians had only the faintest idea of the geography of the mass of jagged mountain peaks or Cordillera that ran from the Arctic Ocean down through South America. They were even less knowledgeable about the Canadian portion of the Cordillera, the mysterious Canadian Rockies.

Only a handful of Canadians bothered to take the time to explore or climb the vast alpine terrain of eastern British Columbia and western Alberta. With just a few exceptions, the exploration and discovery was left to the geologists, surveyors and botanists of the day.

Of course, the alpine apathy of the Canadians did not deter members of the Appalachian Mountain Club, the American Alpine Club or the Alpine Club (England) from scrambling the many virgin slopes and peaks of the region—much to the pleasure of William Van Horne and his marketing team.

Clearly, Canada was suffering from not having a formal mountaineering organization, a problem that was remedied in 1905 with the formation of the Alpine Club of Canada (ACC).

A.O. Wheeler wrote the following in his book *The Selkirk Mountains*: "In all probability, few people are aware that a Canadian Alpine Club was duly organized during the summer of 1883, a president selected, a secretary and treasurer appointed and the first meeting held. The organization took place at the most suitable of all spots upon Canadian territory—at the very summit of Rogers Pass. Here seated upon a grassy knoll, amidst the very climax of Selkirk scenery, the meeting was held. What could be more appropriate! Around in full view are all the adjuncts that go to make alpine climbing of interest. The rugged black precipices of Macdonald and Tupper stand as grim sentries over an apparently closed gateway. To the north and west the primeval forest rises to grassy alpine slopes decked with brilliant flowers; beyond are icy glaciers and fields of pure white, sloping gently to the curving ridges that lead upwards to rocky peaks capped with snow.

"The sharp-cut pyramid of Cheops is silhouetted in space; below, the Little Corporal stands at attention, on guard over the hazy blue vistas reaching into the southwest. Around are gently swaying spruce and not a far distance away is a murmuring brook. Aloft, wrapt in silent meditation, the Hermit stands upon his ledge of rock, and gazes for all time upon the marvels of creation that surround him.

"The president was Sir Sandford Fleming; secretary, the late Rev. Principal Grant; and the treasurer, Mr. S. Hall Fleming, Sir Sandford's son. The account of the meeting is given in the president's own words: 'The horses are still feeding and we have some time at our command. As we view the landscape, we feel as if some memorial should be preserved of our visit here so we organized a Canadian Alpine Club. The writer, as a grandfather, is appointed interim president, Dr. Grant, secretary, and my son, S. Hall Fleming, treasurer. A meeting was held and we turned to one of the springs rippling down to the Illecillewaet and drink success of acknowledgment to Major Rogers, the discoverer of the pass and to his nephew for assisting him.'

"The bold idea of climbing Mt. Sir Donald, then known as Syndicate Peak, was conceived as a fitting virgin attempt of the Alpine Club, but the idea was not put into execution; however, Major Rogers declared that it would be the summit of his ambition to plant on its highest point the Union Jack on the day that the first through train passed along the gorge now travelled. On that day, Major Rogers was 75 miles farther west, for on the memorable occasion upon which the last rail was laid at Craigellachie, he held the ends of the two ties connecting the road-bed from the east and from the west, while the spike that completed the great national undertaking was driven by Sir Donald A. Smith."

"In November 1905," writes I.S. MacLaren in his book *Mapper of Mountains*, "a group of engineers, scientists and recreational alpinists pondered how they might promote mountaineering as a national sport. As news of the desire to form a Canadian club circulated, the promoters soon learned that mountaineering appealed to a considerable number of Canadians, but they simply had had neither the opportunity and means nor the know-how to climb. Hundreds wrote to express their interest and to enquire about attending the first annual camp. At the inaugural meeting at the Winnipeg YMCA on March 27th, 1906, M.P. Bridgeland (a Dominion Lands Survey [DLS] assistant) and the assembled men and women agreed on the following constitutional objectives for their organization:

"a) The promotion of scientific study and the exploration of Canadian alpine and glacial regions.

b) The cultivation of the Art in relation to mountain scenery.

c) The education of Canadians to an appreciation of their mountain heritage.

d) The encouragement of the mountain craft and the opening of new regions as a national playground.

e) The preservation of the natural beauties of the mountain places and of fauna and flora in their habitat.

f) The interchange of ideas with other Alpine organizations."

MacLaren continues: "Although the club is best known as a mountaineering organization, climbing mountains did not represent all members' chief interest. So the club established five grades of membership: honourary members, elected for their service or distinction in mountaineering, research or exploration; active members, who achieved at least one ascent of at least 10,000 feet above sea level; associate members, who desired affiliation with the club, but who had not participated on a qualifying climb; graduating members, who had not yet qualified as active members but desired to do so; and subscribing members, who did not participate in the outdoor activities of the club but wished to receive its publications."

The president of the ACC was Arthur O. Wheeler, who also was the head surveyor for the Department of the Interior. He thus truly was the boss of his assistant, M.P. Bridgeland, on both a professional and a recreational level.

A.O. Wheeler had little, if any, mountaineering experience before he began working for the DLS in 1901, surveying the uncharted terrain of the Selkirks. He arrived in Canada from Ireland some years before, trained in the scrub brush of northern Ontario and spent several seasons in the field in Manitoba, Saskatchewan and the foothills of Alberta. He was smart enough to realize he shouldn't push fate by climbing the ice and snowfields of the Rocky Mountains without proper instruction, so he engaged four Swiss guides whom the CPR had brought to the Rockies in an effort to foster expanded tourism. However, he soon dismissed the Swiss guides, deciding his own men—Canadians—were quite their equals. He remained friendly with the Swiss guides, but seldom did he ever again engage their services.

Wheeler's bouts of bad temper and his extremely demanding nature were legendary to those who worked for him. Although M.P. Bridgeland, his long-suffering assistant, was always friendly to Wheeler, the boss, one writer noted that he "hated to see the return of the chief" to camp.

Arthur O. Wheeler was a very public person, with an international reputation as a distinguished surveyor and mountaineer—a reputation he carefully crafted and worked hard to maintain. Those that knew him claimed Wheeler's social circle and influence had a distinctive air of snobbery to it. Wheeler and Bridgeland co-authored a publication entitled *The Application of Photography to the Mapping of the Canadian Rocky Mountains*. However, when the report was published and presented by Wheeler at the Alpine Congress in Monaco by the Alpine Club of Canada, it appeared prominently under the name of A.O. Wheeler. As he aged, Wheeler continued to thrive on his mountain mystique and willingly played the role of "The Grand Old Man of the Mountains."

Only his closest associates and those who worked directly for him saw his raw ability to curse a blue streak when frustrated by an errant horse, bad weather or the physical demands of survey work. A.O. Wheeler was a master at maintaining a public persona of dignity and sophistication.

It was this man who hired the young Austrian guide Conrad Kain to be the official guide of the Alpine Club of Canada.

Edward Feuz Jr. was one of the earliest Swiss guides who were recruited to come to the Canadian Rockies. He was, like most of the guides, a humble, unassuming man who knew his profession and simply did it well. He had no time for airs or pretensions, which may explain why he so often clashed with the abrasive A.O. Wheeler, president of the Alpine Club of Canada.

In the book, *The Guiding Spirit*, by Andrew J. Kauffman and William L. Putnam, Feuz often tells of his confrontations with Wheeler.

"In 1910 I (Edward Feuz) was engaged as a guide for Dr. Hickson; and Gottfried and Conrad Kain were doing the ACC's dirty work. Arthur O. Wheeler, the crusty former president of the Alpine Club of Canada, (was) renowned as the mountain country's surveyor and cartographer...like many self-made men who suffer from incurable insecurity, Wheeler could not grow gracefully into positions of distinction and advancement."

On one occasion, Feuz and Wheeler disagreed over where to set up camp for the day. "Wheeler, of course, knew better because he was both the Son of God and the Surveyor General, or something like that. When I contradicted him, he turned red and grew angry, and, of course, more insistent. Finally, I got angry, too. I went up to him in front of everybody and said to him, 'Mr. Wheeler, I'm the person who's going to climb that mountain with these two gentlemen, not you. I'm the one with the responsibility, and I'm the one who's going to be blamed if anything goes wrong'...Wheeler's red face turned deep purple, just like a peacock. He backed off like he'd been hit with a club."

Or as an old Golden, B.C., folk song (author unknown) puts it:

Arthur Wheeler blew his Feuz
When Whymper guzzled all that booze.
So Uncle Edward took up his axe
And gave old Whymper forty whacks;
And when he saw what he had done
He gave Art Wheeler forty-one.
Tarara-boom-de-ay...etc.

The authors of *The Guiding Spirit* continue: "He (Wheeler) had, however, another side. Towards his subordinates, indeed towards anyone he considered an inferior—and this included (Ed Feuz and Conrad Kain)—he could be savage. Having risen from humble beginnings, he seemed to despise those of comparable origin who failed to match him. He had a brilliant, impatient mind, which tolerated no delay. Those in his employ or at his orders often found him abusive, arrogant, conceited and autocratic. In short, when not on good behaviour, he epitomized the antichrist turned tyrant. His crowning achievement, a task that occupied decades, was the mapping of the Alberta-British Columbia watershed, in the course of which he delineated over 600 miles of the master range of the Rocky Mountains."

Edward Feuz also tells of the time Arthur Wheeler and packer Fred Stephens tangled again over the site selection of the day's camp. "Wheeler and the rest of the party with fast saddle horses charged up the pass. Stephens, following behind, came to a lovely meadow with good feed for his horses, so he camped there.

"Wheeler and the others had kind of a cold night of it at the pass with no tents, no food and no sleeping bags. At dawn, Wheeler wanted to find out what was wrong and rode back down the trail. He found Stephens just packing up and he said, 'Mr. Stephens, I always heard you were a good man, but you're not.'

"'Mr. Wheeler,' Stephens replied, 'I always heard you were a son-of-a-bitch, and you are.'

"With that Fred Stephens unloaded all his animals and led them back to town. So there was Wheeler and one or two others—all alone with a ton of junk and no horses to carry it. Served him right!"

Chapter 11

The Smithsonian expedition into the Canadian Rockies of 1911 included James Shand-Harvey, Reverend George Kinney, Conrad Kain, Donald "Curly" Phillips, Charles Walcott Jr., Harry H. Blagdon, Ned Hollister and A.O. Wheeler—all seen here relaxing around a roaring campfire.

"The late 1890s and early 1900s were considered by many around the world to be the golden age of scientific discovery."

Smithsonian Expedition | Summer 1911

The late 1890s and early 1900s were considered by many around the world to be the golden age of scientific discovery. This attitude was in no greater evidence than at the United States National Museum at the Smithsonian, in Washington, D.C. A.O. Wheeler, the head of the Alpine Club of Canada and lead surveyor for the Dominion of Canada in the Canadian Rockies, proposed a combined survey and scientific expedition into the Mount Robson area in 1911.

He quickly garnered the support of the Grand Trunk Railway, which desperately needed the area surveyed if they were to complete their planned ribbon of steel through Yellowhead Pass. Wheeler leaned on the provincial government of British Columbia to assist with the trip, to little avail. Then he made a call to one of his highly-placed contacts at the federal level and soon he was granted more than enough funding to commence with the expedition. Once the Canadian government was on board, the provinces of British Columbia and Alberta re-considered and decided to pitch in and support the endeavour.

The original party consisted of Wheeler, guide Conrad Kain, photographer Byron Harmon, a cook, outfitter Donald "Curly" Phillips and a late addition in the person of Reverend George Kinney.

With all levels of the government onside, Arthur Wheeler soon enlarged the scope of the expedition. An extensive investigation of the fauna, flora and geology was added to the original topographical work. However, Wheeler's considerable persuasiveness fell on deaf ears when he tried to capture the interest of Canadian scientists in the project. Undeterred, Wheeler contacted Dr. Charles Walcott, secretary of the Smithsonian Institute in Washington, and invited his participation. Walcott enthusiastically jumped on board and soon sent a party of four to join and work with the Alpine Club. He placed Ned Hollister, Assistant Curator of Mammals of the United States National Museum, in charge. Hollister was accompanied by Mr. J.H. Riley, also of the United States National Museum. Hollister was to obtain mammal specimens and Riley was to collect birds. Charles Walcott Jr. and H.H. Blagden were the hunters in the party and it was their duty to secure big game specimens. The expedition had been granted special permits to secure such specimens as well as other animals and birds for scientific purposes.

"Welcome to Canada, Mr. Hollister. We are honoured to have you and your party join us on our expedition to Mount Robson," said A.O. Wheeler in his characteristic booming voice, as 35-year-old Ned Hollister stepped off the train at the Jasper station of the Grand Trunk Railway.

"Pleasure to be here," Hollister replied, swivelling his neck around to take in the spectacular mountain vista.

"Conrad, can you help Mr. Hollister and his party get their luggage and supplies off the train?" Wheeler shouted. "Haul it over to where Curly Phillips is loading everything up."

"Happy to help you out Mr. Hollister," said Conrad Kain, even though this was not the usual duties of the official guide of the Alpine Club.

"We are excited to finally be in the Canadian Rockies. Where are you from, Conrad?" asked Hollister, noting Kain's thick accent.

"I came over to Canada a couple of years ago from Austria. Climbed nearly every mountain in that country and many in Italy and Corsica as well," replied Conrad, as he lugged bulging suitcases, over-stuffed trunks and reams of equipment off the train.

Still in his mid-thirties, biologist Ned Hollister had quickly moved up the ranks at the United States National Museum at the Smithsonian. He had been born in Delavan, Wisconsin, on November 26th, 1876. In 1903 he published a most respected natural species books entitled *Birds of Wisconsin*. He was rugged in appearance, with a full beard and canvas hat pulled down to shield his eyes. Not one to stand by and watch while others worked, Ned Hollister hauled as much luggage as anyone on that spring afternoon.

"What do you think of Canada?" asked Hollister.

"I must admit that sometimes I feel just like a little child who has lost his mother and is alone in the world, but I have come to love the wide-open spaces of the Canadian Rockies. All these soaring peaks are just waiting to be conquered," Conrad smiled, gesturing toward the ridges behind them.

"Well, I am looking forward to working with you. We have a lot of mammal and bird specimens to collect in a few short months but Mr. Wheeler says we can draw on your expertise and professional guidance," said Hollister.

"I'm happy to help out but I am not sure about Mr. Wheeler. I think he will be busy surveying and scouting possible locations for a new hotel at Fiddle Creek Hot Springs (now known as Miette Hot Springs)," said Conrad.

"Surely, he wouldn't leave us alone to fend for ourselves in this wilderness, would he?" asked Hollister, sounding more than a little anxious.

"Don't worry, you'll be in good hands with Curly Phillips as your outfitter, Jones as the cook and myself as your guide," said Conrad, giving him an assuring pat on the shoulder.

Excerpts from A.O. Wheeler's report to the Alpine Club of Canada detail the Smithsonian expedition of the summer of 1911:

"'Swift's' is a well-known stopping place along the trail. Swift himself, an old prospector and miner, settled here 15 or 20 years ago. He has since been engaged in raising horses such as are used in the mountain trails and in growing enough grain and vegetables to supply his family. He is an encyclopedia of information concerning the country and in his role of fairy godfather to all such parties as ours he took most excellent care of us and sent us on our way rejoicing. Later, Hollister and Riley spent some considerable time trapping in this vicinity and then gathered from this natural genius much valuable information concerning the fauna of the region. Seven miles from Swift's, the Miette River flows from the Yellowhead Pass into the Athabasca. At the junction is the government town of Fitzhugh, also the railway terminal of the Grand Trunk Pacific."

Slowly the expedition party made their way up the Miette River Valley to Summit City which "consisted of some three or four makeshift stores, rough log buildings with canvas roofs, as many billiard and soft drink saloons, a railway contractor's camp and a blacksmith shop. The place was tough and rowdy. There was a 'shooting' the night we were there, but no one seems to have been hurt. Outside of the refuse they accumulate and the despoiling of natural beauties, these places, though necessary at the time, are of little moment. They pass with the passing of the steel, and in all likelihood Summit City has passed since our party was there.

"We crossed the Continental Divide, the backbone of Canada, and two and a half miles of tramping brought us to Yellowhead Lake (a mile below the Fraser River flows from the south and meets with the Moose River). Of all the many lakes in the district—their name is legion and the colours of their waters varied and beautiful—the lake appeals to the traveller.

"We then left the Fraser Valley at the junction of the Moose River Valley, the route to Mount Robson lying northward up the latter. At the confluence was a railway camp and a collection of saloons and bunkhouses of the log wall-canvas roof type, for the edification and comfort, or discomfort, of the travellers. It glorified in the appellation of 'Moose City,' or, in railway parlance, 'Mile 17.' There was a good time in town that night. A new brand of 'soft drink' had arrived and, about midnight, its arrival was celebrated by a violent beating of triangles and tin cans. The triangles are a feature used by the boarding bosses to wake the men in the morning and to call them to meals. Some of the artists have it down fine and, as all the triangles are of different tone, a medley of sound is produced that, as a whole, is weird rather than harmonious. There was another shooting that night, but little damage was done. The town was chiefly remarkable for its brand of slick thieves. Conrad had his clothes stolen, almost off his back, a considerable quantity of grub was taken and the cook's stove abstracted while he sat upon it. The stove was staked at a poker game the night of the celebration and beyond that we were unable to trace it. However, in this section one learns to accept trifles of this kind with true philosophy, which in our case meant buy another stove, at twice the price—on account of the freight.

"The west branch of the Moose River joins the main stream about eight miles from its mouth and the trail follows this branch. Travelling up it we soon heard the roar of falling water and through the trees we spied fine twin falls which sent up a dense cloud of mist. The name 'Westmoose Falls' is suggested...Camp was pitched some three or four miles from the falls in a grove of open spruce, directly opposite where the trail crosses the ridge between the west branch and the main stream to ascend the latter. The valley formation here resembles that in the vicinity of Banff.

"The party now got to business. Hollister set his traps, Riley went off after birds with his gun and the hunters were already up on the crags sweeping the valleys with their glasses in search of big game. Phillips saddled up some ponies and took the topographic party up the west branch to explore its sources and investigate the big glacier...a prospectors' path led high over the ridge, near the mountain side, and descended to the western valley, which seemed to come from the very heart of the Rainbow Mountains (called such for the vibrant stone colourization). From the crest of the ridge, through an opening in the trees, we saw high in mid air, out-topping all around, a beautiful, apparently crystalline formation. It showed isolated, sharp and absolutely white against a sky of perfect blue and seemed to belong to a world other than ours. It was our first glimpse of Mount Robson.

"The valley in which we now found ourselves proved to be a find. It was a truly magnificent alpine one and is the main source of the west branch . . . there are grand stretches of rolling alplands from which the snow was just departing and every bare spot showed a brilliant yellow owing to the number of alpine lilies that covered it. Conrad, who had experience in such matters in his own land, remarked that it would be a fine place to pasture a herd of goats. Wide stretches of similar beautiful alplands may be found all through this section of the mountains. From a vantage spot on the alps, 20 good peaks surrounding the circle were counted; a number would furnish excellent climbs. We suggested the name 'Resplendent Valley.'

"Our next station was on the summit of the conical peak referred to as being at the extremity of the eastern arête of Lynx Mountain. This also is on the line of the watershed and commands a splendid view of the peaks encircling Resplendent Valley. One in particular commanded attention. It rises from the centre of a snow massif, like a huge rock-finger pointing heavenward. On seeing it Conrad exclaimed, 'Ach! That is my peak.' So the snow-covered mass was recorded as Mt. Kain and the great rock finger as 'Konrad Peak,' and was thereafter referred to as the 'Finger of Kain.'

"On the way to Reef Glacier Station we nearly had an accident. It happened crossing a steep ice slope newly covered by snow. Up to that time there had been no difficulty and we had not roped. Conrad was leading and the writer (A.O.

Wheeler) following in his footsteps. Suddenly my feet flew from under me and I shot downward, my axe scraping over the hard ice under its covering. Then I stopped. The axe had caught, but only just in time, for my legs and half my body were over the edge, and the rocks below were a long way down. I presume there was an exclamation at the start, for as I stopped I saw Conrad come leaping down the slope with reckless bounds, a look of horror in his eyes. The worst that can befall a professional guide is to lose his man. He grabbed me by the shoulder and gasped 'I've got you'—and then he began to slide himself. My axe held and we were soon on our feet and pulling ourselves together, for I must confess my nerve was somewhat shaken by the closeness of the call.

"To Conrad's disappointment the 'Finger of Kain,' from a more southwest perspective, now showed a broad slab of rock, but it must have been a very thin one.

"Beneath, to the south, lay a deep valley which opened on the west branch valley above our camp…There is little doubt that, as soon as the trails are put in and the proper accommodation for travellers provided, Resplendent Valley will be a general favourite…The valley, moreover, abounded with wild goat and Conrad and Harmon secured two for us, which proved a very welcome addition to our larder. I know of no more revivifying tonic after a hard day's climbing than a bowl of goat soup, and the older the 'Billy' the better and stronger the soup.

"Conrad was detailed to build a raft to cross the Moose River, flowing swiftly close by, and while this was being done the topographic party ascended the high rock buttresses that stood out prominently behind our camp to the northwest. Conrad is a grand climber and a magnificent guide under all conditions. He will, moreover, attempt anything, but this was his first raft. Instead of holding three, according to specifications, it would only hold one at a time and the problem arose how to get across and then to get the raft back for the next man. (Curly) Phillips, who is by profession a skilled river driver, solved the problem by jumping on the raft and, taking one end of a climber rope over, which he tied to a tree, the other end being made fast on our side. A looped rope hitched the raft to this impromptu cable and a second rope was made fast to haul it back. Shouldering the mountain transit, the writer followed suit…the current bore down on the front end until the raft was absolutely vertical and its passenger (A.O. Wheeler) had no choice but to plunge into the river…with the weight on my shoulders I could not get out. Conrad, quick to think and act, instantly hauled the raft back, jumped on board, and hand over hand arrived at the same spot, when the raft dipped again and in he went in exactly the same manner. Here were two of us on the cable and neither could get out. It was a deadlock, and we had to take chances. The writer caught on a snag downstream and did not see how Conrad got ashore, but he was there to help me out.

"On the way through Moose Pass, Charlie Walcott and Blagden had shot a magnificent grizzly, and while here at this camp, assisted by Phillips who was a skillful and tireless hunter, they tramped the mountain sides after caribou, which were frequently seen. Their efforts were rewarded and they secured six specimens, of which one was a magnificent buck with horns in the velvet…Hollister and Riley also were in clover. Splendid catches in the traps and good hunting of rare species of mammals and birds on the alps filled their days.

"The station on Ptarmigan Mountain was a splendid viewpoint. Mount Robson was clear from base to summit and Conrad picked out what he considered a feasible line of ascent. The route selected lay up the glacier to the foot of the Dome and, by steep rock rib protruding from the surrounding ice-falls, to the snowfield leading by an easy gradient to the bergschrund (a crevasse at the head of a glacier which separates the moving ice from that which adheres to the valley walls) present at the base of the precipitous rock wall that forms the southeastern arête (a sharp ridge, edge or rocky spur). The bergschrund presents a great yawning crevasse and will likely be a serious difficulty; but once passed he claims that the wall of the arête can be climbed and this was demonstrated by Hastings, Mumm, Amery and Inderbinen in 1909, on their very nearly successful attempt on the mountain. How nearly they were successful they did not know, as the lateness of the hour forced them to return. Had they reached the crest of the arête there would have remained but a long and apparently easy snow-slope leading direct to the summit. Conrad says that the day will come when the ascent will be made in eight hours from a camp at Robson Pass. I cannot concur in this estimate, but I do think it will be done in one day from a camp on the alps below Lynx Mountain, directly across the glacier from the Dome.

"When camped at Robson Pass, Harmon and Konrad started off one cloudy morning to get some photographs of the crevasses and snow formations in the Robson amphitheatre. Harmon, owing to the dull cloudy weather, got a poor lot of pictures but they, much to their satisfaction, made the first ascent of Mt. Resplendent. They reported this snow-crowned mountain was wonderfully crevassed…The crest is hung with enormous cornices reaching out a great distance. From this splendid viewpoint Conrad confirmed his previous selection of a route up Robson. He stated that the horizontal southeast arête is quite possible, and that, once reached, little further difficulty would be encountered as the slope to the summit does not exceed 45 degrees and the obvious route lies along the edge of a great snow mass clinging to the southeast face of the mountain. He reiterated the statement that a climb could be made from a camp below Mumm Peak in the eight hours, once the route had been established.

"It flows (the source waters of the Fraser River) quietly in many channels over a shingle flat for a mile below Berg Lake and soon again becomes muddied by glacial tributaries. It was at the end of this flat that our camp was pitched. Phillips, having brought our outfit and a two weeks' supply of provisions, had gone back to pick up Hollister and Riley and go round with the horses the way we had come, to meet us again at Kinney Lake in the Grand Fork Valley below the cliffs that prevented our ponies from continuing further in the direction we were going. We had taken advantage of the return of the ponies to pack a fly-camp to Robson Pass and had come back to headquarters the day Conrad and Harmon climbed Mt. Resplendent. They were late that night and we were wondering what had happened to them, when Harmon rushed in breathless, gasping, 'A bear! A bear!' It appeared that quite close by they had seen a black bear and Conrad had been left to herd it towards the hunters.

"Blagden was mixing dough for a pan of biscuits; Walcott was cooking peas and Kinney was washing dishes, preparatory to getting the absent ones supper, for Conrad's yodel had been heard up the valley. At the word 'Bear' there was a general jump for rifles—the peas were left in the pan, the spoon dropped in the biscuits and the other fellows' supper forgotten. Soon rifle cracks were heard in the gathering gloom, quite a number of them, as the chase waxed fast and furious and about ten p.m. the party returned without the bear which was said to have made off again up the hill badly wounded but his trail could not be followed in the dark. Meanwhile, fortunately for Conrad and Harmon, the Chief had continued the supper preparations. Next day the trail of the wounded animal was followed to where it had crossed the river. It was unlucky to lose this specimen for they were scarce and wild and the hunters did not get another chance.

"At the camp, wet and cloudy weather delayed us several days and compelled inaction. Overcome by ennui, Conrad went off one afternoon and did not come back at night; meanwhile the rain was pouring down in torrents. We kept up a good blaze and yelled and shot off rifles at intervals, but to no avail. Next morning we found Conrad had returned some time during the night. He claimed to have made the ascent of Mt. Whitehorn, and I have no doubt that he did. The blackness of the night had delayed his return…the crest was snow-covered and he could not build a cairn there, but had built one at the nearest spot where there was rock. So his story ran. Knowing him I have no doubt of its truth, but it will not count as a first ascent as there is nothing in the way of evidence except his word and that little cairn which may never be seen again.

"August 16th, camp was moved from the Berg Lake flat to near Kinney Lake, beside a little island of spruce in the shingle-floored delta. Here we nearly lost Conrad for between the spruce island and the main shore roared the glacier torrent of the Grand Fork, over which some prospector had felled a tree to effect a crossing, and Conrad had undertaken to go to the other side to get balsam brush for our beds. It was a thin tree and swayed back and forth uncertainly as the powerful torrent caught and held the branches. Returning loaded with an armful of brush and unable to see where he was placing his feet, he slipped and fell. An agonizing yell was the first appraisal of the catastrophe. It was most expressive, and conveying a full quota of dire distress. One grabbed an axe, another a climbing rope, all leaped to the spot to behold poor Conrad clinging frantically to the branches of the dripping tree with just his head above the water and the surging current, stretching his legs downstream like ribbons. The rope was flung and, with the guide's instinct, he immediately secured it to his body thus ensuring his recovery, dead or alive. With our united assistance he was soon extricated, but it was a pretty close escape from that which might have happened had he been obliged to let go and be swept under the tree at the mercy of the rushing water. It is indicative of the man that through it all he held firmly to a small hand-axe which he had borrowed from Blagden, thereby decreasing his ability to hold on.

"On the way home a flock of 10 bighorn were seen cropping the sweet tufts of grass on the opposite slopes…It tantalized Conrad's sporting instincts to see their tails and sides flashing white in the sun as they moved here and there…We had rounded the shoulder of a shale hill; looking back a little later we saw on its crest two bighorn; one a fine ram. Although we had passed quite close our approach had not disturbed them. While working at my transit on the crest, a wild shout from Conrad, who was sitting some 50 feet away, caused me to look up; as I did so a bighorn passed between us within 25 feet of where I stood. Conrad declared it had jumped right over him, but if so he must have been asleep. Again, later, a band of 15 crossed the hill within 100 feet of us, and while on the way home we came on one evidently asleep amidst the rocks. Its back was turned to us, and although we approached within 30 feet it made no sign. Conrad had his .44 Colt pistol with him, but in his wild desire to get it off missed his aim.

"On the way to the peak (Mt. Bastion) we saw two goats at very close quarters and for a long time we could hear them sending down rocks as they slowly took their departure along what seemed to be the vertical face of the cliffs . . . Indeed, so numerous were they that on the way down to the lake, this seeing of goats resolved itself into the game of 'Find a Goat.' The demand would hardly be uttered before Conrad would exclaim 'I see one,' and he would be invariably correct. This Son of Nature has eyes as sharp as needles, and there is little that moves on the slopes or crags that he does not see.

"It had been planned for the party to return by way of Indian trails across the mountains to Laggan on the CPR and thus investigate the possibilities of a favourite tourist route from steel to steel by pack-train . . . the snowstorm rather upset things. I (Wheeler) had to catch a boat at Vancouver on the 29th of September and the Smithsonian party were due in Washington early in October. The snow made it doubtful whether we could make our connections if we went across to Laggan, so I returned with the Smithsonians to Edmonton and sent Harmon, Conrad and Kinney across the mountains in care of Donald Phillips, whom I knew would get through, if anybody could."

"Conrad, I must say I have been most impressed with your guiding and mountaineering skills on this trip," said Ned Hollister, lounging around the campfire on the final night of the trek.

"I do what comes naturally to me and what I am paid to do," replied Conrad.

"You do it very well."

"We saw some magnificent country over the last few weeks—a spectacular alpland of brilliant flowers and so filled with animal and bird life. Walcott and Riley should be pleased with all their specimens."

"More than pleased I would say. My own take of flora and fauna was tremendous," said Ned Hollister. He lowered his voice and glanced around to see if anyone was listening to their conversation.

"Listen, Conrad, I am not interested in stealing your services from Mr. Wheeler but the Smithsonian is planning a trip to the Altai Mountains of Siberia in Russia. Would you consider coming along?"

"I would give it serious consideration," Conrad replied. "I am not indentured to Mr. Wheeler you know—though he may have you believe so."

"I will write you when I arrive back in Washington and have more details."

"What would you be doing there?"

"The Smithsonian is funding my research on small mammals."

"You would go all that way to trap mice?" chuckled Conrad, turning his attention back to the smouldering campfire.

"Conrad, let's keep this information under our hats for now, okay? No need to rouse Mr. Wheeler's ire at this point," said Hollister nervously. "Besides, I don't want him in a foul mood taking us back to Edmonton, especially through all this fresh heavy snow."

"You worry too much, Mr. Hollister. Mr. Wheeler is more bark than bite," said Conrad quietly, before turning and bidding all good night.

Chapter 12

After an expedition in 1912 to the Altai Mountains of Siberia, Conrad Kain returned to Austria and his family home in Hinternasswald—a semi-rural area just outside the Village of Nasswald in the Rax Mountains.

"Through the glare of the pale street lights,

Konrad could see two of Vienna's most

famous landmarks, the Riesenrad (ferris

wheel) and the Stephansdom (cathedral)."

Siberia and a Return to Austria

On the far side, the dark side, of the moon lies a lunar impact crater called the Lyman Crater. It is located to the south of the huge walled plain of Poincare, and to the northeast of Shcrodinger, another walled plain. To the east-southeast is another larger crater called Minnaert. The rim of the Lyman Crater has not been significantly worn and has a well-defined edge and interior features that have not been eroded through eons of impacts. The perimeter is roughly circular with outward bulges along the southern and eastern edges where slumping has occurred. Around much of the interior edge lunar material has collapsed inward to form a ring-shaped pile around the edge of the crater's interior floor. Though there are a few distinctive terraces along parts of the inner wall, the interior floor is relatively level with only a few minor ridges and a small number of tiny craterlets. At the mid-point of the interior floor is a central peak formation, which consists of a main peak with attached foothills to the north and northeast. A series of serrated ridges runs over 10 kilometres.

Born in Boston on November 23, 1874, Theodore Lyman was a U.S. physicist and spectroscopist. He graduated from Harvard in 1897, from which he also received his PhD in 1900. He became an assistant professor in physics at Harvard, where he remained, becoming full professor in 1917, and where he was also director of the Jefferson Physical Laboratory (1908–17). Dr. Lyman made important studies in phenomena connected with diffraction gratings on the wave lengths of vacuum ultraviolet light discovered by Victor Schumann and also on the properties of light of extremely short wave lengths, on all of which he contributed valuable papers to the literature of physics in the proceedings of scientific societies. During World War I, he served in France with the American Expeditionary Force, holding the rank of major of engineers. He was the eponym of the Lyman series of spectral lines. The crater Lyman on the far side of the moon is named after him.

Long before this craggy moon crater was named after him, in early 1912, Lyman wrote Charles D. Walcott of the Smithsonian to inform him of his planned expedition to the Altai Mountains region near the Siberia-Mongolia border. Among the things Lyman requested was the services of an assistant naturalist, who could help in the collection of mammal and bird specimens for both Harvard and the United States National Museum.

Fresh from his successful trip to the Canadian Rockies, Charles D. Walcott, readily recommended the services of Ned Hollister. Hollister had been an integral part of Walcott's party to the Rockies and was now assistant curator at the U.S. National Museum. Hollister eagerly accepted the invitation to participate in the zoological expedition but he knew that he would also require a reliable assistant. Who better to invite than the skilled young Austrian mountain guide from their previous summer expedition in Canada, Conrad Kain.

A LETTER TO AMELIA

Dear Amelia:

It is impossible to tell all of my experiences as a trapper during the past four months. But I must say that the life is at once the finest and most difficult. From October 1st until the end of January I spent about 40 nights in the open, often in fearful cold. I am hard as a beast of prey, but as soon I got into a hotel in Edmonton I took a cold and it became worse every day.

From Edmonton I went to Calgary, and then to my beloved Banff. Now I am in my old home; two Englishmen live below me and play the piano incessantly. It tires me to hear the noise all the time, although I like music and song. I am not homesick, but the world at times seems so monotonous. I am getting tired of bachelor life.

Each day I work in the woods, and when I return tired and hungry the cooking annoys me and I go to the hotel for supper. There are no white cooks there, only Chinamen and the fare is not good. Yes, my dear friend, it has been a long time since the last 'wienerschnitzel!'

I have just heard from my friend, Professor Hollister, that I am to go with him to Siberia, and so shall have the chance to see my home once more. Hollister writes that we shall leave New York in the middle of May, travel from London to St. Petersburg and through Siberia to the Altai Mountains.

We will not climb much, but travel about. My work will be trapping and hunting and observing little animals and flowers. I am happy to have such new experiences. Last summer I collected mice and beetles for the professor and we became friends in the woods. In the early part of May I am to sail from Quebec to Liverpool on the Empress of Ireland.

I will write from Siberia and tell you when I should arrive in Austria. Please do not tell others, even my mother, than I am coming as I do not fully know my schedule as of yet.

With deepest regards,
Conrad

"So we are going to travel halfway around the world to catch more mice?" asked Conrad, as he leaned against the ship railing and shouted in the stiff ocean breeze.

"Oh, it will be more than mice this time, Conrad. We will be collecting large mammals and birds as well," Ned Hollister shouted back against the wind. "Here's your passport—you will need it to get into Russia."

"Professor Conrad Kain. Look Ned, the passport calls me a professor," he chuckled, pointing to the first page of the newly minted document.

"Just thought it would be easier to get you across the border into Siberia if we registered you as a professor," replied Hollister, unfazed by the apparent mistake.

"I like being called a professor," Kain said, puffing out his chest.

"Look here, Conrad, I mean Professor Kain, I'll show you our eventual destination," said Hollister, stepping inside the cabin to roll out a large map on a deck table.

"We are headed for St. Petersburg," he said, drawing his finger across the wrinkled map. "From there we take the Trans-Siberian Railroad to a city called Novonikolaevsk, which is on the Obi River. Then we take a steamer up the river to Biysk."

"That's quite a trip," said Conrad, tamping his smouldering pipe into a nearby ashtray.

"That's just the start of it. Professor Lyman tells me that from there we will go south to the last Russian post, Kosh-Agach, near the Mongolian border. We'll basically be travelling in a horse and buggy for a couple of weeks, and on the backs of pack animals for another week . . . probably camels. That, my friend, is going to be a tough haul."

"Don't worry about me. I just spent four months in the frozen wilds of the Canadian Rockies. I'm pretty much ready for anything," said Conrad, leaning closer to get a better look at the map.

"Have you ever rode a camel, Conrad?"

"I've never seen a live camel, let alone rode one."

"I have a feeling that after eight days on a stinky old camel, you won't forget the experience for a while," said Hollister, trying to hide a wry smile.

A LETTER TO AMELIA

Dear Amelia:

It has been almost four weeks since we have arrived in Siberia. We are near the border of Mongolia. Thus far all has gone well, but now the difficulties will begin. Both Professor Lyman and his assistant Ned Hollister are kind to me; we share everything alike. I have never been spoken to or treated as a servant. Mr. Lyman, like Ned Hollister, is always pleasant. Naturally, I am careful and try to please them. The people and country are very poor and extremely dirty. I am afraid I will have lice in a little while!

I have been out in the mountains from morning to night, trapping and shooting mammals and birds for our collection. You may be surprised, but Edelweiss grows in profusion about our tent, much to my delight. Yesterday a gigantic owl, of a species rare in collections, visited a tall rock spire above the canyon wall two nights in succession. I climbed to the tip of this pinnacle the next day and placed a wolf trap in the proper position. The next morning I awoke the camp with a hearty alpine 'yell' as I climbed the rocky spire and captured the monstrous bird.

These mountains are inhabited by the largest of wild sheep, which, with the ibex, will form the principal big game animals sought by our party. The region is mountainous, not heavily forested and ever so cold. It rains, often snows, almost every day. During the day I am all alone, coming to camp at evening with my specimens and talking over experiences with my friends. We have a half-civilized Kalmuk, who rides in search of fuel, mostly wood and cow-dung. My work is interesting and I like it better than guiding.

I have been thinking of you all day long, and I gathered many flowers for you. Flowers from Mongolia! They will no longer be as fresh and as beautiful as they now are, but I know you will take them anyhow, won't you? It looks like I will be home around the beginning of September. I will mail this letter from St. Petersburg.

Deepest regards,
Conrad

PS: I have just arrived in St. Petersburg. I will immediately mail this letter. In a few days I will take the train to Vienna. I saw the Tsar today. He rode in a carriage pulled by milk-white horses. A little man, but with a wild cruel look in his eyes— like he could eat little children alive! I hope to see you on my arrival in Vienna.

A RETURN TO AUSTRIA

The train journey from St. Petersburg to Vienna was a slow and arduous one. Konrad could ill afford to take the faster express, so he was forced to endure the starts and stops on a local 'milk run' line. With political tensions escalating across Europe every border point was an extra delay. The slow-moving train would grind to a halt, and soon it would be swarming with heavily armed guards, who did more shouting and waving of their arms than actual searching. They demanded that identification papers and passports be produced at a moment's notice, so the documents could be scrutinized by a multitude of official-looking inspectors.

It was approaching midnight by the time the 'milk run' express finally wound its way along the winding Danube River and shuddered to a squealing stop at the platform of Vienna's main train station, the Praterstern. Konrad wiped the humid steam from the train's wide windows and pressed his face to the glass. Through the glare of the pale street lights, Konrad could see two of Vienna's most famous landmarks, the Riesenrad (ferris wheel) and the Stephansdom (cathedral).

His eyes scanned the mob of family and friends who had come to greet their disembarking loved ones—some visitors, some immigrants and some returning residents. He glanced back and forth over the crowd looking for the one face he hoped would be there—in fact the only person who knew he was returning to Austria.

"Amelia, we've been to this train station two nights in a row now and there has not been any sign of your beloved Konrad," said her mother, now confined to a wheelchair since being struck by what the doctor called 'the palsy.'

"Oh, mother, why do you insist on calling Konrad 'my beloved.' He and I are just good friends," Amelia snorted.

"Well, I noticed your correspondence with the young climber hasn't diminished any."

"We enjoy each other's letters."

"So when is the next train from St. Petersburg due to arrive?" the older woman said, shivering and fidgeting in her chair.

"Mother, please be patient. The last train of the week is set to arrive very shortly. I will take you inside if you would be more comfortable."

"It's almost midnight already. A dreadful time to be sitting here on a train platform," her mother complained, taking an annoyed glance at her timepiece.

"If Konrad is not on this last train, then we will continue on to Prague tomorrow for your treatments. Okay?" said Amelia.

"Didn't the little man give you a definite schedule as to when he would arrive?"

"No, mother. For the umpteenth time, Konrad gave a probable date and time, but said he would write again from St. Petersburg to give me a more certain time."

"Well, what can you expect of a man who wanders the earth like a tramp?" Amelia's mother said.

"Mother, you are becoming unbearable. Konrad is not a tramp. You know he is a highly skilled alpinist and mountaineer. Remember, he developed his love of the mountains in our own Raxalpe."

"Then why didn't he stay in the Rax? I think the burgermeister was right when he said, 'I pity Fanny (Konrad's mother). The boy will surely make trouble for her. No doubt he will run away again, and most likely get mixed up with the Socialists and end up on the gallows.'

"Mother, that is terrible thing to say! Even if you are repeating someone else's words. Konrad has always treated me with honour and the greatest respect. He just has a great spirit of adventure in his bones."

"More than a little, if you ask me."

"Don't you remember when we first met him, mother, at the Inn on the Rax? You were as impressed with Konrad as Sister and I were, right? He was nothing but a gentleman to us all—not even wanting to identify himself as the famous climber, Konrad Kain."

As the jam-packed passenger cars slowly started to empty, Konrad finally reached above his head, grabbed his battered rucksack and swung lightly down from the steps to the crowded platform below.

He continued to peer anxiously around, looking for that one familiar face, but search as he might he didn't spy the one person he had hoped to spot the most.

Questions flooded his mind. Where was Amelia? Was she just lost in the crowd? Was there a mix-up in his arrival times? Did his last letter not arrive? Or was it really that she couldn't be bothered to take the time to journey to Vienna to meet him, like she had said she would?

Just then someone jostled Konrad from behind, almost bowling him over. Konrad tumbled forward but caught himself before he fell. Turning around quickly, he heard a deep, hearty laugh emanate from a tall, thin handsome man dressed in traditional alpine clothing complete with a floppy felt hat.

"Well, if it isn't the prodigal son returning to his native soil," the man shouted above the clamour of people and carts.

"Mr. Albert Gerngross, what are you doing here at the train station?" said Konrad, doing a poor job of disguising his surprise.

"Come along, Konrad, let's get your luggage together and I'll tell you the whole story over a hot cup of coffee," said the other man, slapping Konrad on the back.

"I don't have much luggage. Just this rucksack and a small trunk with my climbing equipment."

"Let's grab it and we can get out of this dampness."

Once settled inside a Vienna coffeehouse, with its tall narrow windows and round little tables, the two men eagerly exchanged stories and caught up on old times and recent news. As they gingerly sipped on steaming cups of coffee, the words became a torrent of chatter.

Albert Gerngross, a businessman who lived in Vienna, hired Konrad as his guide many years before, as they trekked through Corsica. They first met in Florence on the way to the Corsican peaks.

Kain describes their first encounter in his autobiography *Where The Clouds Can Go*:

"My fellow travellers were astonished by my woolen stockings and wondered that they were not too hot…Quick as lightning my eyes swept over the many heads. I could not see Mr. G., but I was easy to recognize with my two packed rucksacks and two axes. Mr. G. was soon standing at the exit, and we greeted one another with a cheery, 'Grüss Gott!'

"As Mr. G. did not like to use the rope, I put it in my rucksack. I went ahead and curved toward our track. Mr. G. wanted to do the same thing, but got onto hard snow, his feet slipped and away he went. I shouted as loudly as I could: 'Stick in your axe! Stick it in!' and went after him across the steep snowfield—with much uncertainty. Mr. G. succeeded in stopping himself, but 200 metres more and he would have been lost. He was glad to take the rope after that.

"The steamer left (the island of Corsica) at ten o'clock at night, and at eight the next day we landed in Livorno. We went at once to the station and went to Genoa by way of Pisa. There I took leave of Mr. G....My patron had divided everything with me and I never felt that I was just a guide. As long as I live I will always remember with pleasure the journey with Mr. G."

It was Albert Gerngross who had inquired about Konrad's journey to America, only to find out the trip was in jeopardy because of a lack of funds. "When he heard that I lacked money for travel, he said, 'If there is no other way, then I can help you. Why didn't you come to me when you knew that I was a good friend?'"

Thus it was Albert Gerngross's generosity that afforded Konrad Kain the opportunity to travel to Kanada.

"So you came to the train station in the middle of the night because Amelia couldn't be here?" asked Konrad.

"Yes, her mother needed to go to Prague this week for medical treatments," Gerngross replied.

"Did she tell you when I would arrive?"

"No, not exactly, because I don't think she knew either, but my home is near by and I have been checking all week. Amelia was convinced you would be arriving last week and she met every train coming in from St. Petersburg."

"She did?"

"However, when you didn't show up she started to wonder if you had changed your mind about coming back home."

"Since I left under a bit of a cloud, I didn't want to create any fanfare about my return, though I did send Amelia a letter from St. Petersburg telling her I would arrive on this very train," Conrad said quietly, draining the last drop of coffee from the porcelain cup.

"You say you left under a cloud?"

"Well, it was sort of like Joseph in the Book of Genesis. Remember, he was accused of seducing Potiphar's wife when it was actually the other way around?"

"Yes, I remember the account."

"I had taken the Countess Hoyos climbing in the Rax and the weather closed in on us. So we had to spend the night at the Hapsburg Hut—we've been there, remember?"

"Yes, I remember. So what happened?"

"That's just it. Nothing happened," Konrad's voice rose. "I swear on a stack of Bibles, nothing happened between us that night, but try and convince Lord Hoyos of that fact."

"What was the outcome?"

"The Lord spoke of laying charges against me. Then he thought better of it and said it would be best if I left the area for good. So with the money he paid me as an inducement to leave, combined with your generous patronage, the English lessons from Doctor Pistor's wife, and Doctor Pistor's connection with the Alpine Club of Canada, I thought it was best I head for Kanada."

"Have you told Amelia all this?"

"No, I was hoping to explain it to her on our train trip back to Payerbach."

"I definitely received the impression that she may be gone to Prague for an extended period of time, as I believe her mother is convalescing in a sanitarium there."

"I hope she comes back before I must leave again."

"Tell me Konrad, what is Kanada like?" asked Albert Gerngross, turning the subject away from Konrad's personal life.

"It is a vast, open country and the Rocky Mountains are beautiful."

"So what are your plans while you are back? Maybe we can get some climbing in together?"

"I would like that. I plan to take the train back to Nasswald in the next few days, and it will be a surprise for my dear old mother, bless her lonely heart."

"Where will you stay while you are here in Vienna?"

"Probably at the Mannerheim House."

"No, never Konrad. Come stay at my house, you can share your Kanadian adventure stories with us."

Conrad Kain Campfire Tales

Conrad takes a bath (with the horses):

Upon our return from a rather strenuous trek across the Scott Glacier, we raced the dying twilight back to our camp. We are convinced that, in most instances, approaching darkness is tantalizing in inverse ratio (as Mr. Thorington says) to the distance from the frying pan.

July 4th was a day of rest in camp. The national holiday was celebrated with spasmodic efforts at bathing and laundry, and in the futile attempts to construct steambombs out of jam tins. I was the object of much photographic activity when all the horses of the packtrain followed me into the pond—we had been out from Jasper for more than a week and there was a lot of salt in my hide and the horses' too.

Chapter 13

Magnificent Mount Robson is the highest peak in the Canadian Rockies. Controversy continues to swirl around who actually made the first ascent.

"Ever since I came to Canada and the

Rockies, it was my constant wish to climb

the highest peak. My wish was fulfilled. "

The Mysteries and Legends of Mount Robson

The rumours of mountain peaks reaching 16,000 to 17,000 feet ran rampant in the early mountaineering days of the Canadian Rockies. Famed British botanist, David Douglas, blind in one eye and the other eye clouded—likely with cataracts—creator of the intriguing legend, lay dead in a pit on the Sandwich Islands, his badly broken body entombed deep in a bullock or bull's pit built by natives. He had been warned of such dangers on the Islands, and Douglas had successfully navigated two empty pits earlier in the day. But hours later a passer-by found his little black dog whimpering on the edge of his untimely and unfortunate death trap. It was from Douglas's prolific note taking, while exploring the Canadian Rockies, that he unwittingly created the legend of these massive peaks in the Canadian Rockies.

Douglas had earlier written, "Being well rested by one o'clock, I set out with the view of ascending what seemed to be the highest peak on the north. Its height does not appear to be less than 16,000 to 17,000 feet." The nearly blind David Douglas named the two legendary peaks Mount Brown and Mount Hooker.

Fuelled by speculation and the abundant enthusiasm of early explorers including the likes of the "Reverend Alpinist" of the day, many were driven to discover and, better yet, climb these two legendary peaks. For whatever reason, the relatively new sport of mountaineering seemed to attract a disproportionate number of men of the cloth.

As one writer described it, "the consanguinity of alpinists with clergymen dates from the earliest human being who lifted up his eyes 'unto the hills,'" but was particularly vigorous in the late nineteenth century. Clergymen like the Vicar Frederick Morton Beaumont, William Spotswood Green and his cousin Henry Swanzy, were all Reverends, as well as founding members of the Alpine Club of Canada. Founding members Alexander MacLennan Gordon and S. Harper Gray were also leading Presbyterian ministers. Men of God were a frequent sight in the Canadian Rockies in the early days of alpinism.

It is of little surprise that it was a clergyman, Reverend George B. Kinney, who became obsessed with being the first to climb what eventually proved to be the highest peak of the Canadian Rockies, lofty Mount Robson—another man of God scrambling to be closer to his maker.

In an article written for the Canadian Alpine Journal (Vol. II., No. 2, page 108), Professor A.P. Coleman states: "The mountain (Mount Robson) as a whole is built of nearly flat-lying limestone resting on quartzite, the latter rock showing only on the south side, where the Grand Forks River and its tributaries have cut most deeply . . . From a structural point of view, Mount Robson represents the bottom of a syncline or basin, with gentle inclination from all sides. The more expanded and shattered forms around it, once probably parts of anticlines, have suffered far more from the destructive forces than the slightly compressed and, therefore, strengthened parts of the syncline. In both rocks and structural features Mount Robson is a very simple type. It is surrounded on three sides, northwest, southwest and south by deep valleys, from which it rises in splendid unscalable cliffs. On these sides erosion is going on rapidly by the action of frost and weather, while the rivers are cutting back their canyons to the northwest and northeast.

"As a result of my trigonometric levels, the altitude of Mount Robson is here computed at 13,068 feet. It is derived from transit readings taken at three distinct benchmarks at wide intervals apart—placed by the engineers of the Grand Trunk Pacific Railway—upon signals set on the adjacent peaks bordering the Fraser River Valley. The elevations derived were then carried from summit to summit to the highest point of the mountain. In one case the reading from the benchmark was directly upon the crest of Robson. The deduction is not absolute. It is impossible to make it so where no distinct signal, such as a rock cairn, has been sighted upon; and none can be placed on Robson, as the summit is covered by an immense snow cornice. Altogether, five sights were obtained on the crest from other summits, of which the altitude had been obtained through sighting on rock cairns built upon them, and one from the benchmark referred to. Two of these were discarded as uncertain, as they had been carried for long distances. McEvoy established a height for Mount Robson of 13,700 feet, but I do not think that any systematic series of observations were employed by him. It is the fate of great peaks to have their reputed heights brought down, and I fancy that more extended observations will find Robson no exception to the rule. The Massif with its glaciers and glacial lakes covers an area of over thirty square miles and measures three miles through at its base where it rises one and three-quarter miles into the air above the Grand Fork Valley.

"When the circuit of Mount Robson becomes an established route through the building of a pony trail by the Moose River, Smoky River and Grand Fork Valleys, it is likely that a chalet or a commodious hut will be built on the Berg Lake side of the Robson Pass, in full view of the Tumbling Glacier, where visitors may sit at their ease and see the ice fall into the lake as the avalanches come crashing from the heights. For magnificence of alpine scenery and grand spectacular effect this particular spot is unique in the Canadian Rockies. I have already selected a camp site for an Annual Meet of the Alpine Club of Canada and, as soon as a trail up the Grand Fork is available, one will be held there.

"It is only by spending some time in the close vicinity of the mountain that its wonders and various phases are seen. The peak is generally clear at early morning and clouds up by nine o'clock. On August 8th, we had a glorious view from our camp at the Pass while at breakfast. The mountain rose like a creation in crystal sugar into the clear blue sky and the rising sun coloured the snow a delicate pink; across this lay a straight black band, perfectly regular and probably cast by some stationary cloud; below the band the pink slowly deepened to a full rosy glow and then turned brilliant gold, finally fading to silver; next the Helmet caught it and became a wonder-world of rose and golden towers and palaces; and then a great rolling mass of fog came up the Smoky Valley and poured into the Pass, obliterating everything and casting a wet blanket over this glimpse of fairyland.

"Sad to relate, all along the north side of Berg Lake the slopes are disfigured by the gaunt and whitened skeletons of fire-killed timber. They have, however, one redeeming feature: the ground is ablaze with alpine flowers. I never before saw them in such profusion and brilliancy, and all species were larger and finer and in greater quantity than anywhere else we had met them. Our Smithsonian confreres made a good collection of the flora and have reported upon it.

"The name 'Robson Peak' dates back to 1863 on the map accompanying Milton and Cheadle's book and must have been given some time before then. I have been unable to trace its origin with any certainty. It is said to be after the Hon. John Robson, but at that time he was an obscure printer, publishing a newspaper at New Westminster, B.C., and did not become Premier of British Columbia until 1889. Here is the story; I give it for what it is worth:

"In or about 1861, Mr. John Robson, who was Premier of British Columbia from 1889 to 1892, was editor of a paper published at New Westminster, named *The Columbian* or *British Columbian*. While editor, he printed in his paper an article upon Mr. Justice Begbie at which the judge took umbrage and committed Mr. Robson to prison for contempt of court. While in prison, Robson published the best editorial he had ever written, which was headed *Lines from a Dungeon Cell*, or some such title. Robson's imprisonment caused quite a mild sensation at the time and, therefore, to perpetuate the memory of Judge and Victim the mountain peaks bearing their names were called after them. Mt. Begbie is on the west side of the Columbia River, a few miles below Revelstoke."

A more likely origin will be found in the following letter from Mr. H. J. Moberly, the well-known Hudson's Bay Company's factor:

Dear Sir,

Your letter, dated 21st instant, I received a day or two ago and am now answering it stating, as far as I have always heard, the origin of the name given to Mount Robson.

Years before the Hudson's Bay Co. and the Nor'-West Co. joined (1821), it was the custom for the Nor'-West Co. to outfit a party for a two years' trip, hunting and trading. They went west and north, even as far as the border of California. One party, under the charge of Peter S. Ogden, (consisted of) some 200 men, chiefly Iroquois and French-Canadians. When west of the Rockies, he scattered his hunters in different parties under the charge of a foreman, to hunt for the season. One of his camps, under the charge of a man named Robson, was somewhere in the vicinity of this mountain and it was the rallying point where all other parties came together for their return east.

I remain, yours truly,
H.J. Moberly

It was this mountain that became Reverend Kinney's obsession and the source of a hundred years of debate as to who rightfully can lay claim to the first ascent of this icon of the Canadian Rockies—Reverend George B. Kinney, man of God; or Austrian goat herder, Conrad Kain?

A LETTER TO AMELIA

Dear Amelia:

We have travelled to the base of Mount Robson for an attempt at the highest peak in the Canadian Rockies. In my experience of about 500 peaks, I find mountain climbing really a sport of kings; the real success and the peak comes by simply putting one foot in front of the other and always the second a little higher than the first. Just like we did on the Rax.

A storm came up at evening, and I was kept busy nailing shoes. On July 29th we had fresh snow and it was quite cold. In the afternoon I went around Berg Lake with two women and a man. We saw ice break off and fall into the lake. We caught sight of four goats on the way back. It was as if they were hanging on the cliffs across the valley. I told the camp, "Ach, gentlemen, to perform the grand duty tomorrow we also be white goats."

On July 30th we started for an ascent of the Mt. Resplendent: two men and a lady. I took my blankets along, as I was expecting two gentlemen to meet me at the timberline for the following day. It was cloudy almost all the way and the weather was not very fine when we reached the top about one o'clock. It was the second ascent of the mountain, and I shook hands with the first lady to attain it. We made a new route of descent, a fine ridge-wandering that we had to give up because of storm.

Tomorrow, we make the push for the top of Mount Robson. I have a folder of dried alpine flowers, which I will forward to you on my return to Banff. I will report on our ascent in a future letter. I expect to have hard and possibly dangerous work—Mount Robson is a wicked peak.

May this letter find you and your family in fine health.

Deepest regards,
Conrad Kain

CLIMBING JOURNAL NOTES | CONRAD KAIN

July 30, 1913: Returned from our ascent of the Mount Resplendent to the tree-line above Robson Pass. I met my two strong and able climbers, William (Bill) Foster, the deputy minister of Public Works for British Columbia; and an American from Summit, New Jersey, Albert MacCarthy. He said to just call him Mack. I call him a rich American. They were my Herren (clients), ready to tackle Mount Robson.

We gathered up blankets, firewood and our equipment and made our way to the base of the Extinguisher, a rock tower on the Robson Glacier shaped like a candle extinguisher. In the shelter of the stone wall we talked about the next day's assault.

July 31, 1913: Early in the morning I wanted to take a look at the weather, but could not open my eyes for a long time. My eyes were swollen and as if filled with sand—just like snow blindness.

I roused the men by 4:00 a.m., and by 4:30 a.m. we proceeded up the Robson Glacier towards the Dome, under a clear, starry sky. The group cautiously climbed the heavily crevassed icefall on the east side of the Dome. We reached the top of the Dome by 7 a.m., and walked easily across the snow to the foot of the northeast face. At close range the rock face soared ominously above us.

Robson's southeast ridge is interrupted by a flat shoulder between the point of attack and the summit. I believed the ridge could be gained by climbing the rock to the left of the hanging glacier, which should be feasible if we can cross the lip of the bergschrund.

With myself in the lead, we found a snowbridge, which had collapsed on the bergschrund. After every possible attempt we were forced to give up, for at this place the glacier breaks off sheer. Finally after using some awkward manoeuvres, we gained the upper lip and sighted a line of ascent that lay between an ice-glazed rock on the left and the edge of the hanging glacier to the right.

After long chopping at the ice, I stood on a 65-degree slope and Mr. Foster counted 105 steps to a ledge in the rock. I cut zigzag steps by swinging my axe with one hand. At the top of that we had another wall of rock, and above that an almost hopeless ice slope. One could see the tracks of falling stones and avalanches.

On this slope I made 110 steps. It was a relief to climb on rocks again, though they were glazed with ice. But unfortunately the satisfaction was short, and for several hundred metres we had to climb again upon a slope of snow and ice. The snow here was in danger of avalanching. For safety, I lengthened the rope on the dangerous slope.

I was reminded of the comments of Swiss guide Moritz Inderbinen from when he attempted Robson with members of the Alpine Club in 1909: "We should all have been kilt. I never before saw death so near." I again lengthened the rope to increase the protection of the Herren (clients).

Mr. Foster and MacCarthy can do nothing but stand and watch me as I chop away step after step. We finally reached the shoulder and took a mid-day rest. Then came a blizzard that wet us to the bone. We pulled out all the clothing stowed away in our rucksacks. The shoulder turned out to be a narrow snow ridge, with overhanging cornices fringed with long icicles glittering in the sun, a glorious picture. Unfortunately, we had no camera with us.

From the shoulder to the peak the route was no longer so dangerous, but complicated with loose, powdery snow. Never before in all my climbs have I seen such snow formations, soaring terraced walls of snow—like ostrich feathers. Some of the walls were 20 metres high.

I searched in vain for over half an hour to find a way to climb from one terrace to the next. A very steep and narrow couloir offered the only possibility. The wind was so bad here we often had to stop. The steepness alone, apart from the wind, makes step cutting very hard work. I made a handhold in the ice, and swung the axe with one hand ... cutting steps with one hand is a frightfully slow process.

"Just be patient," I called to my Herren (clients). "The bad place will soon be conquered, and the peak is ours." Mr. MacCarthy called back through the gale, "We are all right here, we are only sorry for you. I don't understand how you can still keep on cutting steps."

With the steep, terraced walls behind us the reward was a fairly steep snow slope. We could all three go abreast until we reached another wall but this was outflanked without difficulty. The last stretch to the summit was a snowridge.

"Gentlemen, that's as far as I can take you," I yelled, as I turned to my Herren who were only a few steps from the top of Mount Robson. As we stood alongside each other on the peak, we shook hands and I added my usual alpine greeting in German, "Bergheil." Our barometer showed exactly 13,000 feet.

We stood on the crest of the King of the Rockies and since we were 2,000 feet higher than any of the surrounding peaks the view was magnificent. Unfortunately time would only allow us 15 minutes on the summit—10 minutes of pleasure and five minutes of teeth chattering. The rope and our damp clothes were frozen stiff like a board. It was 5:45 o'clock and now we had to start to consider our long descent.

The descent of Mount Robson proved even more challenging than the ascent. Kain proposed a different route of descent, which followed the glacier on the south side in hopes of finding a safer way down. It quickly became apparent that the climbing party would have to spend the night on the mountain, as the light began to quickly fade. Kain's bivouac motto was: "A night out is hardly ever agreeable, and above 3,000 metres always a lottery."

So Kain was forced to begin chopping descending steps in the ice. The party quickly climbed down the 120 steps he carved and soon were confronted with a 3,000-foot sheer precipice—with no way down or around they soon found themselves climbing back up. Examining the icy trenches that barred their way and the ice cliffs overhanging them, Kain saw a slight opportunity along with the great danger they were in. William Foster questioned the decision to go on but Kain replied, "We can; it is practicable but dangerous."

Albert MacCarthy, sensing the danger and frustration of the situation, added, "Conrad, if it is not too dangerous for you, cutting steps, then don't worry about us. We'll trust to you and fortune." So Kain, sensing the confidence the men had in his mountaineering abilities, left his clients in a sheltered spot and proceeded to make more steps as carefully and quickly as possible. With MacCarthy at the rear the three climbers proceeded with extreme caution and managed to negotiate the dangerous trench in an hour. With the glacier below them now in view the descent seemed more promising, though Kain was still worried about another break-off that could avalanche down on them. So he made the painful decision to camp out on the mountain.

Conrad pointed his axe to the woods below, which were now plainly in sight and said, "It will be a fine night down there in the woods beside a big fire." This prompted both clients to cry out, for "fire" makes a very different impression when one is standing in soaking clothes upon ice and snow from the word "fire" when one is aroused by it from a sound sleep.

As they probed their way through several ice debris fields the sun began to set, leaving the group wishing they had just one more hour of sunlight to utilize. Yet Albert MacCarthy, undoubtedly in an effort to buoy flagging spirits, became very philosophical as he stated, "It is well that the law of nature cannot be changed by men. What a panic it would raise if we succeeded in delaying the sun for an hour! It is possible that somewhere some alpinists will tomorrow morning be in the same situation as we are and will be waiting eagerly for the friendly sun."

Arriving at a ledge of rocks at around ten o'clock, their feet began to feel the effects of 17 hours on the mountain and it soon became apparent that it was out of the question to go any further. It was decided that a ledge of rock about two metres wide would offer them a good place to bivouac for the night. They built a small shelter wall around themselves and tried to enjoy a few leftover stale sandwiches. MacCarthy dug deep into his rucksack and pulled out a large package of chocolate, which was a welcome treat. They removed their boots from their weary feet and Conrad gave Mr. Foster a pair of extra mitts to put on his freezing feet. Both clients then placed their feet in a common rucksack and Kain roped them to the mountain for the night.

Fortunately the night proved to be a warm one though it continually threatened rain. Below in the valley bottom the flickering flames of Alpine Club campfires and the Canadian Northern and Grand Trunk Railways taunted the shivering group of three. Kain soon was asleep only to have that bliss shattered with the massive thunder of a nearby avalanche. As he tried to go back to sleep all he could hear was Bill Foster's teeth chattering.

Conrad dreamt that night of being close to a forest. His Austrian friends kept passing along with loads of wood and dry branches for kindling, while he had forgotten to get a match. He reproached himself for not being able to light a fire and ease their suffering. When he awoke with a start, Conrad bolted upright and looked around, realizing the dream of firewood was fantasy, not reality.

At daybreak the warmth of the approaching day finally warmed Kain's two clients up, after a bone-chilling sleepless night, and they promptly fell asleep. When he awoke the two men, they were in considerable pain and could not open their eyes. Being snow-blind at any height is unpleasant—at 9,000 feet it was outright dangerous. As a result of some quick thinking on Conrad's part, cold poultices were applied and the pain subsided. Soon Foster and MacCarthy could once again open their eyes.

Before resuming the descent Mr. MacCarthy related his own frigid night's dream. He had implored his wife for more blankets, and his wife stopped him with the curt reply, "Oh no, dear, you can't have any blankets. Sleeping without any is good training if we want to go to the North Pole."

After scouting the way down, Conrad returned and told his Herren, "Yes, we can make it without further difficulty." His statement soon proved overly optimistic as they were confronted with more sheer walls and cliffs of rotten rocks. It proved especially unpleasant for Foster and MacCarthy, who were able to only see a few steps ahead of themselves through their glasses and badly swollen eyes.

It took the climbing party three hours to gingerly negotiate some eight hundred feet with Conrad cheerfully proclaiming every few steps, "I will find a way." With the barometer showing an elevation of 8,200 feet, Conrad said, "I am happy to be able to inform you that we have all the dangers behind us. We shall reach the green grass in the valley safe and sound even to our swollen eyes."

Without much further difficulty, Kain led his two clients down through a wild, romantic gorge to Lake Kinney. The gorge offered an exhilarating glissade over an expanse of old snow. At eleven o'clock they stopped for a long rest and an opportunity to devour anything and everything left in their rucksacks.

At five o'clock in the afternoon the three men staggered into base camp, exhausted and starving. Their fellow campers greeted them heartily with food, drink and many congratulations.

Conrad summed up the experience: "Ever since I came to Canada and the Rockies, it was my constant wish to climb the highest peak. My wish was fulfilled. For this ascent I could have wished for no better companions. Each had a friendly word of thanks for my guiding."

Then he added, "Mount Robson is one of the most beautiful mountains in the Rockies and certainly the most difficult one. In all my mountaineering in various countries, I have climbed on few mountains that were hemmed in with more difficulties. Mount Robson is one of the most dangerous expeditions I have made. The dangers consist of snow and ice, stone avalanches and treacherous weather."

Conrad Kain Campfire Tales

Kain dodges falling boulders:

Our ascent of Mt. Hooker involved climbing two 20-foot chimneys which was slow going from ledges to slabs to ledges. We traversed southward and upward across a slanting watercourse and crossed below a large waterfall in the centre of the wall.

We had barely started when there was a whizzing and I cried, "STONEFALLS!" just in time for the rest to take what cover was available. It turned out to be the beginning of a raking fire of stones in which we were all struck, but luckily without damage.

I tried to calm the situation down by saying, "Gentlemen, we must move a little to one side." This relieved the tension and we quickly got out of range in time to avoid a heavy bombardment of larger boulders that came banging down over our intended path and would surely have done us in had we persisted. Mr. Thorington told me later, "We realized afterward that in Conrad's cool leadership, in emergency, we had seen one of the finest things produced by mountaineering art."

Chapter 14

PHOTO USED BY PERMISSION - CAJ VOL. 2 1910 WHYTE MUSEUM ARCHIVES

Donald ("Curly") Phillips, a flatlander from Ontario, stands on a rocky crag on Mount Robson, the highest peak in the Canadian Rockies. Some still claim he and Rev. George Kinney were the first men to summit the peak.

"It should be noted that Curly Phillips had an axe to grind with Kinney. He viewed Kinney as amateurish and he was frustrated by his lack of provisions and severe food-shortage problems."

The Debate

"The wind in the wires made a tattle-tale sound
and a wave broke over the railing.
And ev'ry man knew, as the captain did too
'twas the witch of November come stealin'.
The dawn came late and the breakfast had to wait
When the gales of November came slashin',
When afternoon came it was freezin' rain
In the face of a hurricane west wind."

Parker Stevens smiled to himself when he heard the song come on the car radio. He carefully steered his aging Volvo sedan through the blinding snow blasting across Highway #1 as he headed westward. He could see the faint orangey glow of the lights of Canmore, Alberta, just ahead. He checked his watch to confirm what he already knew. Every disc jockey in Canada liked to play Gordon Lightfoot's *The Wreck of the Edmund Fitzgerald*—all six minutes and thirty seconds of it—right around dinnertime. In fact, he could still remember playing the song himself when he DJ'ed at a college radio station up the highway in central Alberta. It always gave him enough cover time to take a quick bathroom break and then rush next door, where he could grab a couple of slices of artery-clogging pizza at Louie's Pizza and Pasta House.

He had wanted to arrive in Banff before six-thirty and barring the blizzard turning any worse he felt confident he was well on his way.

"Hey, Paulie, you better wake up back there," said Parker, reaching over the seat to give the sleeping, prone body of his team member a good poke.

"Geez, Parker. Leave me alone. Between your gawd-awful twangy music and your erratic driving, a person can't get any rest around here," complained Paulie Kowalachuk, sitting up and rubbing his eyes.

"Don't complain. There were more than a few times I thought we might find ourselves sitting in a snowbank. The way this blizzard seemed to have come out of nowhere is unbelievable."

"What time is it anyways?"

"Five forty-five."

"Paulie, what's thundersnow?"

"Thundersnow, who's talking about a thundersnow?"

"It's been mentioned on every radio weather report for the last hour or so."

"Thundersnow is when you have a thunder and lighting storm in the middle of a snowstorm," said a soft voice from the passenger's seat next to Parker.

"Hey, Sarah. I thought you were sound asleep."

"Pretty hard to sleep when you two are yelling back and forth about thundersnow," said Sarah Ryan. The ginger-haired young woman sat up and started to rub the sleep from her eyes.

"Hope they don't cancel the event," added Paulie from the back seat.

"Oh, they won't cancel this one. They've been promoting it like crazy—you'd think it was a WWE cage match," said Parker, as the Volvo glided through the express lane at Parks Canada's entrance into Banff.

"Don't kid yourself, Parker. These Banff-tonians take their mountain legend seriously," interjected Sarah, as she started to re-orient herself while still staring out into the blinding blizzard.

"Yes, let's just stick to our game plan. I think we have developed a winning strategy. Be positive and upbeat as well as gracious and accommodating. Stick to facts and don't let them throw us off our game plan," said Paulie.

"Geez, Paulie. Listening to you, it sounds like we're going to a box lunch social," Sarah retorted, her nose curling in defiance. "If I get a chance I'm going for the jugular," she added under her breath.

Just then Parker slammed hard on the car's squishy brakes and the three passengers inside could feel the centrifugal force pushing them firmly back into their seats. The old Volvo spun wildly out of control before crashing with a deafening crunch in a frozen snowbank on the opposite side of the highway.

"Damn it, Parker. What the hell are you doing?" screamed Paulie, as he peeled his face from the cold, clammy side window.

"Just about broadsided a monster elk," Parker said in a wheezing whisper, his heart hammering against his chest. "Come on Paulie, let's get out and start digging."

"Can't open the door. I think we're trapped inside," shouted Paulie from the back seat.

Jake Renshaw was the first person at the scene of the accident. He had driven up the Columbia Valley through Kootenay National Park and over the Vermilion Pass. He hadn't hit the blizzard until he was making his way off Storm Mountain to the Highway 1 exchange heading east.

He parked his car with the four-way flashers on and sprinted across the four-lane highway toward the blue Volvo. He could detect movement as he hammered on the windows to see who was inside. He latched on to the passenger's side door handle and reefed as hard as he could. The crumpled door flexed, vibrated and suddenly sprang open with a distinctive popping noise.

"Is everyone okay in there?" shouted Jake, pushing his head inside to look around. He found himself staring straight into the bloodied face of Sarah Ryan. Her seatbelt had softened the impact of the crash but somehow her nose had still hit the dashboard and was bleeding profusely.

"I think we're okay, just a bit banged up. Didn't see that elk at all, came out of nowhere," said Parker, still tightly gripping the steering wheel.

Jake reached in his pocket and pulled out a crisp, clean handkerchief and scooped up a handful of snow. He leaned forward and pressed it gently against Sarah's bleeding nose.

"That should help a bit," said Jake. "Anybody in the back seat?"

"Well about time somebody remembered I'm stuck back here. Can you give my door a heave-ho, too? Maybe you can spring me out of here," Paulie said in an agitated tone.

Jake once again heaved on the back door, but it wouldn't budge. By this time both Parker and Sarah had climbed out of the open passenger door. Jake climbed back in the cavity of the car. He reached down as far as he could and found the lever that folded the seat forward. Within seconds Paulie scrambled out of the back seat and was standing by his two friends at the side of the road in the middle of what the radio was calling thundersnow.

"Whatever the heck that is," thought Paulie to himself.

"Look at the time. It's almost 6:30 and we have to get to The Banff Centre by 7:00," said Paulie, rubbing his bruised cheekbone and sore knee at the same time.

"Sarah, if you jump back in and steer, I think the three of us can push the old girl out of the snowbank," said Parker, twisting his neck back and forth, trying to work the stiffness out.

With a couple of wild guns of the frail Volvo engine, the old car shuddered and spun back onto the icy pavement.

"Thanks for stopping and helping us out," said Parker reaching over to shake Jake Renshaw's hand. "Where you headed?"

"On my way to the Conrad Kain-Mount Robson debate at The Banff Centre," Renshaw replied.

"We're one of the debate teams," Sarah piped up, as she now stood outside with the rest of the group.

"Can I give someone a ride?" asked Jake.

"Take Sarah, she's our debate captain. It would be good to get her there as quickly as possible," said Parker.

It was 6:57 p.m. when the highly touted debate team of the University of Calgary re-assembled in the lobby of The Banff Centre. Parker had nursed the battered old Volvo into the parking lot—one sorry headlight dangling by a couple of electrical wires and its passenger side crinkled like an accordion. Sarah's nose had stopped bleeding, Paulie's cheekbone hadn't started swelling yet and Parker's stiff neck was getting stiffer by the minute. They quickly gathered their briefcases full of notes and their dress clothes, which seemed to have survived the ordeal quite well, and headed for the dressing rooms at the side of the massive stage.

According to a legacy brochure found in the lobby of The Banff Centre, "The University of Alberta founded The Banff Centre in 1933. It was, in part, through the largesse of a grant from the U.S.-based industrialist and philanthropist Andrew Carnegie and his foundation. The Banff Centre began simply as a single drama course. Its success soon generated additional arts programs and the Centre quickly became known as the The Banff School of the Fine Arts in 1935. While arts programming continued to expand and flourish, meetings and conferences were introduced in 1953 and management programs came on board in 1954.

In 1970, to acknowledge the broader educational role of the school as well as its move toward a centre of experiment and innovation, it was renamed The Banff Centre for Continuing Education (The Banff Centre for short). In 1978, Alberta government legislation granted The Banff Centre full autonomy as a non-degree granting educational institution under the governance of an appointed board.

In the mid-1990s, The Banff Centre, along with most public institutions in Alberta, sustained cuts to its operating grant. The Centre responded in an entrepreneurial way and launched a successful capital campaign (The Creative Edge) to raise funds for state-of-the-art revenue-generating conference facilities, as well as a new Music & Sound complex. The new facilities opened in 1996, the same year the Centre's fourth division, Mountain Culture Programming, was created. A few years later, in 1999, The Banff Centre was recognized as a National Training Institute by the federal government and was awarded $3 million over three years for artistic training programs.

Today, in the 21st century, the Centre continues its role as a catalyst for creativity. A globally respected arts, cultural, and educational institution and conference facility, The Banff Centre is a leader in the development and promotion of creative work in the arts, sciences, business and the environment.

It was difficult to believe that the massive Eric Harvie Theatre, which seated over 900 people, was almost completely sold out, especially on such a wintry November night. In the middle of the stage sat a large lectern with The Banff Centre emblazoned across the front. To each side of the lectern sat a heavy wooden table with three chairs tucked behind it. On each table sat a large pitcher of water along with three short, squat water glasses. From one table hung a banner which read University of Calgary Debate Team complete with a bright red logo, and on the other table hung another banner identifying the University of Alberta and its Edmonton-based debate team, also complete with their green and gold logo.

Further toward the front half of the stage another heavy wooden table sat half facing the audience and half facing the lectern. Seated at this table were a short, balding man who looked vaguely like George of *Seinfeld* fame, a large man with a short-trimmed white beard and a chiselled face, framed with horned-rim glasses, and next to him a lithe woman with strawberry-blonde hair, and big silver loops hanging from her ears. Dressed in a bright lime-green Lululemon-knockoff outfit, she looked like she had either jogged to the event or arrived straight from her yoga class.

At 7:30 p.m. sharp, the short, balding man stood up, strode across the empty stage with confidence and made his way to the lectern. He bent forward to adjust the pencil-thin microphone, which he proceeded to clear his throat into, as if exercising some perverse method to ensure the microphone was actually working.

"Ladies and gentlemen, may I have your attention," he said, his Adam's apple bobbing up and down, as he cleared his throat once more. Gradually the din of the settling crowd began to subside.

"Ladies and gentlemen, my name is Nobel Wiseman, I am executive director of the Rocky Mountain International Mountain Festival and it is my pleasure to welcome you to The Banff Centre. As a prelude to the opening of the 25th Annual Mountain Festival we are pleased to present tonight's debate: 'Who should be credited with the first ascent of Mount Robson, the highest peak in the Canadian Rockies? Reverend George Kinney or Austrian guide Conrad Kain?' The resolve being: Conrad Kain, the official guide of the Alpine Club of Canada should rightfully be recognized with the first ascent of Mount Robson.

"First of all I would like to introduce our distinguished panel of judges for this evening's debate," Wiseman continued in a nasal monotone. "To my left and your right is Rhea Harte, marketing director of the Spine of Rockies Tourism Consortium. To my right and your left is Brice 'The Edge' Edgerley, executive director of the Adventure Operators of the Canadian Rockies. And, of course, myself, Nobel Wiseman, executive director of the Rocky Mountain International Mountain Festival."

After a smattering of applause, Wiseman droned on, "To my left is the debating team from the University of Alberta represented by John Haskins, third-year physics student; Randall Romich, fourth-year physical education major; and Corbin Jones, fourth-year environmental sciences major. And to my right the somewhat battered and banged-up team from the University of Calgary, which unfortunately ended up in the ditch on the way to The Banff Centre this evening. The U of C team is made up of Parker Stevens, third-year biology major; Paul Kowalachuk, second-year political science major; and Sarah Ryan, third-year law student. Now to set down the debate format for this evening I would like to invite Ms. Rhea Harte to come forward."

"Good evening, ladies and gentlemen and debating teams. Welcome to The Banff Centre and the 25th Annual Rocky Mountain International Mountain Festival. The debate format we will use tonight is as follows: We will flip a coin to determine which team will present the affirmative and the negative. Upon this determination, the Affirmative Position Team will lead with an eight-minute presentation in support of the resolve. This will be followed by an eight-minute presentation by the Negative Position Team as regards the resolve. This will be followed by the two-minute recess before entering into the rebuttal stage," explained a pert Ms. Harte, as she nervously tugged at her oversized earrings.

"The Affirmative Position Team will then have four minutes to rebut the position of the Negative Position Team, followed by another four-minute rebuttal by the Negative Position Team of the Affirmative Team's position. Then each team will be provided two minutes to summarize and make a closing argument in support of their positions," she stated, never once looking up from her script. "May the best team win," she added, looking around momentarily as if confused, then heading back to the judge's table without introducing the next speaker.

Moments later, the large, aging body of Brice Edgerley lumbered to the podium where he roughly adjusted the microphone. "Welcome everyone, it is my pleasure to invite the debate team captains forward, Corbin Jones and Sarah Ryan, to call the coin toss." Edgerley reached into his pocket to pull out a freshly minted loonie.

"When I toss this coin in the air, Corbin Jones, you must call heads or tails. The winner will be the Affirmative Position Team and the loser the Negative Position Team. Ready, here goes," shouted Edgerley tossing the coin high into the air.

"Tails, the U of A calls Tails," cried Corbin Jones.

Brice Edgerley snatched the falling coin out of the air with one hand and placed it on the back of his other hand. He slowly peeled his top hand off and shouted, "Tails, it is! University of Alberta will argue the affirmative position this evening and University of Calgary the negative."

Sarah Ryan returned to their table and gave her teammates a nonchalant shrug and loudly whispered, "This plays to our strength—I think Kinney was the first to the top anyways." Paulie rubbed his swelling cheekbone, Parker painfully swivelled his stiffening neck and Sarah sat down and tried to smile through the fog of a rising headache.

Affirmative Position as presented by Corbin Jones, captain of the University of Alberta Debate Team:

Ladies and gentlemen and distinguished judges, it is our distinct pleasure to be arguing the affirmative position this evening. As you know, the controversy over who actually reached the summit of 12,972-foot Mount Robson first has raged for over 100 years. Tonight it is our desire to put that controversy to rest once and for all. We will prove without a shadow of a doubt that the Austrian and official guide of the Alpine Club of Canada, Conrad Kain, was truly the first man to set foot on the actual summit of this King of the Rockies.

Take, for example, the testimony of the highly respected American climber, who was a member of the American Alpine Club and the Alpine Club of Canada.

As the official biographer of Conrad Kain, J. Monroe Thorington stated in his book *Glittering Mountains of Canada*, "The highest point (of Mount Robson) was not attained until A.H. MacCarthy and W.W. Foster, with Conrad Kain, reached it during the summer of 1913. Their route was by the dangerous eastern slope, but descent was made in a southwesterly direction, with a night out, to Kinney Lake." Later Thorington noted in the same book, "I have not forgotten what Conrad wrote after the first ascent, in 1913: 'I do not know whether my Herren contemplated with a keen alpine eye the dangers to which we were exposed.'"

Or consider the quotation of English climber and army captain J.P. Farrar who wrote, "My old friend Conrad Kain, a redoubtable little man, who was the first to conquer Mount Robson."

J. Monroe Thorington, in Conrad Kain's official autobiography, *Where the Clouds Can Go,* wrote: "The name of Conrad Kain will always be associated with the conquest of Mount Robson. If his life be in any sense epic, then this was his greatest adventure. It is the highest peak of the Canadian Rockies, raising its massive precipices above the Grand Forks of the Fraser in a relief rarely equalled in other mountain ranges of the world. The pioneer and the scientist had each had his turn at the mountain. (George) Kinney and the Colemans attacked repeatedly in 1908, while Kinney and Don (Curly) Phillips, in 1909, had victory within their grasp—a matter of yards."

In the same book, Conrad Kain recounts the following experience upon his return from climbing Mount Robson: "About five o'clock in the afternoon we came, hungry and tired, into camp, where we were hospitably received by our fellow campers with food and drink and congratulations. From what Donald (Curly) Phillips himself said, our ascent was really the first ascent of Mount Robson. Phillips' words are as follows: 'We reached, on our ascent (in mist and storm), an ice dome 50 or 60 feet high, which we took for the peak. The danger was too great to ascend the dome.' Phillips and Kinney made the ascent over the west ridge. The west side is, as far as I could see, the most dangerous side that one can choose. Kinney undertook the journey from Edmonton alone with five horses. On the way he met Donald Phillips who was on a prospecting tour. Mr. Kinney persuaded Phillips to accompany him. Phillips had never before made this kind of a mountain trip and says himself that he had no suspicion of its dangers. They had between them one ice axe and a bit of ordinary rope. They deserve more credit than we, even though they did not reach the highest point, for in 1909 they had many more obstacles to overcome than we, for at the time the railway, which brought us almost to the foot of the mountain, was then no less than 200 miles from their goal, and their way had to be made over rocks and brush and we must not forget the dangerous river crossings."

More testimony comes from one of the Canadian Rockies' most famous mountain guides and founder of Canadian Mountain Holidays, Hans Gosmer. Gosmer, a fellow Austrian, wrote the foreword of the 1975 reprint of *Where the Clouds Can Go*. He said of Conrad Kain: "One is awed by the skill, drive and mental fortitude which powered the 'Tour de Force' of Mount Robson; yet Conrad never comes across as bravado mountaineer. Rather, one gets the impression of a very humble man who loves life in the out-of-doors, especially in the mountains, but who has the strength and discipline to call on the physical reserves necessary to succeed on Mount Robson." Out of respect for Conrad Kain's achievements, Hans Gosmer named his two sons Conrad and Robson.

Patrick Morrow, the first Canadian to climb Mt. Everest and one of the founders of the Conrad Kain Society in Kain's hometown of Wilmer, British Columbia, states in his recent foreword for *Where the Clouds Can Go*, "Kain achieved renown as the outstanding mountaineer during the Golden Age of mountaineering in this country: the prince of Canadian alpine guides...he made upwards of 69 first ascents (Mount Robson included) or new routes on peaks in the Rocky Mountains and the Purcell Range, a record surpassed in volume, but not in difficulty, by Swiss guide Edward Feuz, Jr."

In his book *The Cloudwalkers*, Paddy Sherman stated that, after some 50 years, Reverend Kinney finally conceded that he was probably mistaken and was actually, "a few feet short of the summit."

However, the most conclusive proof came in 1959 when Kinney's summit register and his flag were found by a group of climbers from the Harvard Mountaineering Club. In the latter part of July 1959, a Harvard climbing party was ascending the steep south face of Mount Robson just below the Emperor Ridge at its foremost western corner. This discovery finally settled the matter—Kinney and Phillips had gotten so close to the peak of Mount Robson but fell short by mere yards or feet.

In view of the evidence presented, it is necessary to draw only one conclusion. Conrad Kain, lead climber, along with A.H. MacCarthy and William Foster, was undoubtedly the first to reach the actual summit of Mount Robson.

Corbin Jones returned to his seat at his team's table to the enthusiastic applause of a clearly pro-Kain audience.

Negative Position as presented by Parker Stevens, captain of the University of Calgary Debate Team:

Ladies and gentlemen and distinguished judges, on behalf of the team of Sarah Ryan and Paul Kowalachuk it is my pleasure to be arguing the negative position this evening. First of all let me say that there is no question that Conrad Kain was a tremendous alpinist and probably one of Canada's finest mountaineers. However, I will argue tonight that he was the second climber to reach the top of Mount Robson, not the first.

I remind everyone here this evening that hearsay and circumstantial evidence can hardly be used and depended on to snatch away the tremendous achievement of Reverend George Kinney and his greenhorn guide Donald (Curly) Phillips.

The mountaineering establishment of the day, namely the freshly minted Alpine Club of Canada, led by its strong-willed, dictatorial president, A.O. Wheeler, found it hard to believe that a man of the cloth and a young country "hick" dressed in riding boots who had never climbed a hill, let alone a mountain, would have the audacity to claim to have conquered the highest peak in the Canadian Rockies. The fact is the ACC establishment of the day simply did not want to believe it. They studied the mountain two years later and Wheeler wrote the following in the Canadian Alpine Journal: "...the route looked impossible... Kinney took a desperate last chance and succeeded. He has been criticized rather severely by practical mountaineers for taking on so extremely dangerous a climb with a companion who had no previous experience."

If I may draw your attention to one critical phrase in the above quotation, Wheeler wrote, "Kinney took a desperate last chance and succeeded." As of 1911, Arthur O. Wheeler, president of the Alpine Club of Canada, believed and publicly stated that Reverend George Kinney and Curly Phillips succeeded in their quest to make the top of Mount Robson.

It has been suggested that Kinney's desperate dash to reach the summit was motivated by a sincere desire to ensure that a Canadian climber was the first to summit Mount Robson. This was confirmed when he passed a British team of climbers consisting of Mumm, Hastings, Amery and Swiss guide Inderbinen on his way out of the Mount Robson area. Kinney, rightly so, proudly announced that he and Phillips had just conquered the peak for Canada. Undeterred, the crack British team, with experience climbing in Europe and the Himalayas, carried on but failed to reach the summit, almost perishing in a series of avalanches trying. It should be noted that this team of expert climbers was never known to doubt or discredit Kinney's claim.

It is said the truth of Kinney's shortfall leaked out on the return trip back to Laggan from Jasper. The 120-mile trip saw George Kinney, Conrad Kain, Curly Phillips and photographer Byron Harmon and their string of packhorses make the journey in just 11 days. There has long been speculation that Phillips "spilled the beans" after a night of heavy drinking. It was from then on that Phillips would make the statement, "We didn't get up that last dome." When asked by A.O. Wheeler's official biographer, Elizabeth Parker, how high the dome was, Phillips reportedly told her, "between 60 and 70 feet."

It should be noted that Curly Phillips had an axe to grind with Kinney. He viewed Kinney as amateurish and he was frustrated by his lack of provisions and severe food-shortage problems. This was exacerbated by the fact that Kinney had brought along a rifle with a bent barrel, which proved useless in garnering any game for food and insisted on not travelling (or climbing) on Sunday, "the Lord's day."

To quote lawyer, author and mountaineer Bruce Fairley, "Kinney had to overcome a lack of standing in the emerging world of Canadian mountaineering... Wheeler undoubtedly nourished the dreams of the Alpine Club of Canada being credited for the first ascent of the peak...There never was any kind of official inquiry or investigation of Kinney's claim, yet the single most damaging piece of evidence contesting Kinney's claim—the statement of Phillips—does not stand up to careful examination. It would not even be admitted into evidence in a court of law, either in his day or in ours, because it is simply hearsay and therefore unreliable and unable to be tested or verified . . . The decision taken was to quietly sweep Kinney's claim under the rug and so the evidence for and against the claim was never properly assessed."

Fairley continues, "The impact of the ACC's decision was quite dramatic. By 1913 the authenticity of Kinney's claim was universally discredited . . . (Conrad) Kain suggested that his party had made the first true ascent. And, for the first time, he quoted those words of Curly Phillips that have always been used to discredit Kinney. According to Kain, Phillips told him: "We reached, on our ascent (in mist and snow) an ice-dome 50 or 60 feet high, which we took for the peak. The danger was too great to ascend the dome."

Sounds convincing, sounds reasonable, but to me it sounds well crafted—rehearsed or staged. It sounds like well thought-out strategy to undermine the credibility of George Kinney. Lawyer Bruce Fairley, having climbed Mount Robson himself, argues that what Phillips purportedly described, "a 60-foot-high ice dome on the summit of Robson,"simply does not nor ever did exist. He states, "The entire top of the mountain is one great cap of snow . . . climbers ascend a broad back of snow at a constant angle. There is nothing difficult about the climbing."

Our distinguished opponents made reference to Swiss guide Edward Feuz, Jr., who to his dying day believed that Kinney reached the summit of Mount Robson. Feuz most certainly ranks as one of the greatest of mountain guides in the Canadian Rockies, even outstripping Conrad Kain in first ascents. Still, the record shows that Feuz and Kain had a high regard and mutual respect for each other. Again, lawyer Bruce Fairley reasons, "What is especially interesting about Feuz's conclusion that Kinney really did reach the summit is that Feuz knew most of the players, and Feuz also appreciated the political aspect of early Canadian mountaineering. He had guided Kinney on previous climbs, and his opinion was reached based on a knowledge of the characters of both Kinney and those who disputed his claim."

In view of the evidence presented, I believe it is necessary to draw only one conclusion. That Reverend George Kinney, a man of the cloth, and his sidekick Donald (Curly) Phillips were without question the first to reach the summit of Mount Robson, despite an orchestrated strategy to undermine and discredit them.

Parker Stevens headed back to his seat to a smattering of applause accompanied by a subtle chorus of hisses and boos. Brice Edgerley hoisted his large frame erect and slowly made his way to the lectern, holding his hands up as if to summon quiet.

"Ladies and gentlemen, there will be now be a quick two-minute break before John Haskins of the University of Alberta presents his rebuttal. Please remain in your seats. Thank you."

Good evening, my name is John Haskins and I will present a rebuttal to the Negative Position presented by our opposition from the University of Calgary:

As much as there was an effort to discredit and besmirch the reputation of A.O. Wheeler, founding president of the Alpine Club of Canada, Mr. Wheeler was a respected authority among his peers and in his later years was affectionately referred to as the "Grand Old Man of the Mountains." Hardly the conniving schemer our friends from the U of C would like you to believe.

On the other hand, may I point out that Reverend Kinney was noted as an "eccentric man" who damaged his own credibility by writing in the Canadian Alpine Journal (1910), "During the 20 days we were at Camp Robson we captured five virgin peaks including Mount Robson, and made 23 big climbs." This baffling statement most certainly was an exaggeration—if not an outright lie—undermining Kinney's believability for years to come.

May I also point out that many years later Kinney is quoted as telling John T. Coleman of *B.C. Magazine*, "It was not until a few months ago (the article was published in March 1957), after years of controversy, that George Kinney was finally convinced that they had not reached the summit of Mount Robson."

As for the testimony of Edward Feuz, Jr., it is tainted by tension that existed between himself and Arthur Wheeler. For whatever reason Feuz and Wheeler were like oil and water—some say it resulted from an earlier misunderstanding and dispute over unpaid wages. Feuz knew that Wheeler wanted the credit for the first official ascent of Mount Robson to go to the Alpine Club of Canada, but Feuz would never support his old rival in anything, let alone let him claim rights to the first ascent of the highest peak in the Canadian Rockies.

However, I believe you will agree that the most damning evidence is the sheer improbability of a greenhorn flatlander from the bush country of Ontario—Donald (Curly) Phillips, dressed in leather boots, cowboy jeans and equipped only with a walking stick, and the near-mad "Man of God" Reverend George Kinney succeeding on one of the most technically challenging and dangerous climbs, even today, in the Canadian Rockies. It is no wonder that the mountain climbing establishment of the day was suspicious from the start and why we can say today that Kinney and Phillips most certainly fell short of their objective in 1909.

And, in conclusion, remember that the Harvard Mountaineering Club found Kinney's summit register and flag at least a thousand feet beneath the summit on a ridge that levelled off, which evidently Kinney mistook as the summit of Mount Robson.

Let us therefore rightly conclude: The resolve being Conrad Kain, the official guide of the Alpine Club of Canada should rightfully be recognized with the first ascent of Mount Robson.

Thank you and good evening.

John Haskell smiled and waved to the cheering audience. He slowly made his way back to the table, basking in the adulation of the crowd. His teammates leaned over and shook his hand, whispering congratulations for a job well done.

Sarah Ryan approached the lectern with confidence, determination and a throbbing headache. Her strawberry hair against the bright stage lights gave her a fiery presence as she began to speak:

Good evening, my name is Sarah Ryan and I will present a rebuttal to the Affirmative Position presented by our opposition from the University of Alberta.

I have never heard so much poppycock in my life. A.O. Wheeler was universally known as a tyrant—a man who demanded and got his own way. Wheeler had both Conrad Kain and Donald (Curly) Phillips under his big fat thumb. Let's face it, Conrad Kain was a semi-illiterate immigrant who hardly spoke English, he was sponsored by the Alpine Club of Canada, and Phillips was a guide beholden to the Club for future employment and economic prosperity. Wheeler wanted the glory for the Alpine Club of Canada but, most importantly, Wheeler wanted the glory for himself. Wheeler travelled the world from Great Britain to Monaco, rubbing shoulders with the climbing elite. He wanted the world to know that it was his club that bagged the highest peak in the Rockies, not some "nutcase" Reverend from the Pacific Coast.

And, if I may, I would like to present one more piece of evidence as recorded by Chic Scott in his book, *Pushing the Limits, The Story of Canadian Mountaineering*. Mr. Scott relates a conversation old-time guide Ken Jones—a longtime friend of Conrad Kain's—had with the Austrian guide in Invermere.

"I asked him (Kain), 'What's this controversy over Phillips and Kinney not getting to the top?'

Kain said, "That was Wheeler. That was Mr. Wheeler's work . . . Kinney and Phillips were on top. They got to the top."

Apparently they found a piece of stick at the top. Kain said, "We found that stick there. It looked like a piece could have been broken off from one of Curly Phillips' sticks."

If you would like to follow me to downtown Banff and pay a visit to the Whyte Museum of the Canadian Rockies, I would like to show you a map that sports Conrad Kain's signature. On this map Kain drew a dotted line that traces his ascent up Mount Robson and right above his signature he wrote, "Showing route taken on the second ascent of Mount Robson, July 13, 1913." People, what more proof do you need—Conrad Kain acknowledged and signed a document clearly stating his was the second ascent of Mount Robson.

As for the discovery in 1959 of Kinney's summit register and flag by the Harvard Mountaineering Club a thousand feet from the summit, could it not be possible that in some 50 years the tin can could have been swept up by an avalanche or debris and moved hundreds of feet from its original resting place?

And if you need more evidence, J. Monroe Thorington wrote in Volume 16 of *The Canadian Alpine Journal*: "MacCarthy and Kain have always given credit for the first ascent to Kinney and Phillips, who were on the mountain in 1909."

It is true everyone liked the affable, kind and good-hearted Conrad Kain, but let's not forget his somewhat checkered past. If you remember, as a youth Kain stole bread, he was known as a poacher, he often claimed he was from the prestigious Tyrol region, when in fact he was not, and he told the fantastic story of the millionaire guide—a totally apocryphal account—time and time again.

Sarah Ryan reached down and took off her shoe and—shades of Nikita Khrushchev—she banged it hard on the lectern and shouted, "To most of you Conrad Kain was a saint, the Prince of the Mountain Guides—to me Conrad Kain was the king of the convenient little white lie."

From the front row to the back, an audible gasp of disbelief rolled through the audience. Then a chorus of angry catcalls and boos was directed back at Sarah Ryan who was now literally clinging to the lectern.

Suddenly, with a sizzling, popping sound, the auditorium lights flickered and dimmed. They then surged bright white and snapped off, plunging the Eric Harvie Theatre into an abyss of darkness. The stunned audience went silent as a loud crack of what sounded like thunder echoed through The Banff Centre. "So that's what the weather reports meant by thundersnow," thought Parker Stevens, as he rushed forward to help a dazed and swaying Sarah Ryan back to her seat.

The dim emergency lights flicked on after a few minutes, bathing the auditorium in a pale, eerie light. Nobel Wiseman, sensing that the situation was deteriorating, rushed headlong to the front of the stage and shouted, without the aid of an operative microphone, "In view of the unfortunate power outage we have experienced, the judges have determined that we will not be able to continue tonight's event. We therefore declare the debate a draw. Thank you for your attendance. The ushers will escort you out and please be careful on your drive home this evening."

"My Gawd, Sarah what were you thinking?" shouted Paulie Kowalachuk as he burst through her dressing room door which had been left slightly ajar. "I thought we agreed to take the high road and not attack Kain personally."

Paulie looked around the vacant room, lit only by the faint glow of the emergency lighting system.

"Sarah, Sarah, where are you? Are you in here?"

Where was she? he thought, as his cellphone went off.

"Paulie, get down here right away. Sarah's collapsed," yelled Parker into the phone.

"Where are you?"

"In the hallway behind the stage curtains. It looks like Sarah never made it back to her dressing room," he hurriedly explained. "She must have collapsed right after the debate ended."

"Did you call 911?"

"Yes, but I am having trouble getting through. It must be the storm that is creating havoc with the phones."

"What's the matter?" enquired a deep, low voice out of the pitch-blackness.

It was Jake Renshaw; a long, thin flashlight in his hand shot a stream of bright light in the direction of the empty dressing room.

"Sarah's collapsed and we need to get her to the hospital," said Paulie frantically.

"I can take her in my car. The passenger's seat folds back. Remember the back doors on your old Volvo are stuck shut," Jake said.

"Okay, let's go find her and Parker."

They soon discovered Parker, knelt over the prone body of Sarah, her face ghostly white and her eyes shut. She was sprawled against the wall of the narrow hallway—her head just missing a heat register when she fell.

"Is she breathing okay?" asked Paulie, giving Parker a worried glance.

"It's a bit shallow but steady," Parker replied.

The three of them managed to gently lift her up and carry her safely through the dark theatre and out a side door into the snowy night. They gently tucked Sarah into Jake's car. Jake threw a light emergency blanket over her to keep her warm.

He sped through the nearly abandoned streets of Banff as fast as he could—despite the raging blizzard with its strong gusts of wind. He arrived at the emergency doors of the Banff Mineral Springs Hospital in short order.

The Banff Mineral Springs Hospital was established in 1930 by four Catholic nuns from Antigonish, Nova Scotia. They purchased the hospital from the estate of Dr. Brett. Dr. Brett, along with his sons and colleagues, had first started to deliver health services to the Bow Valley from a small log cabin in 1886, which was an improvement from the boxcar that was previously the medical facility.

The single-storey brick and stucco building with a large H on its most prominent facade faces south and hugs the central downtown area of Banff. Surrounded by the spectacular peaks of the Canadian Rockies, the hospital sits in one of the world's most picturesque settings.

About 45 minutes after Sarah Ryan's admission, the doctor—who looked more like a teenage snowboarder than a medical doctor—came through the double doors leading into the waiting area. He was dressed in a white smock coat and his plastic ID badge read Dr. Geoff Rose, Intern.

"It looks like she is suffering from a low-grade concussion, obviously the result of her face smacking the dashboard," said Dr. Rose, directing his attention to Parker Stevens.

"Is she going to be okay?" asked a shaken Paulie Kowalachuk, echoing the sentiments of the others.

"She'll have a nasty headache for a few days, but she'll be fine with a couple of nights' rest. It's the sort of thing we see all the time when these young hockey players take a shot to the head or a snowboarder wipes out on an icy track," explained Dr. Rose.

"Is she awake? Can we go in and see her?" asked Jake.

"Yes, she's awake, but still pretty groggy," the doctor said. "I would suggest keeping your visit brief. Sarah really needs some rest."

"Any idea when you will release her?" asked Parker.

"She will have to stay in overnight for observation, and barring any complications she should be able to go home tomorrow afternoon," said Dr. Rose.

"What happened?" asked Sarah, as the three young men gathered around the foot of her hospital bed.

"I guess you collapsed on your way back to the dressing room. The doc says you have a concussion," said Paulie.

"What, from the debate?" asked Sarah, not fully comprehending what had happened.

"No, the car accident," said Parker. "Remember, you banged your face on the dashboard and your nose really bled. I'm sorry that happened."

"Hey, it wasn't your fault. That big old elk jumped right in front of us," said Paulie.

"Sarah, you are going to have to spend the night. They will check on you in the morning," said Jake, moving to the head of the bed.

"Listen Sarah. The storm has quieted down outside. Paulie and I have an early morning hockey tournament at the university tomorrow," said Parker. "Are you okay if Jake drives you back to Calgary tomorrow afternoon?"

"Yes, that's fine, if it's okay with Jake," Sarah said. Her eyes fluttered with fatigue several times before she drifted off to sleep again.

Parker turned to Jake and said, "Are you sure you are okay doing this for us?"

"Yes, no problem," said Jake. "You and Paulie get going before they decide to close the highways."

"It's great meeting you," said Parker, stretching to shake Jake's hand. He flinched as he felt a sharp pain run through his neck again.

Paulie shook Jake's hand as well and thanked him again for his help.

"Don't worry. I'll make sure Sarah gets back home to the dorms safe and sound. I'll check in with you before I leave Calgary," said Jake, pulling up a chair to sit next to Sarah.

Two months after Sarah Ryan graduated from the University of Calgary, she moved to Cranbrook to article for a local legal firm.

Less than a year after being pulled out of Parker Stevens' old blue Volvo by Jake Renshaw, she married the sports reporter of the *Cranbrook Daily Townsman*.

The day after the wedding, James Gunn, the editor of the paper and Jake's boss, ran their wedding picture on the front page under the headline, *Love/Hate of Austrian Mountain Guide, Conrad Kain, Brings Couple Together in Marriage* with a subheading that said, "Big-city lawyer nabs our small-town sports reporter."

Conrad Kain Campfire Tales

High on the reaches of Mount Hooker:

Morning came, a cheerless dawn, but we had been watching for it. The snow seemed to be lessening; the fog ebbed and billowed. Just before four o'clock the snow ceased; the fog wavered and lifted, so that as we looked out we could see the ground below us and the way to the pass. We were a stiff lot, but I made a leap for my boots and it seemed to startle everyone. It is hard work putting on half-frozen shoes, and I was first out, pushing over the snow-crusted boulders in the doorway. Miserably uncomfortable as we were, Mr. Thorington said it was impossible not to think of Samson and the pillars of the temple!

By the campfire that evening, I remarked that Mount Hooker was the most interesting mountain I had climbed in recent years, and that the summit arête reminded me of Mount Cook in New Zealand. There are few Canadian peaks that I find worthy of such praise.

Chapter 15

Conrad Kain brought his love of skiing and ski jumping to the Canadian Rockies. He founded the first ski club in Banff and would regularly practise his jumping.

"As early as 1887, Scandinavian woodcutters working for the CPR near Banff hand-carved skis and used them to move through the deep snow in the winter."

The Birth of Skiing in the Rockies

By the 1890s Rossland had become a booming mining town, feeding ore to the giant smelter owned by Augustus Heinz in Trail, located some seven or eight miles down the mountain on the banks of the Columbia River. The famed Le Roi Mine was reported to have produced over $30 million in gold in short order. The thriving mining town sported more than 40 licensed bars and saloons, a certain sign of success for any frontier town.

The ever-increasing need for miners brought gung-ho individuals from all corners of the world. This influx included one Olaus Jeldness, a 39-year-old Norwegian mining engineer whose love of skiing soon became evident. The deep powdery snow that blanketed nearby Red Mountain was a dream come true for a skier of exceptional talent and passion like Jeldness, who described skiing as "the Royal Sport of the Northlands."

Around the same time that Olaus Jeldness arrived in Rossland, an article appeared on the front page of Revelstoke's *Kootenay Star* newspaper—proving that skiing was taking hold throughout the mountains of western Canada. The article read, "Yesterday a young man mounted on a pair of Norwegian snowshoes (what is now called skis), essayed the task of skimming over the snow-covered surface of Main Street, but owing to its being considerably cut up by traffic, he did not make much headway. These snowshoes (skis) are simply thin slats of wood, about three inches in width and 10 feet in length, turned up in front like the bow of a canoe. The feet are fastened to these slats by leather straps in the centre, leaving about five feet clear fore and aft which is not lifted clear of the snow but glides along the surface. A pole about six feet in length is carried either for steering or as help in propulsion."

Olaus Jeldness was a native of Stangvik, Norway, which is located in the midst of the Nordmore ski district. It is said that he set a record in ski jumping, at only 15 years old, of over 92 feet. Jeldness emigrated to the United States in 1873 and subsequently worked in mining in Michigan, Missouri, South Dakota and Colorado. In 1896, he arrived in the booming town of Rossland and quickly got involved in the buying and selling of land and mining claims. He reportedly netted $75,000 in one lucrative transaction.

Jeldness, who had rediscovered his love of skiing on the slopes of Colorado, must have been a strange sight when he disembarked from the train with a pair of ten-foot "Norwegian snowshoes" slung over his shoulder. Over the next decade he was in the forefront of setting up competitive ski-running and ski-jumping competitions on Red Mountain. Proving his own prowess, Olaus Jeldness captured the championships four years running from 1897 to 1900.

As one observer wrote about Jeldness, "The sight of this latter-day Viking with his queer elongated snowshoes, ski-sliding down from the top of Red Mountain . . . was nothing short of fantastic."

In an effort to spur the development of skiing at Red Mountain he donated the Jeldness Trophy, which has inscribed on it the following...

Play not for gain but for sport,
Leap not for gold but glee,
Oh! Youth play well thy part,
Whate'er life's game might be.

However, the interior of British Columbia wasn't the only place the popular winter sport of skiing was popping up. As early as 1887, Scandinavian woodcutters working for the CPR near Banff hand-carved skis and used them to move through the deep snow in the winter.

A LETTER TO AMELIA

Dear Amelia:

Now I am back in Banff from the survey with Dr. Longstaff and Mr. Harmon. It has been too cold and I have been too tired to write. We were in Banff for the Christmas celebration. In the second week of January a fearful storm came, with great cold. For three days no train got through. The coldest day was –52°. It may have been a little warmer in the tent, but not much, for we had a bad stove. It would not burn well except on one evening—and then the tent caught fire. Luckily we could save most things, but my blankets are badly burned. I was damaged the least, for I was not in camp that evening. I had gone with the dogs to Banff to get provisions, and reached camp at one o'clock in the morning, half-frozen. We always wore snowshoes. The snow was four to five feet deep. One always sleeps clothed. One gets hardened to it.

Minus 20 does not seem so cold, but when it goes below –30° then all comfort ceases, and during such weather one's thoughts often turn toward home or to a warmer climate. The engineer in charge wanted to take me with him for two years to Hudson Bay, but I told him that I did not want to go so far from the mountains. He gave me a good recommendation in Banff. I have often used the instruments without making serious mistakes. To be sure, Amelia, there is no great skill required, but no workman in Austria would ever be allowed to do such a thing. Now I am cutting ice at $2.50 per day. I have not spoken German for so long that I am almost afraid I shall forget it.

Yesterday a lady, sent by the railway, came to me for information as to the possibilities here for skiing and tobogganing. I talked to her about sport for nearly two hours. Several weeks ago I founded a ski club in Banff. The people seem to take to this sport. We practise every Sunday, jumping as well, and many people assemble. My longest jump is 50 feet, about 12 feet beyond the last record.

At our winter sport festival we had more than 400 onlookers. It lasted all night. We had more than 100 lamps. A tent was put up and refreshments sold. We collected $55. I think I have a good beginning. No wonder the lady from the railway wanted to speak with me.

Amelia, as you know, I remember watching the skating when I was in Vienna. How poor I was then—could not skate and could not join in. But it will be otherwise when I am there again; maybe we can skate together. Now I can skate and have the money. I am continually thinking of home, of my mother and my good friends. But I have no desire to remain there, for it is certain that Canada is better for the workman; he has a freer course and more opportunity.

Winter makes us sleepy with thought, and spring awakes us. The past comes to mind. I recall, Amelia, that three years ago today we made our lovely excursion in the Wienerwald.

Kindest regards,
Conrad

Chapter 16

Englishman Sir Edward Whymper, who led the first successful ascent of the Matterhorn, was hired by the CPR to publicize mountaineering and alpine tourism in the Canadian Rockies.

"I guess you could say the guides got their

peaks, Whymper his booze, and the CPR

very little."

Sir Edward Whymper to the Rescue

William Van Horne sat behind his large roll-top desk, from where it is said he ran every detail of the CPR, poring over the passenger volume reports to the Canadian Rockies for the previous season.

With numbers trending dramatically upward, passengers carried increased from 1.8 million in 1886 to over 3 million in 1894. Van Horne felt somewhat reassured that his marketing strategy to bring alpinists and mountaineers westward to the Canadian Rockies was on the right track. However, as with most things, William Van Horne believed the potential had just been scratched and much more opportunity awaited.

To bolster his marketing efforts he had recently added two key men to his well-oiled publicity department. They were David McNicoll and the flamboyant former newspaper man, George Ham.

Van Horne threw down the reports he had been deciphering and marched across his office. He grasped the ornate door handle with enough force to rattle the entire room, swung open the heavy wooden door and strode down a long narrow hallway—pausing only to give a stern rap on several doors as he passed by.

Everyone knew what that knock meant. You would immediately drop whatever you were doing and fall into lockstep with Van Horne as he thundered toward a small, cramped meeting room at the very end of the hallway.

"The purpose of this meeting is to give you a timely update on passenger loads to the west," said Van Horne, in a forceful, no-nonsense manner. "Though the numbers are up, let me tell you this is not a time for complacency. We have a lot of work still to be done."

"I have heard through the grapevine that westward passenger numbers have been way up," said someone from the back of the room.

"That is true," confirmed Van Horne, blowing a billowing ring of blue smoke from his cigar in the general direction of the commenter. "But we can't be resting on our laurels."

"Resting on our laurels! I've never worked so hard at any newspaper as I am working here," moaned George Ham.

"We need something big, a big idea! Something that will impress the world," replied Van Horne, ignoring the previous remark.

"What do you have in mind?" asked publicity boss David McNicoll.

"I don't really know. All I know is that we need something that will reach out and grab some international attention. Headlines in every major newspaper—some way to reach out to the mountaineering crowd," said Van Horne, his face flushed with excitement.

"How about someone, rather than something?" George Ham said thoughtfully.

"Ham, was that you? Can you elaborate, man. Don't keep us in the dark—what did you have in mind?" Van Horne demanded.

"I have been following the writing of Sir Edward Whymper in the *Times of London*. If you read between the lines of his adventure stories, it would appear old Ed Whymper is itching for a new challenge," said Ham.

"Who's this Edward Whymper? How can he help us?" asked Van Horne.

"Well, Mr. Van Horne, Sir Edward Whymper is a British climber who just happens to be the most famous mountaineer in the world. First to climb the Matterhorn, in fact," replied George Ham.

"It took him seven or eight tries, didn't it?" said McNicoll, sounding cool to the idea.

"Yes, but he did it. He was knighted for his achievement and lionized among the British public," said Ham.

"But old man Whymper has a pretty big blotch against his reputation, don't you think?" retorted McNicoll.

"True, Sir Edward lost eight climbers on the descent of the Matterhorn, but accidents do happen in the mountains," said Ham.

"There were even rumblings about ropes being cut to save Whymper," replied McNicoll, crossing his arms tightly across his chest.

"That was all rumour—nothing was ever proven. He still remains the most famous mountaineer in the world to this day," Ham added, tiring of the argument and turning in the direction of Van Horne as if to seek his support.

"So what are you suggesting George?" demanded Van Horne, impatiently rapping his fist on the table.

"I say we should bring Sir Edward Whymper to Canada. Do a travelling road show starting in Montreal all the way to the Rockies. Get him to climb a few mountains, give some speeches and write it up in reports to the *Times of London*," explained Ham.

"Do you think he would actually do that?" asked McNicoll, somewhat skeptically.

"My God, why are you such a naysayer? With the right financial inducements and a few extra bottles of whiskey, Sir Edward would be over here in a flash. One last hurrah for an aging climber," argued Ham.

"George, I must admit, I like the possibilities," said Van Horne, sitting back down to contemplate the idea.

"It'll blow the top off our publicity campaign, I can guarantee that. Every alpinist or would-be climber will want to follow in the footsteps of the great Sir Edward Whymper," said George Ham.

"Brilliant, George. Absolutely brilliant!" said Van Horne, his voice rising with excitement. "Let's contact Mr. Whymper immediately. Offer to pay his way, his accommodation, offer him free passage to Canada. Whatever it takes to get him here."

"I'd be careful on this one. It could backfire on us," warned McNicoll, adding quietly, "I've heard he's a bloody lush."

"Nothing ventured, nothing gained," shouted Van Horne, jumping up and again smacking the table with the palm of his large hand. "George, wire him immediately. Spare no cost. I agree this idea could send our visitation to the Rockies through the roof."

"Brilliant, George," said McNicoll, rolling his eyes. "You can manage the old boy when he falls off a mountain smelling of booze."

"Now let's get back to work," Van Horne's voice boomed through the little room, as he chose to ignore or simply didn't hear McNicoll's concerns—more likely the former.

William Van Horne stood at the end of the conference table rubbing his hands together at the delightful prospect of attracting the world's most famous mountaineer to the Canadian Rockies. How could he lose with a man of Sir Edward Whymper's stature?

WHYMPER IN CANADA

Upon his arrival in Banff in 1909, Conrad Kain couldn't help but be impressed with the Canadian Rockies from the very first day. A.O. Wheeler of the Alpine Club of Canada first assigned him to help the club move into their new clubhouse in Banff. He was then assigned to the Club's camp at spectacular Lake O'Hara, with its azure-blue water, plunging waterfalls and nearby soaring peaks. Though he hardly had time to admire the scenery, he worked tirelessly on the grounds and readied the tents for the upcoming camp.

He watched as an impressive lineup of the world's climbing's elite arrived, including British notables like A.L. Mumm and Leopold Stuart Amery, H.B. Dixon and, of course, the dour 69-year-old Edward Whymper. The conqueror of the Matterhorn and the Andes, Whymper arrived with his usual posse of guides and porters, but he was a shadow of the man he once was, for now he drank too much and climbed too little—though it didn't seem to stop him from enjoying some wild times at the Field Hotel. He addressed the camp with the speech of a sad and lonely man.

"Ladies and gentlemen, live, live, while you can. We're born to live, but born to die. Unite prudence with courage. Take heed to your steps lest you fall. Whatever you set your hands to do, do it with all your might. Act well your part, there all the honour lies. This, ladies and gentlemen, is the first and it will be the last occasion on which I shall have the honour to speak to you. I came out from Europe expressly for this meeting and tomorrow I start back. But, if unable to be with you in body, I shall, so long as I live, be with you in spirit, and wish you success and prosperity."

For the first six days, Conrad led the British contingent around the Yoho Valley, though it is unclear if the party included Sir Edward Whymper, who only remained in Yoho for a few days. The trekkers spent most of their time above the timberline, climbing the likes of Mt. Habel and Mt. McArthur and ending the trek by climbing Mt. Stephen.

"So, I hear you have just arrived from Switzerland?" said Edward Whymper, as he tried to peer through the swirling smoke of the smouldering campfire, nursing a large, dark bottle of rye.

"Yes, I have been hired by the Alpine Club to be their mountain guide," said Conrad hesitantly, in his broken English. "But I actually came from Austria not Switzerland."

"Austria, Switzerland, Germany. They are all the same to me," Whymper said, with a wave of his hand.

"Yes, but only if you are from Britain," relied Conrad.

"Here, have something to drink. What did you say your name was?" Whymper asked, reaching over to fill a nearby tin cup to the brim.

"Kain. Conrad Kain, certified Austrian mountain guide."

"Well, young man, your career is just starting but mine is finished. It's been almost 40 years since I climbed the Matterhorn. I must tell you there is not a night that passes that I don't have nightmares of that damned rope breaking on our descent," Whymper said, his face in his hands. "Conrad, I lost them all. I was frozen, helpless, as I watched my four companions slide off the edge of that bloody cliff, arms outstretched, to their death below."

"Accidents do happen in the mountains," said Conrad, after a few minutes of awkward silence.

"Conrad, it took me seven bloody attempts to climb that mountain. Then when I did, it came back and bit me hard," said Whymper, in not much more than a slurred whisper.

"Have you ever thought about hanging up your climbing boots?"

"I would have quit a few years ago, but for the CPR enticing me to explore the Canadian Rockies. Mind you I haven't climbed many mountains of late. I just sit around the fire and wait for the others to do the climbing for me."

"Fresh air never hurt a man," said Conrad, struggling to think of things to say as the old man continued to ramble on.

"Conrad, I once knew a guide here in the Rockies, a dry, humourless old stick named Martin. On this particular portion of the trail, which we had to walk up and down every day, was a fallen log. Eventually, it got on my nerves. I said, 'Martin! Come here and cut that log.' Martin, who's lying on the ground resting, barely looks up but says, "Well, Mr. Whymper, I've been up and down this valley many times and every time that log has been there, and I'm thinking Mr. Whymper, if you want that log cut you'll have to cut it yourself.'"

"So what did you do?"

"I jumped up and yelled, 'Martin! You're fired.' But I guess Martin was used to me firing him, and a short while later he was still lying there resting. So I shouted again, 'Martin, come here!' And when he showed up at my tent I had a bottle in one hand and a mug in the other, and in exactly the same tone I ordered, 'Martin, have a mug of beer,'" said Whymper, now chuckling loudly.

"Such are the ways in the mountains," Conrad nodded.

"Saddest thing I ever saw in the Rockies was on my first trip here," the old man continued. "It was my first time to Canada, 1903 I believe. I had met Sir James Hector, geologist, botanist and surgeon from the Palliser Expedition back in the mid-1880s. He had just returned to Canada from New Zealand with his younger son, Douglas, a young man of a brilliant mind and great promise. Ever heard of them?"

"No, can't say I have."

"They reached Glacier House in early August, and the son started to show severe signs of illness so he was removed to the Revelstoke Hospital. There he died—from peritonitis, I believe—and on August 17th his body was laid to rest; within the sound of the river his father had explored so many years ago, and in the shadow of the mountains where his best manhood had been spent, the son lies today."

Whymper paused to drain the last few drops of whiskey from the bottle he had been cradling all night and then he continued.

"I was contacted and quickly made my way to Revelstoke to attend the burial of young Douglas Hector. I found Dr. Hector most congenial, despite his tragedy, willing to talk about his old exploring days, but come the next morning he turned his face westward and returned to New Zealand by the vessel which had borne him to our land. I tell you, Conrad, mountains have no mercy."

"It is true," said Conrad.

"And the worst part of it all, Conrad, was that my bloody foot was so infected I could hardly walk. I had it treated by a Dr. Schaffer, who I later found out was an ophthalmologist, which probably explains why it took so long to heal."

"Could be," nodded Conrad.

Edward Whymper stood up and staggered dangerously close to the waning campfire before sitting down hard again on a rough stump of wood.

"Look at those glaciers," he said, pointing to the snowy peaks that surrounded them.

"They look impressive in the moonlight," said Conrad.

"You know, Conrad, glaciers fulfill three purposes."

"What's that?"

"They polish rocks, supply ice to hotels and provide chasms for tourists to tumble into," he said, with a mighty laugh. Then the old man, with the face of bulldog, rose slowly and staggered off to bed with a most unsteady gait.

"Good night, Conrad," he waved as he ducked into his tent.

"Good night," Conrad replied, exhausted by Whymper's inebriated ramblings.

Edward Whymper died two years later in Chamonix, France, where he had gone on a round of visits despite being in extremely bad health. According to an English newspaper, during his last days he was haunted by the tragedy on the Matterhorn, which carried his name all over the world.

Within a week the old mountaineer was buried in the midst of the mountains, his coffin carried to the grave by 10 of the most famous guides in the district. All the villagers and every passing tourist attended the funeral, various alpine clubs being represented by individual members, every club in Europe sending wreaths of alpine flowers.

"Nothing could be more melancholy," wrote an eyewitness, "than the long procession under a grey sky, pierced here and there by lofty aiguilles (sharp, pointed mountain peaks) brilliant in newly fallen snow."

Among the humble friends present who had known Edward Whymper for 50 years was an old man who had helped to carry down the bodies of those killed on the Matterhorn in 1865.

In 1901, he being in his sixty-second year, Whymper first came to the Canadian Rockies. Upon his departure from London, rumour had it that he was en route as the conqueror of the Matterhorn to now conquer the Matterhorn of the Rockies (Mount Assiniboine). He made base observations but he never did attack Assiniboine.

Much to the dismay of the CPR, Whymper never published an account of his Canadian explorations. The CPR brass had hoped he would write a climber's guide for the Rockies similar to his popular Swiss guidebooks. About all he produced was a dry statistical report which he forwarded to the CPR. Disappointingly, it had none of the literary charm of some of his previous books.

As one writer lamented, "If his pen had not lost its cunning, the impressions of a climber so eminent in the Alps and Andes would have been an addition of great value in the literature of the Canadian Rockies."

When the young Bosnian dissident, Gavrilo Princip, raised his pistol and fired a deadly hail of bullets into the open-air car in which the Austrian Archduke Franz Ferdinand and his wife were riding through the streets of Sarajevo, on June 28, 1914, it plunged the world into an irreversible march toward the bloodiest conflict mankind had ever experienced.

Thousands of miles away, Austrian guide and Austrian army conscript, Conrad

Kain, was busy doing more of the "dirty work" for Arthur O. Wheeler, Alpine Club of Canada president and chief surveyor of the Dominion of Canada. Conrad had just returned from a winter season of guiding in New Zealand and was once again in the employ of Wheeler, hauling heavy crates of surveying and photographic equipment to the ridges of the Rocky Mountains in the wilds of the barren, windswept Crowsnest Pass.

"I don't know what Mr. Wheeler has in these crates, but they are breaking my back," said the packer who was accompanying Conrad Kain.

Conrad only grunted and continued to trudge slowly, but deliberately, up the steep mountain slope.

"Two more crates each and I think we have it beat," panted the packer.

Conrad shrugged, his shoulders sagging under the weight, focusing his attention on the spire above them.

"Back home in Austria, mountain guides are not expected to be pack animals," Conrad finally said, as they crested the blustery summit.

The two men sat down on a rocky outcrop to catch their breath. Reaching into their rucksacks they pulled out a lunch of sandwiches and tea.

"See that big lone mountain over there?" said the packer, pointing across the valley, through the swirling mist, at the birthday cake-shaped Crowsnest Mountain.

"A beautiful mountain, if I do say so myself," said Conrad.

"Legend has it that it was that peak that defeated the legendary climber Edward Whymper."

"How's that?"

"On one of his publicity trips to the Rockies for the CPR, Whymper took to the bottle—a bit more than usual. First one drink, then another, then a pint, a fifth and, finally, over a quart a day."

"I heard Whymper make a speech to the Alpine Club once. He truly was a sad man, drowning himself in sorrow and booze."

"Well, the story goes that on the day the party was to climb Crowsnest Mountain, old Ed was too hung-over to even stick his head out of the tent. So his Swiss guides and climbing partner scrambled to the top and back before he awoke from his stupour."

"Well, they said you could always find Whymper's campsite, just by the large number of discarded liquor containers that were scattered about."

"I guess you could say the guides got their peaks, Whymper his booze, and the CPR very little," the packer laughed.

"Let's get those last two loads up here and then we can do what Sir Edward Whymper couldn't—scramble to the top of Crowsnest Mountain," said Conrad, turning his back to buffer the howling wind from the west.

Little did he know, at that very same moment, the winds of World War I were swirling just as viciously across Europe.

Chapter 17

Conrad Kain in the company of a trio of women mountaineers, including Cora Best and Annette Buck. The dashing Kain was a favourite guide among female alpinists.

"Women referred to him as 'dear Conrad,'
and men saw him as the epitome of what
they might like to be—an independent
spirit admired for his achievements and
loved for his warmth and humour."

Dear Conrad—Kain's Ladies

"Conrad Kain was a man of slightly less than average height. His brown eyes were his most notable feature. They had depth in colour and expression and reflected instantly his every mood." So writes Phil Dowling in his book, *The Mountaineers.* "His clothing always appeared rumpled. He did, however, frequently wear a necktie on climbs in deference to his clients, who always appeared to him to be of a higher social status than his. Few paid as much attention to these matters as he did, however. His personality was so vibrant that he captivated everyone who met him. Women referred to him as 'dear Conrad,' and men saw him as the epitome of what they might like to be—an independent spirit admired for his achievements and loved for his warmth and humour. He was a merciless wit, and when he told stories around a campfire he could render his audience nearly sick with laughter."

The Swiss guide, Rudolph Aemmer—who at one point played John Barrymore's double in the Canadian Rockies-filmed movie, *Eternal Love*—and Conrad Kain were considered two of the most handsome guides in the Rockies.

"One might almost have called (them) picturesque," wrote Dowling, of the pair of guides. "(They) both looked precisely the way a guide should. As inveterate pipe smokers, (they) had friendly brown eyes, rosy cheeks and both sported a magnificent black mustache. (Rudolph) sported a gold band in his earlobe. With (their) dark and becoming tans, it made (them) appear dashing and gypsy-like."

Definitely dashing enough to make the ladies swoon, though this was nothing new for Conrad Kain as he often told his climbing partners when they gathered around a roaring campfire, their clients having long since crawled into their tents for the night.

"Once when I was climbing in Italy, near Milan, I ended up in a carriage with a newlywed couple. I took a book to hide my face behind, while the two quarreled," Conrad grinned and continued his story. "I asked the bride, when her new husband departed, why she had married him? She just made a face and called him insipid and an idiot. I bid the young bride adieu. I engaged a room, changed my clothes and went into the dining room. I had scarcely finished eating when I heard the woman ask the waiter whether a young man, an Austrian, had come in. The waiter came and got me, she greeted me with a friendly manner and asked me to accompany her to the Exposition. Suspicious, I hid my pocketbook."

"Was she after your pocketbook or was she after you?" asked one of the other guides.

"No, but on the train to the Exposition, she told me her story of woe. We had a glass together in a beer hall. Viennese waltzes were playing, and my companion was gay and light of heart—until her husband showed up. He spoke sharply and accused me of seducing his wife."

"How did you wiggle out of that one, Conrad?"

"I said, 'Sir, don't get angry, let your wife tell the story.' But all she did was start crying bitterly and didn't say a word. I told the man I had met his wife at the Exposition, where she was waiting for him, and was about to guide her back to her hotel. The outraged husband would have none of it and most forcefully begged my pardon. Off they went and I thought I had seen the last of the bride.

"Next a knock came at my door. 'Sir, there is someone here who wishes to speak to you,' came this familiar voice through the door.

"I shouted, 'In a moment.' I dressed and opened the door. Who was it? The lady again. She asked me if she might come in. Remembering her irate husband, I said quietly, 'Get away from me,' but she walked in, put her arms around my neck and kissed me, then fell on her knees and begged me to forgive yesterday's unpleasant scene with her husband. She began to call me her 'dear Conrad' and she wanted me to take her back to Vienna. I advised her to return to her husband, but she begged me to meet her that afternoon."

"So what did you do?"

"Just to get rid of her I said yes and goodbye. God be praised, I was free! I told the waiter to tell the woman, if she came again, that I had gone. Thank goodness, I never saw her again."

One of the mountain guides, Edward Feuz, got up, still chuckling at Conrad's story, and grabbed another armload of wood. He stoked the campfire, once again, into a roaring blaze.

"It reminds me of the time I was at Glacier House, 1905 or '06, when Mr. Hearst, the newspaper Hearst from California, arrived with a bunch of his girls," said Edward Feuz, a Swiss guide for the CPR. "Young girls, office girls, you know—I must say very good-looking girls, jolly, happy girls. And he wanted them to have a good time. And he's a good-time fellow, he was a nice fellow that Mr. Hearst. Of course he was worth lots of money and we fussed around him, you know."

"What about the girls?"

"Anyway, he wanted to go camping up the Asulkan Valley with the girls. He gave us big tips in $5 gold coins, which he said his father had mined in California. So, we went up with the girls with tents, and the pony boys with the horses up the trail. They took me along to go on the glacier ice, and they wanted to stay out all that night. We went with the horses up there to the last timber, and we saw a bear—way up the slide. Showed him to the girls and all they did was scream. Time went on, we went up there and made camp and made a huge fire—we had dinner and it clouded over. It was quite dark and it looked like a big storm was coming on."

"The girls, Ed, what about the office girls?"

"So we were singing a song there, and it was soon time for bed—as soon as it gets dark you go to bed in the summer—it was 10 or so. I was standing there by the fire, and the girls disappeared, and then finally Mr. Hearst disappears. I stood there with the fire, smoking a little bit, you know—nice and quiet and figuring out for the next day to go up under the ice, when here comes Mr. Hearst, running back."

"He says, 'Ed!'"

"Yes, Mr. Hearst, what's wrong?" I asked.

"I'll tell you, the girls is all scared. They're scared in the tent of that bear they saw—they think the bear will come around. Would you mind sleeping with the girls, Ed?"

"What did you say, Ed?"

"I says, Mr. Hearst, a great pleasure, Mr. Hearst, in the mountains, to sleep with the girls."

The mountain guides looked at each other and laughed uproariously.

Conrad threw another log on the fire and its sparks jumped and crackled into the night sky.

"So I went in there and it was a nice peaceful night. There wasn't a thing around—not a hint of the bear," said Ed Feuz, grinning from ear to ear. "Oh, I was young . . . there were six girls . . . yes, yes. They had a big bell tent, you know. Oh, there were a lot of things that happened like that in the Rockies."

With his first summer season of mountain guiding over, Conrad Kain found himself without a job. Desperate for work, he found employment with an Austrian farmer who had settled near Fort Saskatchewan, Alberta. It probably would have been a typical, cold prairie winter, except for the fact that the farmer had a daughter and he was certain Conrad would make her an ideal husband.

Another jug of schnapps was passed around the campfire as Conrad began to regale the other mountain guides with another of his amorous tales.

"Marie was her name. A young, attractive, strong-bodied girl, well developed from farm labour," he said with a twinkle in his eye. "Her family plied me with whiskey, homemade sausages and sauerkraut—it was just like being back in Austria. The farmer soon had me out in the barn looking at a newly born colt, but I soon found myself alone with Marie. Suddenly, she's embracing and kissing me—quickly becoming flushed, she opens her eyes wide and suddenly bursts out, 'Do I please you? Do you love me?'

"Gee, Conrad, she would have made you into a good farmer," one of guides snickered.

"I was nearly overwhelmed with her affection, but all I could think of was being stuck far away from the mountains in the middle of the prairie," Conrad continued. "I thought to myself, 'One must be a man, not a fool.'

"Things cooled down for a month or so, and then her parents invited me over after Sunday church service. When evening came Marie and her parents insisted I spend the night—conveniently in a room right next to Marie's.

"Soon there was a knocking at my door and Marie was there with an extra blanket. Her room was much warmer, she said. I was sorely tempted to follow her . . . I could feel my flesh weakening.

"Marie would not let up. She soon returned to my room concerned about noises. She asked me to comfort her. In desperation, I explained we were not married. Suddenly she's embracing me again and turns out the light. I chided her for her behaviour, and then she starts to cry and asked for my forgiveness. Soon we are both asleep—in separate beds."

"It was over?"

"No, when I went to the kitchen for breakfast the next morning, Marie's mother asks boldly and hopefully, 'Were you with her?'

"No! was my reply and then the mother turns and starts to weep but I said I was proud to have been the master over myself.

"She was a beautiful girl," he said, wistfully, sitting down hard on the round block of wood and holding his hands out toward the fire. The other mountain guides stirred nervously and nodded in recognition of his resolve—but wondered what they would have done in the same situation.

"Tough to top that story, Conrad," chimed in Ed Feuz, taking a deep draw from the fresh tobacco he had just stuffed his pipe with. "But I'll do my best.

"I remember when Van Horne decided to send out old man Whymper to publicize the Canadian Rockies. Darn near backfired in every conceivable way," Feuz said. "Whymper, supposed king of the mountain men—conqueror of the Matterhorn—decides to stay in Field one night. Early in the evening the hotel guests had gathered, as was customary, in the lounge next to the lobby to enjoy a few pre-dinner libations."

"Drinks, Ed, we call them drinks."

"So be it, drinks then. Anyways, all at once polite conversation is interrupted by a piercing female scream of terror from the corridors above.

"'RAPE!'" she yells.

"A split second later a dishevelled middle-aged Victorian lady streaked past the assembled guests and ran breathless to the reception desk.

"'Help! There's a MAN! He chased me down the hall. He was STARK NAKED.'

"The manageress, one of the Mollison sisters, I believe, smiled, unperturbed. 'Oh madam, not to worry. That must have been our good friend, Sir Edward Whymper. He's not so young as he used to be and he has a few little eccentricities, you know.'"

"Old Whymper, stark naked? Now that would be a sight to see," laughed the guides.

"I'd have to say the CPR definitely got their money's worth bringing over Whymper to the Rockies," one of the guides concluded, a touch of sarcasm in his voice. "If he wasn't chasing women, he was stinking drunk and expecting one of us to tow him up to the top of some peak."

It was around this glowing campfire that Conrad Kain told his most notorious story concerning himself and the ladies who flocked to climb with him.

"How is it," the guides asked, "that when you are in the Alpine Club camps the ladies all want to climb with you?"

Conrad smiled, struck a match and puffed through his pipe. With a glint in his eye and the reflection of the harvest moon lighting up his face, he explained.

"Wal, dot is very easy thing to explain," Conrad began, his accent thicker than ever. "You see, when the ladies come into camp they are a little afraid. They want to climb a peak, but they think maybe they cannot make her. So when I see one who look a little bit timid, und if she be young and a good-looker, I say, 'You want to climb a mountain? Dot is fine; I guarantee you make her.'

"So next morning we go off. Und after a little while I say, 'Now, young lady, you must excuse me a little while, but I must sit down for a schmoke.' Und so we sit down.

"After a while we go on again, and presently I stop. I pick up a rock und I look at it and turn it over, und I tell the girl all the geology I do not know. Und after a while if she is very tired, maybe I make a little bit loving to her.

"Very harmless, you understand, but dot little loving bring her to und we are on the summit. Und, say, she is pleased!

"Dot is why, afterward, every day in the camp, those womans say, 'Oh, Conrad, will you not be so kind as to take me on the mountain.'"

Conrad turned and kicked another log onto the fire, a grin plastered across his dark, weathered face.

The list of ladies that Conrad guided through the years to the summit of many of the highest peaks in the Rockies included Annette Buck, Cora Johnstone Best, Audrey Shippam, Phyllis Munday and Caroline Hinman, not to mention Mrs. Jane Thomson, the adventurous, 59-year-old widow he led across the New Zealand Alps.

Mrs. Thomson once wrote that Conrad was "a splendid guide, with a genius for finding new routes. He never took an established route unless it pleased him to do so. Competent judges say he was the finest mountaineer ever in New Zealand." She adds, "In those days he was a handsome man with a pleasing personality and fund of entertaining stories of his life, told in broken English." While another writer stated, "I hope Conrad's married life was as happy as it deserved to be. But somehow I don't think he could ever have given his real heart to any woman; the mountains were his life and his love."

"Conrad, tell us about your adventures back in Austria. Tell us about the 'fensterln' (window-visiting)," asked one of the younger guides.

"It's getting late and we have a big day ahead of us tomorrow," Conrad complained, trying to avoid another round of stories.

"Just a quick one, okay Conrad?"

"It reminds me of that farmer girl Marie. Her mother said for a young Austrian, I acted very strangely! She said it doesn't matter if you go to Marie; she's a strong, healthy girl, and it would be quite natural," reminisced Conrad. "How could a mother do that?"

"What do you mean?"

"I know that I am not, and have never been, an angel. I have gone 'window-gazing' in many parts of Austria. I talked about love and its meaning with many girls and women, but never in my life have I heard a mother utter such words about her child," he said, turning to spit in disgust.

"What about the window-gazing?"

"Fensterln goes on chiefly in the mountain regions where the houses are separated and lonely and the young people are unable to meet as they do in cities. The young mountaineer—like me—has just as tender feelings toward the feminine sex as the young fellows in town. In the mountains there is not a dance or a concert every Sunday but the young want to get together. What else is there to do but to take a ladder, go to the window of one's beloved and chat for an hour or so?

"I regard it as a special pleasure, almost as a sport, because at the window one can show whether he is wise or stupid, cowardly or courageous."

"Sounds sort of dangerous, don't you think Conrad?"

"True, everyone who is well acquainted with life in the mountains knows that there are numerous obstacles," said Conrad, outlining them one by one.

"One, the dog." (The guides grinned.)

"Two, the position of the window, and how to reach it." (The guides chuckled.)

"Three, the kind of ladder that is needed." (The guides chortled.)

"Four, where the old folks sleep." (The guides whooped with laughter.)

Just then one of their clients poked his head out of a nearby tent and shouted, "We're trying to sleep! Would you guides keep it down out there?"

Conrad stood, stretched, then headed for his tent. "Dat is a goot idea. See you in the morning boys."

THE NEW ZEALAND SEASONS

Conrad Kain guided in the Southern Alps of New Zealand three times starting with the 1912/13 climbing season. In his relatively short time there, he proved to be one of the country's most successful climbers.

One of his most ambitious undertakings was accomplished in 1914/15, when he led the New Zealand widow, Mrs. Thomson, to the top of 12,349-foot Mt. Cook—the highest in the country. Kain later wrote of his excursion with the 59-year-old woman, "I had just finished explaining to Mrs. Thomson that this was not a place to linger, when we heard the reports of falling stones. 'There she comes, follow quick!' I shouted. We made a dash for an enormous ice block a few feet from us; it was a race with death. Fortunately our shelter withstood the impact of the avalanche and only fine snow rolled in on our feet and buried the rope. As the close call did not upset Mrs. Thomson's nerves, we continued the ascent by rounding a few large crevasses and snow walls, and gained safer going on a small plateau. The view was magnificent, the most striking sight being the ridge up to the highest point. Mrs. Thomson made some remarks about the steepness, but I assured her that it would not be so terrible when she got nearer. On some occasions, motherly words from the guide on a climb are a good stimulant.

"We made good progress along the ridge, which we found less steep than it appeared from the middle of the peak, and stepped on the summit a few minutes before three o'clock. It was as warm and calm as on a tropical sea beach. Mrs. Thomson was delighted to gain the highest point of her native land. Ladies, as a rule, do not tell their age, especially to males; therefore I was surprised when she told me that she would be 60 on her next birthday and would like to celebrate the occasion on Mt. Cook.

"We climbed more than a dozen peaks together, some of them long and tiresome snow tramps and some more difficult, but she never played out or showed fear."

"He (Conrad Kain) was wonderful in the mountains, seeming to have an instinct for finding new routes," wrote Mrs. Thomson, some years later. "I had absolute faith in his guidance, and never disputed it. He was very entertaining, frequently relating interesting and amusing stories about the people in the different countries he had lived in. He is very modest about his prowess as a mountaineer: 'I am better than some, and not so good as others,' I once heard him remark."

———————————

"I am sorry, Mr. Kain but your application to guide next season in New Zealand has been denied," said the New Zealand customs official, dressed in a navy blazer and finely creased grey pants.

The officer opened one of his desk drawers and took out a large rubber CANCELLED stamp. He carefully inked it on a red blotter and, with a loud thud, applied it to Kain's visa renewal application.

"There must be some mistake." said a bewildered Conrad Kain.

"No sir. No mistake. Your application has been denied."

"I've guided in New Zealand now for three seasons and was hoping to come back next season too. There's never been a problem."

"Well, there is a problem now."

"Not to brag or anything, but I have done the Grand Traverse, made 59 ascents and almost 30 of them were first ascents at that."

"Mr. Kain, are you not listening? It doesn't matter what you've done. Your visa is null and void. The government of New Zealand has turned down your application."

"But I've even rescued dying men off your peaks, and escorted a 59-year-old woman to the top of Mt. Cook."

"Does the battle of Gallipoli mean anything to you Mr. Kain?"

"No, why?"

"I lost my brother in that battle and New Zealand lost over 2,500 soldiers trying to take the peninsula. All slaughtered by Germans and Turks." The customs officer looked like he could have spit at the little mountain guide.

"Oh, that is what this is all about. But sir, you don't understand, I am a naturalized Canadian citizen. I live and work in the Canadian Rockies."

"Maybe so, but you won't be guiding again in the Alps of New Zealand," the official replied. He stood up abruptly, slammed shut his thick black binder, scraped his chair back across the concrete floor and twirled around to leave.

"But . . ."

"Good day, Mr. Kain, this conversation is over."

The year 1916 proved to be the last season for Kain in New Zealand, writes author Phil Dowling, in his book *The Mountaineers*. The tourist department would not reissue licences to private guides. No real reason was given for their decision, but Kain believed it reflected wartime prejudices. Although he was now a Canadian citizen, he was regarded as an alien in New Zealand because of his Austrian origin. He was very hurt and disappointed by this experience. He wrote many years later about this period of his life, "It was wartime. I could tell some very interesting stories in connection with this patriotic sentiment, but it is better to forget it."

Kain left New Zealand, never to return to those faraway Southern Alps that had taught him so much about ice and snow—and about man's inhumanity to man.

Conrad Kain Campfire Tales

The story of the swearing parson:

That night I entertained the party around the campfire with an amusing story of the mountaineering parson who I had once travelled with. The parson was much worried about the future salvation of my soul and tried to convert me to his fold. He said one day, "Conrad, when you have been in a tight place on the mountains, has the Angel of the Lord never stood by you and told you to be unafraid?" I, believing I am an amiable, open-minded philosopher, replied that no such angelic visitation had ever occurred, but that I was ever hoping for such a miracle. The parson earnestly advised me to pray for it, adding, "I am sure that there are mountains in the afterworld. I have always desired to make the ascent of the Matterhorn, a feat which my financial condition has prevented. The afterworld is, therefore, made up for different degrees of attainment. If I live my life righteously, I shall perhaps find my Matterhorn in the world to come. You, remaining an unbeliever, will surely pass eternity on a prairie."

The doom sounded harsh to me. A few days later, on the trail, a straying horse snagged a pack and fell bodily into the creek. Much to my surprise, the parson burst into expressions of profanity that are seldom associated with the clergy. I wheeled my horse and rode back. "Shake hands, parson," I said, "Sometimes I think you are almost a man. I don't know for sure how far down in dot afterworld you come; but chust be yourself and maybe yet we climb dot Matterhorn together!"

Chapter 18

Albert MacCarthy, W.W. Foster and Conrad Kain, after their ascent of Mount Robson, at the Alpine Club of Canada camp at Mount Robson in 1913.

Albert (Mack) MacCarthy

Albert (Mack) MacCarthy was born in Ames, Iowa, in 1876, the first year of Canadian confederation. He was educated at Des Moines and from there he entered the U.S. Naval Academy at Annapolis and graduated in 1897. Little did he know then that the newly formed country north of the 49th parallel would have so much influence on his life.

MacCarthy spent ten years in the U.S. Navy and saw action in the Spanish-American War. He was discharged from the Navy in 1907, with the rank of lieutenant commander, at the age of 31.

Two years before his discharge he married Elizabeth (Bess) Larned. She was the sister of the then reigning American tennis champion. She was a fine tennis player and athlete herself. It was Bess who discovered mountaineering in the Canadian Rockies. Following his wife's prompting, Mack followed her example by making the first ascent of Mt. Daly in the Waputik Icefield.

As one alpine biographer stated, "Thus began Mack's passion not only for mountaineering but his love of Canada."

It was around this time that Mack and Bess took a pack train trip through the Bow Valley from Castle Mountain to Windermere, in the Columbia Valley. The trip resulted in the couple falling in love with the Windermere Valley. They quickly bought a ranch in the foothills of the Purcells. They named it Karmax and it became their summer headquarters for many years. Later on MacCarthy bought a second ranch on the Rocky Mountain side of the Columbia River, which he called the K2 Ranch.

Mack MacCarthy joined the fledgling Alpine Club of Canada (ACC) in 1911 and in August 1912 he made the first ascent of the Strathcona Matterhorn, rechristened Elkhorn Mountain, the second tallest peak on Vancouver Island. This ACC trip was organized by Colonel William (Billy) Foster but led by Edward Oliver Wheeler, son of the Alpine Club's founder and president, Arthur Wheeler.

Thus cemented his friendship with Billy Foster, which led to MacCarthy and Foster teaming up with Conrad Kain the following year (1913) to make the first "official" ascent of Mount Robson. Although MacCarthy's alpine experience was somewhat limited, his excellent physical condition and unique abilities made him a force to be reckoned with on the slopes of the Canadian Rockies.

In 1914, after attending the annual ACC camp at Upper Yoho, MacCarthy received a telegram from Conrad Kain, who was returning from a winter in New Zealand, offering his services, once again, as a mountain guide. MacCarthy jumped at the opportunity to climb along with Kain and on August 10th they made the first ascent of Mt. Farnham, in the Purcells. Farnham was a mountain that one climbing party had publicly stated "was considered absolutely unclimbable."

During the climbing season of 1915, MacCarthy again hooked up with Conrad Kain and they made multiple first ascents in and around the Purcell Mountains. That summer they conquered Mt. Ethelbert, Commander Mountain, Jumbo Mountain, Mt. Peter, Mt. McCoubrey and Spearhead Peak, while throwing in a number of second ascents for good measure. MacCarthy wrapped up the climbing season by making a solo ascent of Mt. Sally Serena.

Over the next two seasons, Mack MacCarthy and his wife, Bess, hired Kain on a full-time basis. They made the first ascent of Mt. Louis and then ventured into the Bugaboo Range to claim ascents on the difficult Howser Spire and the daunting Bugaboo Spire. The two climbers were accompanied by Bess MacCarthy on their climb of Mt. Hungabee—she thus was the first woman to climb this impressive peak.

For many years the MacCarthys were annual fixtures at the Alpine Club of Canada annual camps and they made numerous climbs throughout the Rockies. As their experience and confidence grew their climbs with guide Conrad Kain became increasingly few.

Mack MacCarthy's pinnacle of achievement came in 1925 when he led a team on the first ascent of Mt. Logan in the Yukon, Canada's highest peak. MacCarthy reached the summit on June 23, 1925, with a group of climbers, including his friend and frequent climbing partner, Billy Foster. They battled daunting odds, horrendous conditions and vicious weather, all of which nearly resulted in the entire climbing party being lost. The epic story of their climb became a hallmark of Canadian mountaineering lore. The ascent resulted in Albert "Mack" Mac-Carthy being made an honourary member of the Alpine Club of Canada.

As a result of the Depression years, which hit Canada particularly hard in the 1930s, MacCarthy was forced to make major changes in his business affairs. This caused him to "take back" a property he had once owned called Carvel Hall near Annapolis, Maryland. He spent much of his remaining years there due to the close proximity to his other love in life—the ocean. Back in Maryland he became closely connected with the SPCA, particularly in respect to dogs for which he established ambulances that were in touch by radio with his own station. He even created dog hospitals. Friends remember Albert MacCarthy fondly, talking about his Logan expedition and his rehabilitation of a preyed-upon sled dog. He would affectionately refer to himself as the "official dog catcher."

MacCarthy's health began a gradual decline in the 1940s, though he continued to attend ACC camps until 1952 when he was 76 years of age. It was in 1952 when his horses bolted from his Assiniboine camp and he was forced to walk back to the Bryant Creek staging area; he rode from there to Spray Dam, and trucked to Banff—a big day for a man of 76.

Albert "Mack" MacCarthy died in Annapolis on October 11, 1956 at the age of 80.

TELEGRAM: CONRAD KAIN TO ALBERT MACCARTHY | SPRING 1914

Dear Mr. MacCarthy,

I am writing to inform you that after a successful winter of climbing in New Zealand, I am returning to the home fires of the Columbia Valley. I am hoping we can arrange a trip into the Purcells.

I am pleased to once again offer my service as mountain guide to you and Mrs. MacCarthy. There are many spectacular peaks in the Purcells and I look forward to guiding you and Mrs. MacCarthy to the top of them.

Regards,
Conrad Kain

"Conrad, it is good to see you," said Albert MacCarthy, as he stepped out onto the veranda of his Karmax ranch house to greet Conrad Kain on his return from New Zealand.

"Yes, it is good to be back in Wilmer. It feels like home," replied Conrad, shaking Mr. MacCarthy's hand and surveying the beloved mountain scenery.

"So tell me, how was your season Down Under?" enquired MacCarthy, motioning for his friend to sit down. "Bess, Conrad is here, can you send us out some coffee?" he yelled through the screen of the open window in the general direction of the kitchen.

"In New Zealand I climbed 48 peaks, including Mt. Cook, the highest, but Mt. Sefton was the most attractive of all," said Conrad.

"How does the climbing compare to North America?"

"Ah, Mr. MacCarthy, climbing the high peaks of the Southern Alps was hard and strenuous work because the timberline was much lower than in other countries. Therefore the climber is compelled to carry a camp outfit on his back up the mountain to a certain height, from which he can reach the summit the next day."

"Interesting," said MacCarthy, leaning over to give Conrad a match to light his pipe.

"I can tell you, carrying heavy packs and sleeping—if you can—on cold rocks takes a great deal of the pleasure away."

Conrad flinched as the kitchen screen door suddenly flew open and banged shut. An attractive, dark-haired woman with a slim and graceful figure came out onto the veranda carrying a tray of coffee and biscuits.

"Conrad, let me introduce you to Henriquita Ferrara," said Mack MacCarthy. "Bess has just hired her on to help with the household duties. She seems like a very pleasant girl. Comes from the West Indies I believe?"

"Mr. MacCarthy, you don't have to talk about me as if I wasn't here," said Henriquita Ferrara, in her soft, lilting accent.

"It's a pleasure to meet you, Miss Ferrara," said Conrad, somewhat flustered and immediately jumping to his feet.

"It's Mrs. Ferrara," said Henriquita, leaning forward to shake Conrad's hand. "And Mr. MacCarthy, the truth of the matter is, as you know, I come from British Guiana, not the West Indies."

Conrad found himself staring into the dark hazel-coloured eyes of Henriquita, eyes that sparkled with intensity.

"Pardon my mistake," replied Mack MacCarthy, with a growing grin on his face.

"Help yourselves, gentlemen," she said, breaking away from Conrad's stare and motioning to the tray of coffee and goodies.

"A bit of a spitfire, wouldn't you say, Conrad?" Mack said in a low whisper, as Henriquita whirled around and headed back into the kitchen.

"Yes indeed," said Conrad.

"Her husband died back in British Guiana, so I think she came to Canada to get a fresh start," Mack added.

"How long will she be staying here at Karmax?" asked Conrad.

"I believe she signed on for the next few seasons. I leave all those details to Bess, you know," he added.

"Now, let's forget about the servant girl and talk about our upcoming climbing season in the Purcells. Where should we go? What peaks should we climb?" asked Mack MacCarthy, as he settled back in the chair with a steaming cup of coffee in one hand and a buttered biscuit in the other.

"This is the year for Farnham," said Conrad, taking a sip of his own coffee.

"We have talked about that mountain long enough—let's climb it," agreed Albert MacCarthy.

———————————

The Horsethief Valley lies behind the little town of Wilmer, hometown of Albert MacCarthy, and soon-to-be resident Conrad Kain. A trail winds up and out of Wilmer for a good eight miles before it enters the valley proper. About ten miles from Wilmer the Horsethief Creek Valley widens at the gateway to the old Starbird guest ranch.

Evidently the creek, which was formerly called Creek No. 1, received its more colourful name—Horsethief Creek—because of the exploits of an American and a Swede, who years before rustled some pack ponies from a whiskey peddler.

They were pursued up the creek, captured and taken to Fort Steele where the episode was brought to trial but the alleged thieves were discharged. Whiskey, it is said, is generally not looked upon as a peacemaker, but evidently was in this case.

Further up the valley is the most striking peak of the area, Mt. Farnham at 11,342 feet. It is the highest point of the Purcell Range and looming beside it is the Farnham Tower. This geographical anomaly was considered by many to be absolutely unclimbable.

Yet, in 1914 Conrad Kain and Albert MacCarthy became the first two men to climb Mt. Farnham and its Tower.

Kain described it: "In 1914 the most interesting climbs I made were Farnham and the Farnham Tower in the Purcell Range. The tower offered rock work to my liking, and these ascents compared well with climbs in Dauphine.

"I told Mr. MacCarthy of the rumour associated with these two peaks, that 100 dollars was being offered to the first party to climb these peaks and bring back a piece of rock from the top. We packed down a good-sized rock, but we failed to locate the man with the hundred dollars."

The massive mountain was so named for a mining prospector who is said to have spent a fortune on the Ptarmigan, a mineral claim on an adjacent mountain.

"Conrad, tell me, what makes a good mountain guide?" asked Mack MacCarthy one day as the two men struggled to load up the pack train.

"I have learned that the leader on any climb must hold the confidence of the party," replied Conrad, stopping only to quaff down a canteen of cold water—feeling the heat of this late summer afternoon.

"And this is not always so easy, but there are four essential points to remember," he added.

"What are your four points?" Mack MacCarthy was curious to hear the answer.

"First, the mountain guide should never show fear," Conrad explained.

"Makes sense."

"Second, he should be courteous to all, and always give special attention to the weakest member in the party."

"Yes, that's true," MacCarthy said, nodding in agreement.

"Third, he should be witty, and able to make up a white lie if necessary, on short notice, and tell it in a convincing manner."

"You have no problem there, Conrad," MacCarthy chuckled.

"Fourth, he should know when and how to show authority, and when the situation demands it, should be able to give a good scolding to whomsoever deserves it," Conrad concluded forcefully.

"I've seen evidence of that too and have been on the receiving end a few times," said Albert MacCarthy, knowing he had just heard the wisdom of a true professional.

"Come on Mr. MacCarthy, let's get this pack train loaded. The spire of the Bugaboos is waiting," said Conrad, as he threw another load on a horse and began to rope it down.

The Bugaboo Spire, hidden away in the isolated Purcell Range of eastern British Columbia, was originally known simply as No. 3 Peak. The Howser and Bugaboo spires are a two-day horse ride west of Spillimacheen in the Columbia River Valley. The rugged crag of a peak jutted over 10,000 feet into the air and was long considered to be virtually unclimbable.

At the time, the two spires were unnamed though T.G. Longstaff referred to them as "The Nunataks" while the well-known Swiss guide Edward Feuz Jr. suggested the name "Aiguilles," as the spires reminded him of the sharply defined rock pinnacles of Chamonix, France.

On August 29th, 1916, the day after their traverse of nearby Sextet Ridge, a group led by Conrad Kain and consisting of Albert MacCarthy, his wife Bess and John Vincent, broke camp at 4:30 a.m. for a try on No. 3 Peak.

Since time was of the essence, the group wasted no time in scrambling up, through and over peaks No. 1 and No. 2.

The lower reaches of No. 3 above the saddle, wrote Albert MacCarthy in the following year's *Alpine Journal*, varied in angles of 30 to 60 degrees, for about 1,200 feet. To make matters worse there were two thirty-foot chimneys, one smooth slide and a whole stretch of the most interesting rockwork.

Not to be deterred, Conrad Kain set a fast pace, as did climber John Vincent following closely behind. A most difficult stretch at around 10,000 feet, a real "piece de resistance," took two hours to negotiate. The very sight of the daunting task ahead led the MacCarthys to the quick conclusion that the name "Bugaboo" was most appropriate.

Mounting the ridge, the group studied the route to the summit. They soon realized they were now confronted with a most challenging "gendarme" or sharp spiked pinnacle. After trying to skirt around it the group's progress slowed to a snail's pace.

Conrad Kain describes, in his autobiography *Where the Clouds Can Go*, the rest of the assault: "We returned to the gendarme and after a short rest I tackled the perpendicular 15-foot wall. Several diagonal cracks offered firm handholds, but were not large enough for the toes; the old proverb 'half a loaf is better than none' comes often to the climber's mind. Near the top I was stuck for a few minutes, the edge being smooth and without holds of any kind. I applied the vacuum grip and pulled myself up and over.

"The only possible way out was to the left. There was not room for two on this edge, nor was there a projecting rock or crack for anchorage, so I had to depend entirely on myself. I managed to wriggle over the holdless slab, and when I tried to get into the crack I was stopped. Convinced that I had started wrong, and as there was no chance to change my position, I crawled back to the edge and began again. To my surprise I found myself in exactly the same position as before; but I grew bolder and stood up, balanced on the toes of my left foot and made great efforts to get into the crack, but could not find a hold. The endurance required in balancing one's whole weight on the toes should be cultivated. Again I returned to the starting point."

This predicament reminded Conrad of a similar situation he had once found himself in years earlier on the mountains of the Tyrol. There he was able to use the leverage of his ice axe to move upward.

He continued: "My plan was to place the axe in a position to take the weight of the left foot, the only one I could make use of, and at the same time lift myself a few inches higher. This I thought would enable me to put my arm into the crack, which appeared just wide enough so I could use the elbow on one wall and the palm on the other.

"All went well according to this plan. Once in the crack the axe was not only useless but proved a real nuisance. I found myself in such a position that I could not dispose of the axe in any other way except by letting it drop. This I would not do, so there was nothing to do but to go back once more and make other arrangements. Finally I succeeded in pulling myself up the crack and across the overhang. To my great relief a slanting crack about two inches wide led me to a safe place. I was now only 70 feet above the others, but it had taken me an hour and a half to cover this stretch. While coming up I heard Mr. MacCarthy whisper to the others that he felt confident I would not descend over such a place if any other possible place could be found. I concealed my fear carefully."

"Camp was reached at 8 p.m., just as darkness was setting in and we were more than ready for rest. Just how Conrad Kain managed to finally get into that crack is a mystery to me," Albert MacCarthy marvelled later on around the campfire. "We were all just waiting for him to reappear and suddenly he pokes his head out, about 70 feet above us, and says, 'I made it.' That day I saw evidence of all four points that Conrad had so pointedly and powerfully instructed me on earlier in the trip."

The next day the group reluctantly turned their backs on the many spires of the Bugaboos, whose intimate acquaintance they had not yet made, but with a resolve to return to conquer them at the first possible opportunity.

Chapter 19

Henriquita (Granito) Ferrara—Hetta—married Conrad Kain in June 1917. Here she stands in front of a stack of straw in a field in front of the couple's modest home in Wilmer.

"His marriage to her was to be a source of
great happiness to him after so many years
alone." ·

Conrad Gets Married

The original area of "Guiana" included present-day Suriname, French Guiana, Guyana and parts of Brazil and Venezuela. So states the book *Guyana: Politics and Development in an Emergent Socialist State* by Kempe Ronald Hope.

Christopher Columbus first sighted the area in 1498. Subsequent voyages by Sir Walter Raleigh took place in 1595 and other explorers thereafter increased European interest in the region. The first European settlers were Dutch. They came in the late sixteenth century. The local Amerindians welcomed them as trading partners. Over the next 150 years the territory alternated between Dutch and British rule, interrupted only briefly by a short period of French rule. Although the territory had been, in effect, ruled by the British since 1796, it was not officially ceded to the United Kingdom by the Dutch until 1814.

The book *Guyana* continues: "In 1831 the settlements were consolidated into the colony of British Guiana with Georgetown as its administrative centre. In 1833 an Act of the British Parliament directed that slavery be abolished within five years. The abolition of slavery resulted in the departure of the Blacks from the plantations. Those who remained were in a favourable position to demand relatively high wages as the planters were forced to compete for the scarce supply of labour now available. In view of the resulting shortage of labour, coupled with a decline in the market price of sugar, the planters suggested in 1837 that indentured labourers should be imported. This resulted in a diversification of the population, as indentured servants were brought in from Germany and England.

"The Portuguese arrived from the island of Madeira, and also from Brazil, Chinese from China, and Blacks from Africa and the West Indies. The largest number (238,960), however, came from India. Between 1838 and 1917 a total of 340,962 immigrants arrived in British Guiana. In 1917, as a result of public protest in India against the humiliating treatment of Indian nationals in Guyana, the Government of India abolished the indenture system and no more Indian labour was allowed to enter the colony."

Guyana is an Amerindian word meaning "land of the waters." It was formerly known as British Guiana when it was a colony of the United Kingdom. It became independent on May 26, 1966. The country is the only English-speaking nation on the South American continent and has a population composed of six ethnic backgrounds. It is bordered by the Atlantic Ocean, Brazil, Suriname and

Venezuela. Its some 83,000 square miles is approximately the size of the State of Idaho.

Guyana is divided into three areas: an inland forest which covers about 85 per cent of the total area; a grass-covered savanna-like region of 8,000 square miles in the interior; and the coastal plain covering about four per cent of total land mass. The country is watered by four main river systems, namely the Essequibo, Demerara, Berbice and Corentyne.

The climate of Guyana is tropical; however, the northeast trade winds dampen the heat along the coast, where temperatures vary between 72 degrees and 90 degrees Fahrenheit. The country receives an average rainfall of 80 to 102 inches depending on which part of the country you are in. The coastal rainy seasons are from April to July and November to January.

Georgetown is the capital city and is also the main centre of commerce, being the largest city and port. It is located on the northeast coast at the mouth of the Demerara River. New Amsterdam is an old Dutch town situated on the eastern bank of Berbice River near the ocean—it too is an important harbour port. The city of Bartica is located at the convergence of the Essequibo and Mazaruni rivers and is an important port for large ships.

Conrad Kain spent the winter of 1916/17 in the wilds of the Canadian Rockies, primarily along the Simpson River. It was a time of isolation and melancholy. He saw no one for months on end. He lived in a tiny log cabin, which he purportedly shared with his dog Bruno, sixteen mice, an ugly toad, and a snake named Satan who loved music. He whiled away the days reading the Bible, writing his friends and family back in Austria and reflecting on his self-worth and the value of his occupation as a mountain guide.

A LETTER TO AMELIA

Dear Amelia,

I have written the dear lady, Mrs. Jane Thomson in New Zealand, so I am writing you a similar letter. I am far, far away from towns and peoples. I am once more a trapper, and I enjoy life in the wilds and amongst the wild animals to the full extent. I have not seen or spoken to anybody since 29th September 1916, till today. What date it is I don't know; this man who came this morning to me thinks it is somewhere round the second week in February. He is going to civilization and he will post this letter for me. I will go with him halfway to help him to break the trail. The snow is in some places four-five-six feet deep, but I won't go out till late in spring.

I have enough food, and I feel so well here alone that I really dislike to think of leaving my nice little log cabin which I have built all by myself. I have a long beard and my face is round and brown with sunburn. I am physically and mentally well, as I was not for a long time. In December-January it was bitterly cold, yes, too cold to go outside the cabin. Such cold spells one never gets in New Zealand.

Then I receive daily visits from the few winter birds who stay here. Well, it seems to me they all love me. I know that I love them all. I find them better friends than one does amongst people. No doubt some people would think me mad—crazy— but I am all right.

I sometimes think that I must have been mad that I did follow up mountain guiding as long as I did. I do not say that mountain guiding is foolishness, no, by no means. I think it one of the finest healthy sports. I love the mountains, the climbing, and the view from a summit, but I think it is first-class folly to try to make a living off it. Of course, we must all have our own experiences before we are wise.

I once had a position which would have given me a great name, and very likely I would be well off now, but I did not like the life I had to lead. I never told you nor anybody else about it. Nobody but my friend Mrs. Thomson in New Zealand knows about it, but as I now have decided to give up mountain guiding I will tell you.

If you write me in the future, write care of Post Office Banff. I will make Banff again my stopping place, but don't address it to the Alpine Club. You see I must forget them all, otherwise I might go climbing again, and I must not make myself a fool again. I get climbing enough as a trapper.

Now this fellow man of mine is up (a long awaited visitor from Banff), so I will have to stop and cook some supper. We shall start out early in the morning. I hope he does not lose these letters. I would not mind to go out myself, but it is too early for me.

This winter melancholy has convinced me it is time to seek a wife. If you were here or I was there I would most certainly seek your hand in marriage. You are a dear friend but circumstances dictate we must go our separate ways. I will always consider you a dearest of friends.

Warmest regards,

Conrad

Whether it was an antidote for loneliness or simply love at first sight, within a matter of months of Conrad Kain returning to the Columbia Valley from his winter exile on his lonely trap line, he married Henriquita (Granito) Ferrara in June 1917. She was in the employ of his friend and climbing partner Albert MacCarthy. She was a quiet but an interesting woman and the best possible partner for him. One writer describes her as "an attractive, dark-haired woman with a slim and graceful figure. His marriage to her was to be a source of great happiness to him after so many years alone."

Hetta, as she was called, was born at Georgetown on the Demerara River in British Guiana, June 8th, 1884. She attended a convent school and she spoke English, Portuguese and some Hindustani—"coolie" labour being common on the plantations. She first married J. Ferrara, and by him had one daughter. When her first husband suddenly died, Henriquita immigrated to Canada in 1913. She lived and worked at different places around the Wilmer/Columbia Valley area and for some time she was a maid at the Karmax Ranch, which was the estate of the MacCarthys. It was here that she undoubtedly met her future husband, Conrad Kain.

The somewhat harsh economic realities of life dictated that Conrad needed to do more than be a seasonal mountain guide, so to supplement his income he worked for surveying and hunting parties. He also tried his hand at farming—with limited success—and trapping in the vicinity of his new home in Wilmer.

Although raised in a household in British Guiana where servants did most of the heavy work and, of course, educated in a convent, Hetta soon fit comfortably into farm life in the little rural community. She was a capable and sociable hostess as she looked after the home fires while Conrad was away on his surveying, hunting and climbing trips. Yes, climbing trips—Conrad's resolve to give up climbing didn't last too long.

For the first three years of their marriage Conrad and Hetta lived on the MacCarthys' ranch. In the summer of 1920, they pooled their resources and managed to purchase 8.3 acres of gently sloping land near the Village of Wilmer. Not only did it offer a picturesque view of the Columbia Valley, it was intersected by an irrigation ditch which channelled water throughout the property, keeping it fertile and green. Next to a landmark old poplar tree, Conrad Kain and his wife Hetta constructed "a small, two-room, white clapboard house, which, under Hetta's care, was soon covered with columbines and sweet peas."

The little farm quickly brought out Hetta's talent for handling animals, the care of which largely fell to her. In addition to a regular lineup of farm animals, the Kains also had a small fur farm.

"Hetta, I have an idea," said Conrad across the breakfast table one morning.

"Oh, Conrad. You and your ideas, what is it now?" replied Hetta, his wife.

"Mr. MacCarthy and his wife Bess are planning a trip into the Purcells next week and they want me to guide them again. So I thought you might enjoy coming along," he said.

"Conrad, you said you were going to give up guiding and climbing. And now you want me to come along too?"

"Hetta, I am Austrian. Climbing is in my blood. It is all I know."

"Yes, as they say, you can take the man out of Austria, but you can't take the Austrian out of the man," she replied, with a twinkle in her eye.

"So you will go?"

"Let me think about it for a bit."

"You wouldn't have to do any actual climbing. Just an easy hike into the base camp and you could stay there while I accompany the MacCarthys up the surrounding peaks."

"I don't know. I would feel sort of silly just watching you traipse off with the MacCarthys, and me staying back at the camp."

"No need to feel bad Hetta," he said, reaching over to pick up his smoking pipe. "The MacCarthys will understand."

"Conrad, remember, we have an agreement. There is to be no smoking in the house."

"Yes, Hetta," he said in a resigned tone.

"Take your pipe out on the front porch if you must smoke."

Hetta Kain decided, in the end, to accompany Conrad and the MacCarthys. The trip was rather uneventful but on their return Conrad was heard to say, "Hetta was too much afraid the white blankets would get dirty."

After their marriage in June of 1917 Conrad and Hetta settled down on a little farm in Wilmer. Hetta's talent for handling the animals meant that the management of their small fur farm fell primarily to her. Over the years, with varying success, they tried raising mink, marten and even chinchilla rabbits, depending on what demand, price and the season dictated in the fickle fur market.

THORINGTON, SIMPSON AND KAIN CONQUER THE NORTH TWIN

"I tell you that outfitter Jim Simpson knows how to handle an axe," J. Monroe ("Roy") Thorington wrote in his book *The Glittering Mountains of Canada*. "We're going through a dense forest and in places there are windfalls—the tree trunks piled up high and crisscrossed like giant straws.

"But if those windfalls lie across the trails, Jim Simpson is off his horse—he is always in the lead—and in seconds he's making the chips fly and the woods resound with the echo of his chop, chop, chopping.

"You know them windfalls are dangerous, the packs on the horse can be caught and snagged awry but that's when Jim's axe comes into play.

"Soon the trail is clear and horses all back in a line—yes, there's a trail vocabulary especially designed for wayward cayuses. Pretty soon Jim's got the outfit swinging along a trail steep and muddy, slippery for beast and man and 3,000 feet to the river below.

"We forded the Blaeberry that day, our long procession of horses trailing neck-deep through that swirling, muddy water.

"Much of the trail is washed out by the shifting river; what is left becomes a tangle of undergrowth and obstructive timber, keeping Jim out of his saddle, axes flashing and chips and curses both flying in every direction.

"It's good to be under the care of Jim Simpson; he's for more than 20 years pioneered these Rocky Mountains."

Thorington's account continues:

"A black bear preceded us, and from his uneven, sprawling track we concluded he was in somewhat of a hurry; at least we never caught up with him, and his pace was by no means slow and dignified.

"All afternoon a second bear—perhaps a neighbour of the first one we saw—wandered about our campground, and we could see the tips of his ears above the scrub bush as he cautiously raised up to investigate our presence. One of the boys chased him and he clambered up to the top of a tall pine and sat disconsolately on a limb, whimpering.

"(We spent) evening by the campfire with the last rays of sunshine on the back of the spire of Mt. Forbes. Summer evening is a long twilight in the Rockies... and on this night a full moon rises, shedding its silvery glory over the meadow. We can hear the distant jingle of bells as the horses move slowly through the marsh grass. Jimmy Simpson tells stories of old explorers who passed this way in the long-ago; tales so fantastic that if the shade of David Thompson or of Dr. Hector had walked in to listen, we should have been unsurprised.

"We were riding leisurely along, admiring the impressive panorama of Mount Forbes' towering peak when suddenly Jim Simpson, who was ahead of me, began to urge his horse into a full gallop. We followed closely and on a small gravel-cliff had the unusual experience of catching a baby goat that apparently had strayed from home. The little animal was headed off by a horse on each side and a stream in front. When several of us approached, the kid gave a frightened leap and fell into the water and was rescued, kicking and struggling in the arms of Tommy Frayne—our cook. It really was only coincidence that the cook should have made the catch, but the wee beast no doubt expected immediate consignment to the pot. It was interesting to see that the animal remained limp, as if dead, as long as it was held tightly; but ready to stiffen like a steel spring and bolt if the chance offered. We soon released it, and in our last glimpse it was proceeding with all speed, but with a damp and injured air, down the river gravel-bars.

"That evening we watched, through binoculars, the big billy-goats come out to feed on the high alpland above the cliffs. And once when we came back late into camp, a cow moose with her calf plunged back into the timber."

"It was early in the spring when we arranged our plans. Our outfitter, of course, would be no other than Jim Simpson. He was quite keen to go again into the north country which he knows so well. He wrote to say that Tommy Frayne, the best of the cooks, would be with us again; and that one Ulysses La Casse—because of his broad grin more conveniently known as 'Frog'—would come as horse-wrangler. Finally, and luckiest of all, we secured the promise of Conrad Kain, super-guide and philosopher, whose stories have since quieted our nerves over many a day of bad weather, to lead us up the icefield peaks.

"It was June 27th when we left Lake Louise with a procession of horses. We had quite an audience, for the start of a pack-train is a thing not seen every day. Such a commotion! Boxes and saddles; duffle bags and pans. Squealing horses tethered in the scrub-pine, breaking loose now and then and galloping through the clearing, bells clanging and pack-covers flapping. The cayuse that is being packed—how sleepily he stands, with belly forcibly distended lest the rope be too tight; the shrewd look in his eye as an uncovered axe touches his rump. A heave and a buck, profanity and the operation repeated…off at last with the horses fighting for their place in line."

———————

"Jim Simpson and Conrad are lying flat on the shale, with a map spread out, there is a great pointing of fingers toward distant valleys, and the remarks which come to my ears indicate that fur-bearing animals next trapping season had best look out for themselves. William Ladd and 'Frog' are dividing the last piece of cheese, and 'Frog' is not getting the best of it. Tommy—the cook—and I sit with our backs against the summit cairn; one corner of it decked with mossy fringe of hoarfrost, which is dripping in the sunlight and falling into several cups to which we have constructed elaborate aqueducts of flat stones."

———————

"As we skirted the western slopes of the Snow Dome, North Twin loomed apparently close at hand; but distances are as deceptive as on the ocean, and nearly level snow hides many deep depressions. We circled widely to avoid crevasses at the head of Columbia Glacier, which slopes to the Athabasca Valley. The Twins are an isolated pair, ringed by cliff and icefall, North Twin alone being connected with the icefield by a snow col—a ribbon of snow—leading down toward Havel Creek. And after weary hours fatigue mirages set in; when one has crossed the last long slopes and plateaus, it is necessary to lose altitude in crossing this deep saddle to gain the peak.

"Fatigue mirages—momentary illusions—began to appear; for an instant I am convinced that the dark line of a distant crevasse was a staff planted on the summit of North Twin; and I berated Conrad (Kain) for bringing us so far only to let us be cheated of a first ascent. Mr. Osgood Field, whose party crossed the icefield during the next summer, reported a similar experience—bushes and trees at various places on the icefield, and groups of people pitilessly watching the slow progress across the snow. All a mirage."

———————

"Our own peak—North Twin—is immediately above us; its corniced summit ridge intermittently hidden by snow flurries and wind-blown mist, rose in a slope of glistening snow, steep and unbroken. Conrad Kain is leading, I (Roy Thorington) was second and William Ladd last on the rope. The wall of snow was ever before us as we went up; there was considerable step-cutting, not in hard ice, but in crusted snow, and our pace slowed before the top of King Edward came into view above the sharp arête of South Twin. We reached the summit just 13 hours after leaving camp: fleeting glimpses of winding rivers in the west and of shining summits in the direction of Maligne Lake and Wilcox Pass were blotted out in the closing mist."

"Someone following our track may one day understand that journey back across the icefield's vastness. For an analytical mind, it will at least afford insight of the psychology of fatigue: the half hour in a blizzard, obscuring the trail and exhausting us; the clearing at sunset, with crimson and orange light banded against masses of lead-blue storm clouds behind The Twins.

"We had brought some portable fuel and a small kettle with us and left it on a snowy hummock far out on the icefield against our return. It was dark when we approached it, but we soon had some water melted to slake a burning thirst. While Conrad and Ladd were attempting to make tea, I walked on alone to the slopes below Castleguard. The unbroken snow was hardening a little, the air comfortably cool, and only a gentle wind stirring.

"It is not easy to thread crevasses in the dark—lucky that we knew the way, but how we cursed the lantern (flicking from the camp in the distance). When we pulled into camp it was three o'clock and morning was on the hills as it had been when we departed.

"Twenty-three hours we had been out; we were very tired, and the grass beside the campfire seemed luxurious in its softness as we sat there breakfasting in the light of the rising sun."

"On awakening after our long and weary journey to North Twin, I found the sun high in the heavens. Tommy—the cook—had the fire going and was putting together a tremendous lunch. From the teepee came intermittent strains of a harmonica, for which Conrad could be blamed; and you missed real music if you have not heard his orchestrations! This time, however, it sounded as if he were suffering from sunburned lips.

"Let no one think that Mt. Columbia (our next summit) is a mere snow-hump rising from a neve; it is a distinct peak in every sense, looking its height and quite worthy of its place. In a little while we were back at the campfire; just six hours from the summit. We had supper by the cracking logs, with the cross-lights from fire and western afterglow. The shadows lengthened, blue-black at the forest edge, and Conrad told us stories until there was no light remaining save that of the glowing embers, and the stars that peeped out above our heads."

J. Monroe Thorington became the compiler of Conrad Kain's posthumous autobiography, *Where the Clouds Can Go*. The book was compiled from notes and letters Thorington received from Kain's Austrian friend, Amelia Malek. In the foreword, Thorington acknowledged her important role: "For much of the material contained in Book One (The Alpine Years), as well as parts of the first Canadian season, I am indebted to Miss Amelia Malek, of Reichenau, Austria, who had the wit to preserve the scattered notes and letters which he (Conrad Kain) continued to send her."

Chapter 20

A group of climbers gather at the base of Mount Robson; included in the group was Phyllis Munday and the somewhat notorious American climber Annette Buck.

" . . . no woman had made the ascent. Mr.

Wheeler chose two—led by Conrad Kain—

Mrs. Munday, representing Canada, and Miss

Buck, the United States."

"Well, Lady, Here Is the Top" | July 1924

The following tribute to Miss Annette E. Buck, at the time of her death, appeared in the 1947 edition of the *Canadian Alpine Journal:* "Miss Annette E. Buck, long a member of the Alpine Club of Canada, passed away in San Francisco on November 4, 1946, after an illness of many months. She was born in the State of Pennsylvania, but spent most of her life in New York City.

"Miss Buck was a great lover of the outdoors, especially of the mountains, and lost no opportunity to spend her leisure time in the open whenever possible. For many years she was a member of most of the outdoor clubs, which carry on their activities in or near New York City and Philadelphia, and of the American Alpine Club. After her introduction to the Canadian Rockies at the Assiniboine Camp of the Alpine Club in 1920, she attended a number of annual camps.

"She made many difficult climbs in the Canadian mountains, both with the Club and privately with Swiss guides. Among her climbs were Victoria, Magog, Temple, Robson, Sir Donald (twice, by different routes), and a goodly number of the more strenuous climbs in the Glacier, B.C., Lake O'Hara, and Paradise Valley regions. Previous to her introduction to the Canadian mountains she also did some climbing in Colorado and in the New England mountains.

"On the climb of Mt. Temple the party was caught in a blizzard near the summit, and the cairn was found only by accident. The leader, Mr. Geddes, was compelled to devote his attention to assisting a disabled member of the party, and to Miss Buck fell the problem of leading down. All footsteps had been obliterated, visibility was reduced to a few feet and only the remarkable sense of direction, which she always displayed, enabled her to choose a route and to discover after the party had passed below the storm that they were almost exactly on the route of ascent. She always seemed to regard it as a response to her prayer as she started down.

"Prior to the time of Miss Buck's climb of Mount Robson, no woman had made the ascent. Mr. Wheeler chose two—led by Conrad Kain—Mrs. Munday, representing Canada, and Miss Buck, the United States, to share the honour of being the first women to reach the top of the highest peak of the Canadian Rockies.

"Miss Buck made many warm and lasting friendships at the Club camps and while climbing in the Canadian mountains, and her happy memories of the camps and her correspondence with those friends helped very much during the years when she was unable to go to camp and especially while she was ill."

———————————————

Vancouverites Don and Phyllis Munday were known respectively as the "the Dean of Mountaineering" and "the Grande Dame of the Mountains." Their alpine exploits were legendary in mountaineering circles—they climbed over 150 peaks and were credited with some 40 first ascents.

As much as they shared a passion for the high alpine, they were an odd match physically—Don Munday was small in stature, with a slight, wiry frame whereas Phyllis, six year younger, was long-limbed, robust and several inches taller.

In 1924, the Alpine Club of Canada (ACC) made it known that it would be assembling several groups to climb lofty Mount Robson—a mountain not climbed since it was summitted by Conrad Kain, Albert MacCarthy and William Foster in 1913.

The Mundays had been one of the first to put their names on the sign-up sheet posted by ACC President Arthur O. Wheeler. After climbing nearby Mt. Gendarme, they were pulled aside by Wheeler and told they had been selected to be part of the second group of climbers who would tackle Mount Robson.

It was reportedly an unexpected move by Wheeler, who was well known as an autocratic, paternalistic president—not to mention his gender bias against women climbers.

CLIMBING JOURNAL NOTES | PHYLLIS AND DON MUNDAY

July 24, 1924: It was with amazed joy that I heard from A.O. Wheeler's lips that I was chosen to accompany my husband on the second (climbing) party.

July 25, 1924: The first party to climb Mount Robson would be prominent club members Malcolm Geddes, T.B. Moffatt, Harry Pollard, J. Monroe Thorington, A.J. Ostheimer—all guided by Conrad Kain.

After a restless night's sleep, the second party left Robson, which consisted of the Mundays, Andy Drinnan, Fred Lambart and latecomers J.T. Porter, and second guide, Joe Saladana, to work with lead guide Conrad Kain, and the notorious Miss Annette E. Buck.

Robson will be the first serious climb on which my wife and I were not members of the same rope party. We vowed it would be the last.

The climb was hot, steep and dry, and we reached the camp shortly before 8 p.m. Three tents, food and other equipment had been placed on a high shelf . . . the highest point a comfortable camp could be placed.

July 26, 1924: At High Camp we prepared supper and awaited the arrival of the descending first party . . . with two missing climbers—Thorington and Ostheimer, who it was discovered, had turned back when tons of ice and snow crashed down over the climbing route soon after the rest of the party had surmounted the summit.

In the wee hours of the morning Conrad's famous yodel signalled the return of the rest of the first group. Unbelievably, Kain would turn around and attempt the mountain again the next day with the Munday group.

Frustrated that Kain, understandably, needed rest. Kain crawled into his tent and spent the day resting and sleeping. As he slept, we lamented that we were unable to take advantage of the perfect sunny weather. We were itching to go.

July 27, 1924: At 3:30 a.m., Conrad Kain roused us and we moved off. At about 8,000 feet we gained the ridge, just in time to see the troublesome ice-front of the southwest face discharge a mass of ice down the sheer cliffs.

What concerned us the most was that we had to cross the bare cliffs for nearly 100 yards directly under a 100-foot glistening and shattered wall of ice and snow hanging over our route.

A few stray blocks crashed down, but we passed safely. The next 2,000 feet presented good rock climbing. Then we worked our way across cliffs of 200 yards and tackled a 150-foot face.

Conrad now roped the climbing party up. With a steady head and foot we crept along a protruding ledge with 8,000 feet of thin air below us. Now came a steep icy face, which caused Kain to ply his ice axe vigorously. After Conrad cut small handholds, he stood on one foot while he chopped a final step and he soon surmounted the crest and disappeared.

I (Phyllis) had been anchored to Conrad with the rope around my ice axe thrust in a hole in the ice. Now it was my turn to follow . . . never had I such an excess of nothingness under my heels or so much impending above.

The glare of the noonday sun was felt even through our snow glasses. The snow was soft or "rotted." The second guide, Joe Saladana, attempted crossing a crevasse. He suddenly plunged out of sight, getting a severe shaking up and dropping his ice axe deep into the crevasse.

Joe resurfaced from the crevasse, his face bleeding. It took over an hour of precious time to recover his axe from the bottom of the 50-foot chasm. We had the uneasy feeling that this delay would prohibit us from reaching the summit and returning to camp before dark.

Kain was busy cutting steps when the tail-ender (Miss Annette Buck) on his rope ignored his implicit orders as to the mode and time of crossing the rotten bridge, and she fell in as Conrad had predicted.

An excerpt from Don Munday's unpublished manuscript describes this harrowing event in more detail: *"Conrad, relying on his party's obedience to his careful instructions, was intent on cutting steps on a steep slope above an ice-bridge nearly as fragile as a greenhouse roof. His back was to them and he had thrown down about 24 feet of rope slackly between himself and Mrs. Munday.*

"The woman (Miss Annette Buck who made the fourth on the rope) now ignored orders to move only one at a time and to drag herself prone across this essential

bridge. Consequently she dropped into the crevasse and jerked the unprepared man above her from his footholds. We four on the other rope watched helplessly while my wife, unaided, braced herself to hold the double weight. Conrad snatched in the slack frantically, knowing he could not possibly check the three if they fell together any distance. But my wife held them and the second man regained the footholds before Conrad took in all the rope."

July 27, 1924: No. 3 on the rope was not in position to stand a strain as he had no reason to expect it; fortunately No. 2 (Phyllis) was well braced, otherwise all four almost surely would have plunged into the crevasse.

The top of the south ridge was a slope unlike anything else in the Rockies. It was an absolute chaos of ice blocks on a slope of 45 degrees. The sight was both fairylike and at the same time sinister, hostile and menacing.

We crawled on hands and knees—even laying down and wriggling along—utmost care was required to avoid giving the shattered mass of snow and ice any kind of jar.

Conrad was thoroughly anxious about the slope below the great cornice. It was excessively steep and without cohesion; the steps broke away repeatedly, but the slope as a whole held. An avalanche here would have shot us down 3,000 feet.

"Well, lady, here is the top of Mount Robson," said Conrad, taking in the slack as I (Phyllis) came up beside him and looked down both sides, seeing Berg Lake a mile and a quarter below—the time was 4:30 p.m.

The loss of time caused by both incidents meant we must now spend the night on the mountain. We huddled at about 9,500 feet, on a rock ledge.

July 28, 1924: Conrad again roused us the next day at about 3:00 a.m. and we reached High Camp two hours later. That afternoon we returned to the main camp and telegraph messages were sent off to the newspapers announcing the successful ascents and, importantly, the first female ascents.

Embarrassingly for the Mundays, the newspapers of the day—especially the American press—reported that Miss Annette Buck was the first woman to summit Mount Robson, the highest peak in the Canadian Rockies. As Don Munday writes, "As Phyl and Annette Buck were on the same rope it was assumed by the general public that they were on the summit simultaneously. Robson's summit was too small to allow more than two people at a time, so Kain brought the climbers to the summit in their rope order, first Phyl, then Lambart, then Annette Buck."

And to further clarify the situation, Don Munday took the unusual step of issuing a statement to the press, *"a correction of the impression being spread in Canada by American publications and news services that an American woman was the first woman to reach the top of Mount Robson. Mrs. Don Munday was the first, preceding the other woman (Annette Buck) by some 15 or 10 minutes; while those*

who know Mrs. Munday realize she is not the one to wish to press unduly the dis-
tinction, the first person is the first, and this is so well recognized in well-informed
mountaineering circles that on a first ascent, for instance, the guide steps aside just
short of the highest point to let one of his party be the first to reach the top."

Phyl and Don celebrated their ascent of Mount Robson by spending the next day quietly in the lower camp and then on July 30 they ascended nearby Mt. Calumet with other ACC members.

"IT'S COMING DOWN"—THORINGTON'S
FAILED ATTEMPT AT ROBSON | JULY 1924

American climber J. Monroe Thorington had journeyed to Mount Robson years earlier to scout out the magnificent peak. He wrote: "Mount Robson is the highest summit in the Rockies of Canada; but, like many a lesser peak, its height has diminished with recent measurements. The first triangulation resulted in a figure of 13,700 feet; but the more recent determination of the Interprovincial Boundary Commission has brought this down to 12,972 feet. Thus an old illusion is shattered, and no peak of the Rockies in Canada attains 13,000 feet."

After riding a Great Northern freight train, which had derailed, and walking back to the Lucerne station to catch a Canadian Northern train on the other side of the Fraser River, Thorington finally arrived at the base of Mount Robson at midnight.

He writes: "And suddenly the vision appeared! Mist and vapour play strange tricks with one's judgment of size and distance—moonlight affects it to perhaps an even greater degree...There it was; Robson, 'the mountain of the spiral road,' seeming to touch the very heavens, flooded with soft light and gleaming like molten silver. I had seen higher peaks before, but nothing has ever equalled the impression of stupendous height that Robson gave on that starlit night."

CLIMBING JOURNAL NOTES | J. MONROE THORINGTON

J.M. Thorington noted that it was not for a number of years—the Great War had come and gone—before he and his fellow climbers could come back again to Robson.

July 17, 1924: It was cloudy to be exact, when Conrad Kain, Alfred Ostheimer and I unloaded our packs before a crowd of curious tourists at Robson Station. This time we had come to climb; there would be more hard work and less senti-ment than on my first visit many years earlier.

July 19, 1924: We had not seen the top of Mount Robson; weather seemed to be getting worse instead of better. Fog hung in the valley, blowing in from the Fraser; then, in a change of wind the fog came back in.

July 20, 1924: Enforced inactivity was making us jumpy. Although it was cloudy and there was a high wind blowing, we all decided that something must be done. It occurred to us to try 11,200-foot Mt. Resplendent.

We roped below a little schrund (short for bergschrund, which is a crevasse at the head of a glacier separating the moving ice from that adhering to the valley walls), as well guided a party as has ever tackled a Canadian mountain. Ostheimer, with Kohler and Streich, made one rope; while Conrad and I followed behind, showing wisdom therein, as we could use them for a wind-break while they cut steps.

Conrad and I then went ahead and found some quite delightful climbing in a short stretch of chimneys and slanting slabs. Resplendent is not an easy mountain on which to lose the way, and though there was no view to be had, Conrad led us through the fog to the steep-corniced summit in another ninety minutes.

July 21, 1924: Camp was being put up for the annual activities of the Alpine Club of Canada, and the first hikers arrived.

July 22, 1924: Although the clouds hung low, a large party on three ropes ascended Lynx Mountain, an attractive peak of the Robson cirque. It took six hours to reach the highest point. Down the Resplendent Valley we could see the slender needle known as the "Finger of Kain."

Writing in the *Canadian Alpine Journal*, Conrad Kain said of the southwestern ridge of Mount Robson, *"There is no doubt that this ridge will be the future route to ascend to the summit of Mount Robson. But the climb cannot be done from Lake Kinney in one day. It will be necessary to build a hut at the head of the Lake Kinney Valley. The snow conditions on the highest peaks in the Canadian Rockies can never be compared with those in the Alps, as there are more avalanches in the Rockies on account of the dryness of the atmosphere, which leaves the snow powdery and unpacked. And so I may say that Mount Robson will always be a risky climb, even on the easiest side, on account of avalanches."*

Kain continued, *"In all my mountaineering in various countries, I have climbed only a few mountains that were hemmed in with more difficulties. Mount Robson is one of the most dangerous expeditions I have made. The dangers consist in snow and ice, stone avalanches and treacherous weather."*

During the ten years since, I believe Conrad has no doubt modified his opinion somewhat of the mountain; but his view in regard to the length of the climb was unchanged. The danger from falling ice could never be ignored.

July 23, 1924: Messrs. Geddes, Moffat and Pollard, Ostheimer and I—all members of the Alpine Club of Canada—packed down to Kinney Lake. Conrad, of course, led the way, adding considerably to our remarks about the uncompromising weather. Thus we decided to spend the night at the lake rather than go up to the higher level.

July 24, 1924: Mount Robson may be considered as a gigantic wedge. The next day it took five hours to mount the steep trail through the woods to the climbing-camp. Conrad had the heaviest pack of all—only slightly smaller than himself—and was forced to "build a fence" of willow twigs in order to accommodate a pail and several loaves of bread on top.

The afternoon was spent in camp work: chopping wood, carrying water, and in constructing a well in the nearby gully. Sitting on the limb of an ancient, storm-gnarled tree, one felt that it would be quite possible to throw a stone into the grey waters of Kinney Lake, 3,000 feet below.

July 25, 1924: During the night the clouds rolled back and we started out at four o'clock on the finest of clear mornings. Early in the morning it was quite safe to cross close below these falls. Then up and up the crest of a long, rocky ridge, where the sun met us.

On such a level, a place of breakfasting, Conrad told us how a hut should be constructed. We sat there, eating bread and jam, a little below the first snow and looked across to the shoulder.

We would soon be on the snow; Conrad, Ostheimer and I on one rope. We stopped to reconnoiter, while the other rope came up. In the ice-cliff there was a choice between a frozen chimney, near by, blue and steep. Conrad pronounced it too hazardous for the leading man and a lateral traverse on horizontal, snow-covered ledges seemed to afford access to the higher slopes. The traverse seemed the only course; but it looked nasty.

It was past the noon hour, the ice was in the full light of the hot sun for the first time in a fortnight; and the summit of the mountains, although less than 2,000 feet above us, showed us plainly enough that to go on undoubtedly meant a night bivouac.

Just then there was an ominous cracking, and Conrad shouted, "It's coming down," and we all ducked under the nearest ledge. I made up my mind that the amateurs on our rope must turn back. On this day, toward the end of a long and successful season, I was not willing to take a chance on the good behaviour of those ice-pinnacles.

The others felt differently about it and were inclined to go on. Conrad said, "Gentlemen, it is risky. I am willing to go on if you wish." So we decided that Conrad should rope with them and continue, while Ostheimer and I on the rope remaining should descend the ridge below. So we parted, wishing each other the best of luck.

We built a little cairn and sat down to watch the climbers' progress. All at once there was a grinding crash in the direction of the couloir, and some large blocks of ice came tumbling down. The men were still out of sight, but that shower of pieces must have been uncommonly close to them. They were untouched, and a little later we gained the icecap.

Still later as we descended, we saw them high up on the snow, half hidden at times by veils of mist. We had come down nearly to the lower icefalls; we stopped to finish off some sardines and coffee.

Something made us turn our gaze to the lower ice. As we looked the entire front of the pinnacles began to move. Slowly the green wall of ice tottered and sank, sweeping the path through which we had come in the early morning.

Then came the crashes. We sat as if petrified until the last echoes died away. Conrad heard the noise, on top of Mount Robson. He told me afterward that they spent the night near where we had been sitting. He thought the avalanche had caught us.

July 26, 1924: Conrad and his successful party came in at four o'clock the next morning, all rather tired—a night on the rocks is never restful. I got up, did what I could to help get breakfast ready.

After more than a thousand miles of trail riding in the Canadian Alps, with success on many high peaks, in more than one long season, I have not conquered Robson—yet. Perhaps it were best that I should never attain that height; I might think the less of it.

"What if I live no more those kingly days?
their night sleeps with me still.
I dream my feet upon the starry ways;
my heart rests in the hills.
I may not grudge the little left undone;
I hold the heights, I keep the dreams I won."
—J. Monroe Thorington

In a letter to his friend Amelia Malek in Austria, Conrad Kain states, in regard to his 1924 ascents, "In two weeks I have ascended Mount Robson four times."

Writing later in the *American Alpine Journal*, J. Monroe Thorington noted that he received the information too late to include it in Kain's autobiography, *Where the Clouds Can Go*. Thorington writes: "His round-trip times from the timberline camp were as follows: first, 26 hrs.; second, 23 hrs., third, 17 hrs.; fourth, 15 hrs. This information is not in the records of the ACC. One must add Kain's first ascent and traverse of the mountain, July 31, 1913, and his almost successful attempt from the S.S.W. a few days later, making a total of five complete ascents and one incomplete ascent. An amazing feat by any standard."

Conrad Kain Campfire Tales

Conrad's stories:

One evening, our last night in camp with the outfit, Mr. Thorington tells me, "It is my conviction, Conrad, that you are the reincarnation of Scheherazade (the legendary Persian queen and the storyteller of One Thousand and One Nights), with several hundred extra yarns thrown in."

At all the events I try to entertain the guests with a few tales of adventure: snake-collecting in Egypt, sheep-herding in Australia, gold-washing in the Northwest, wandering the South Seas, hunting in the Siberian Altai. But the most beautiful in the world, I believe, is the island of Madeira. I would like to spend a little of my old age before retiring to a cottage in the Tyrol. And the most interesting place of all is New Zealand.

Chapter 21

Professor Winthrop Ellsworth Stone, president of Purdue University, gazes out over the Canadian Rockies. The Professor tumbled to an untimely death on Eon Mountain near Mt. Assiniboine in 1921.

The Agony of Mrs. Stone

A statement isolated between a question it poses
a question unanswered - how she endured seven days
on the mountain
Her husband fell from the summit of Eon
into death's isolation
"I can see nothing higher" he had shouted
from the mountain's height
then fell . . .
—by Jon Whyte

At the head of the Marvel Lake Valley stand four glorious mountain peaks, namely Mt. Gloria, Mt. Assiniboine, Aye Mountain and Eon Mountain. At 10,860 feet, Eon Mountain is the second highest of the group and its odd name comes from British mountaineer James Outram, who thought the name appropriate considering the great spans of time involved in building such an impressive peak. Mt. Eon was soon to become linked forever with the name of Winthrop Stone.

Winthrop Ellsworth Stone was the first child of Frederick and Ann Butler Stone. He was born in Chesterfield, New Hampshire, and attended Amherst High School and Massachusetts Agricultural College (now the University of Massachusetts), where he received his degree in 1882. After studying chemistry and biology at Boston University for a short period, he studied chemistry at the University of Göttingen, Germany, where he received a PhD in 1888. In 1889 he was appointed chair of chemistry at Purdue University in West Lafayette, Indiana. After the death of President Smart in 1900, Stone was appointed his successor. In 1907 he was awarded the honorary degree of Doctor of Laws by the University of Michigan. He was also the brother of Harlan Fiske Stone who was to become Chief Justice of the United States.

In 1920 Dr. Stone, president of the prestigious Purdue University, and his wife, Margaret, both avid mountaineers, attended the Jubilee Camp of the Alpine Club of Canada at Lake Magog at the base of nearby Mount Assiniboine. The Stones soon learned that Eon Mountain was a "virgin peak" and they could not keep their eyes off it. They snapped numerous photographs of the soaring peak and made a pact to return the next summer for they were "anxious to crown a big one."

They did return the very next summer to the camp at Mount Assiniboine, eager to do more than participate in Arthur O. Wheeler's somewhat mundane "walking tours." So on the morning of July 15th, the Stones struck out over Wonder Pass and were soon descending to the Marvel Lake Valley. From there they continued on over the Marvel Pass and readied themselves to make the first ascent of Eon Mountain via its southern slopes.

After spending two days sizing up the mountain, they determined that the "key" to the mountain was a yellow-capped outlying tower with a level ledge that would give them access to the peak of Eon. With this tower as their point of attack, the Stones first ascended three slopes and broken-down ledges to an elevation of about 8,000 feet. This was followed by a series of steep ledges and couloirs of firm rock taking them another 500 feet, and then another series of broken-face ledges led to the 9,500-foot level. From this arête they soon reached a band of firm snow, which they used to kick-step their way up. Above this band of snow and ice, the route spiked upward over more broken ledges and sheets of unstable rock and onto a final wide, steep, irregular chimney that opened up to the dangerous sloping top sides of the summit.

On reaching the base of this last rock chimney, Dr. Stone placed his wife Margaret in a secure spot at the base of the chimney, securely away from any possible rock falls.

"Winthrop, what can you see?" implored Mrs. Stone, as her husband scaled higher and higher.

"Can you see the top?" she called again.

"I see nothing higher, Margaret. It is the top," he shouted back before disappearing above the chimney.

"You must not leave me here alone, Winthrop. Winthrop?" she cried, as a large slab of stone, without warning, plunged down the face, narrowly missing her as she craned her neck to see where her husband had gone.

To her horror, the plunging rock was followed, seconds later, by her tumbling husband.

"Winthrop, hang on. Winthrop, rope yourself in. Winthrop, Winthrop . . ." she screamed.

A white-faced Dr. Stone catapulted through the thin mountain air, tightly clutching on to his ice axe with his right hand but he didn't utter a word as he careened downward.

"I've got the rope. I can save you," she gasped, bracing herself to take the jerk of the rope. Only then did she realize that there was no resistance on the rope— Winthrop had unroped himself so he could reach the peak of Mt. Eon, which had been just beyond the rope's length.

The Doctor first fell about 60 feet to a narrow ledge which triggered a cascading fall as he continued to bounce off ledge after ledge until it appeared to Mrs. Stone he must surely have fallen right to the bottom of the mountain.

Dazed, nauseated and in a total state of shock from the horrific events of the last few minutes, Mrs. Stone struggled to maintain her composure as darkness began to settle in over Eon Mountain. Immobilized at the bottom of the fateful chimney, some 40 feet from the summit, she readied herself for the longest night of her life.

With the eventual first light of dawn, she began inching her way down, peering intently over every ledge, hoping to see her husband waiting below, somehow miraculously unscathed, but knowing in the back of her mind this would be an impossibility.

"Winthrop, Winthrop. Can you hear me? Are you all right? Winthrop, Winthrop . . ." she cried out time and time again. Not a sound came back but the howling of the rising wind.

She made decent progress on her initial descent, but owing to her unsettled state coupled with a lack of food and water, she quickly became weaker and more disoriented. With darkness once again setting in, she was forced to seek shelter under another rocky ledge for a second night.

"Winthrop, Winthrop. Are you there? Winthrop, hang on, I am on the way to get you help," she cried out several times in the night, mistaking the moaning wind for her husband's voice.

With the break of dawn again, Margaret once more began her uncertain descent. In her haste or state of confusion, or simply because she was intent on getting help to rescue her husband, she went astray. She worked her way along a narrow 100-foot ledge which suddenly seemed to dead end, but peering down through the mist she could see another ledge that looked like it would lead to the timberline bottom. Taking her rope and securing herself, she belayed her way down to the next narrow ledge, but she had misread the distance and was ten feet short of making it to the ledge below. She was forced to undo the rope and drop the last ten feet, which she did only to quickly realize her mistake—there was now no way up or down—she was stranded. She could not climb down the sheer chimney below and the end of her rope dangled ten feet above her head—totally unreachable.

Without food or shelter and dressed only in a flannel shirt and knickerbockers, Mrs. Margaret Stone sat down and sobbed. She knew her own survival was now at risk.

Assiniboine Camp,
Thursday, July 21st, 1921 | 10 a.m.

Dr. W.E. Stone and his wife left here Friday morning, July 15, to climb Mt. Eon. They were lightly provisioned for four (4) days and left word to send relief if they did not return by Monday night, July 18. They have not returned yet. We have found their cache where they left some clothes and provisions evidently intending to return.

Please send at once a Swiss guide and stimulate to head a search party. We will supply the food. Come by way of Trail Centre to the construction camp of the government party working on the new Wonder Pass Trail at which camp we will meet and give all information.

Immediate help is necessary if they are to be saved. We have half a dozen men to assist the Swiss guide. Will he please proceed at top speed by horseback. Embers were found in the fire Sunday evening warm.

—Frederick Burnett

(Letter brought in to Banff by Constable Childs, the rescue trip's packer, and delivered Thursday evening to the Royal Canadian Mounted Police)

When the call for Swiss guides went out, it was Rudolph Aemmer who answered the call. He was a well-known guide based out of Banff at the time. He was reputedly the handsomest of the Swiss guides. As one writer described him, "He looked precisely the way a guide should. An inveterate pipe smoker, he had friendly brown eyes, plump rosy cheeks and sported a magnificent black handlebar mustache. The gold band in his earlobe, with his dark and becoming tan, made him appear dashing and gypsylike . . . women worshipped Rudolph just as they worshipped (actor) John Barrymore. (Rudolph played his double in the filming of *Eternal Love,* which was filmed near Lake Louise in 1928).

Rudolph Aemmer, Bill Peyto of Banff and Constable Childs of the Royal Canadian Mounted Police made the rugged 45-mile trip on horseback from Banff to Mount Assiniboine in just one day. They initially worked their way up Marvel Pass, where they found the Stones' bivouac. The next morning they continued up a broad ledge of Mt. Eon and out to the summit of a south spur at some 7,800 feet. This gave them a view of the lower reaches of the mountain's south face. After a long and careful scrutiny of the mountainside with their field glasses, they were ready to give up for the day, as the light started to fade. They were suddenly startled by a faint, pleading call from a point to the west. They soon discovered Mrs. Stone on a ledge almost a quarter of a mile away and 300 feet below them.

The rescuers quickly fired a shot off to notify her that help was on the way. They worked their way around the steep mountain face and were soon situated on a ledge just above her. Rudolph quickly descended with the aid of a rope and, by the use of a rope from above and Rudolph's assistance below, Mrs. Stone was carefully raised up to the broad ledge above. However, the eight days of exposure with no food and only a trickle of water rendered her too weak to walk. So Rudolph slung her over his shoulder and carried her back around the base of Mt. Eon for about a mile up and down and along several broken and unstable ledges and then down to a basin to the timberline where he made a camp and they spent the night. Eventually, after a great deal of clearing by a trail gang in the vicinity, Mrs. Stone was carried out by stretcher for 14 miles to the Trail Centre Camp. There a Miss Brown, manager of the camp, and another woman, the wife of Dr. Fred Bell, did everything possible to make her comfortable.

JULY 27, 1921 - *New York Times*
DR. W.E. STONE DIES IN MOUNTAIN SLIDE

Wife of President of Purdue University, Who Accompanied Him, Found Alive.

MISSING SINCE JULY 15: Searchers Had Been Scouring Mount Assiniboine in Search of Them—Woman Found in Crevice.

The body of Dr. Winthrop E. Stone, President of Purdue University, Lafayette, Ind., who disappeared with his wife on July 15 from a walking tour camp at the foot of Mount Assiniboine, has been found at the bottom of a very deep precipice.

Mrs. Stone was found alive at the bottom of a 17-foot crevice, according to word received here.

Hundreds of men, led by experienced alpine climbers, had searched the mountainsides surrounding Banff for hours in a determined effort to locate Dr. Stone and his wife. The couple had neither been seen nor heard from since July 15, when they set our for a three-day hike on Mount Assiniboine.

Because of the seriousness of the situation in which it was feared Dr. and Mrs. Stone were placed, Professor Charles E. Fay of Tufts College, called "the father of the Rocky Mountain climbers," was summoned to direct the search for the missing couple.

It was unofficially reported here tonight that a party of the searchers, the one who found the remains of a fire and food and toilet articles belonging to Dr. and Mrs. Stone in a crevice at the base of Mount Eon, also found that a slide had occurred near the camp site chosen by the two missing people.

Dr. and Mrs. Stone are well known at Banff and in the several weeks they spent here this year made a host of friends. They were members of the walking tour camp at Mount Assiniboine.

Before leaving the camp on July 17, Dr. and Mrs. Stone told companions they intended making a three-day climb in order to condition themselves for the big Alpine camp meet at Lake O'Hara this week.

Dr. Winthrop Ellsworth Stone was born in New Hampshire July 12, 1862. He graduated from Massachusetts Agricultural College and then finished his studies at Göttingen, where he remained until 1888. He became Professor of Chemistry at Purdue University in 1889. He has published numerous chemical researches upon carbohydrates and educational papers and reports. Dr. Stone has been President of Purdue University with conspicuous success since 1900. He is a member of the Indiana State Board of Education. He is an active member of the Alpine Club of Canada, the American Alpine Club and the Mazamas.

The heavy work of the rescue, coupled with a spate of bad weather, had taken a toll on the members of the rescue party. This was especially the case with Rudolph Aemmer and it was quickly decided that a fresh party had to be organized to continue the search for Doctor Stone. This decision corresponded with the return to Banff of Arthur Wheeler, director of the Alpine Club, from his duty as a surveyor to the north. Horrified that he may have potentially lost one of his clients, he immediately took charge of the situation and on August 2nd set out with a party that consisted of a who's who list of mountaineers in the Canadian Rockies at the time.

The second rescue party was made up of Wheeler, Rudolph Aemmer (who would not hear of the idea of not continuing), Edward Feuz, Conrad Kain, Lennox Lindsay, Albert MacCarthy and his wife Bess, and Ralph Rink, who was charged with the transportation logistics. They pushed the packhorses as hard as possible and reached the Trail Centre Camp near Assiniboine late the next afternoon. The party was pleased to find out that Mrs. Stone's condition was improving quickly, especially since Dr. Stone's son, Richard, had arrived at the camp several days earlier.

During the night and early the next morning a savage storm blasted through the region leaving a thick blanket of fresh snow on all the surrounding peaks, thus limiting the search party's efforts. With the weather breaking on August 5th, the searchers reached the "key" tower before 10 a.m., and they started to search the upper reaches near the summit of Mt. Eon. With all five members on one rope, and Edward Feuz leading the way, they soon reached the 10,000-foot mark. From this vantage point on the southeast arête, Edward Feuz spotted the body of Dr. Winthrop Stone lying about 300 yards to the west.

A considerable amount of time was required to climb the short distance to the body because a snow band with a fresh dusting of snow on it required a number of steps to be hacked into the icy ascent. A short distance above and beyond the body, Conrad Kain found and recovered the Doctor's ice-axe. It was evident from a large scalp wound across the top of the Doctor's head that he met instant death upon striking the first rocky ledge in his fall of 850 feet.

Albert MacCarthy wrote the following in the *Alpine Journal*: "An examination of the chimney from above, opening onto the summit with its sloping top sides strewn with large unstable slabs, made it evident to us that in climbing out of the chimney and disappearing for a minute or so, Doctor Stone had stood on the summit of the mountain and walked a short distance to make sure that there was no higher point beyond, then upon returning to the chimney he had stepped on a loose slab of rock near the edge that had slipped from under him and carried him over the cliff.

"Traversing the ledge to where the body lay, we were gratified to find that owing to the high elevation and the proximity of large snow patches, thus making the nights cold, the body was in a good state of preservation with no sign that any animal had molested it."

All hands pitched in to build a memorial cairn for the fallen climber and the following wording was written on it . . .

Friday, August 5th, 1921

The monument was built by the undersigned in tribute to their comrade of the mountains, Doctor Winthrop E. Stone, President of Purdue University, LaFayetter, Indiana, U.S.A.; who, July 16th, 1921 (actually the 17th), with his wife, virtually completed the first ascent, reaching a point not more than 50 feet from this spot. Dr. Stone's ice-axe crowned this monument.

—Albert H. MacCarthy, ACC, Lennox Lindsay, ACC, Edward Feuz, Rudolph Aemmer, Conrad Kain

Conrad Kain paused for few minutes and took a picture of the lone ice-axe pointing to the sky in tribute of the Doctor. After careful preparation of the body by using available medical supplies, oiled silk blankets, canvas and lashings and two 100-foot climbing ropes, the arduous task of bringing the body down the sheer rocky face of Mt. Eon was underway. At around 9,600 feet Rudolph Aemmer found the Doctor's rucksack, which still contained Mrs. Stone's sweater, Kodak and a small supply of provisions. Eventually by using a shoulder pole and guy lines, the steep slopes and lower ledges of the mountain were traversed. Upon returning to the camp every member of the rescue party nearly collapsed in exhaustion from their heavy labour and general lack of food.

On Tuesday, August 9th, the rescuers met with Stone family members, which included Harlan Stone, Winthrop's brother, and the Doctor's sons, Richard and David. The next day the Stone family bade a sad good-bye to all and placed the body of Winthrop Stone on an eastbound train en route to LaFayette, Indiana.

Several months later Conrad Kain received the following letter from Harlan F. Stone of Columbia University, New York. It read: *"I am writing this letter in behalf of Margaret Stone, my sister-in-law. She has sent me a sum of money, to which all the members of my brother's immediate family have contributed, with the request that I make distribution of it among all of those who assisted in her rescue and in the recovery of my brother's body at Mount Eon this summer. This I have done, dividing the money as best I could among 15 different people.*

We quite appreciate that no sum of money could adequately express the gratitude which we all feel for this skillful, loyal and unselfish service of you and your associates.

I feel especially fortunate in having personally had the opportunity to see you and to take you by the hand. Some day I shall hope to come back to the Canadian Rockies. When I do come I shall not fail to see you and to express in person the deep sense of obligation which, one and all, we feel toward you and those who were with you on your sad and difficult errand."

Rudolph Aemmer and the other rescuers received funds and a special citation from the American Alpine Club for their heroic efforts. Though grateful, Rudolph accepted his reward philosophically, as it is said of most good professionals. He was heard to say, "Real guides cannot be heroes. When somebody gets into trouble in the mountains, we go after him, take the necessary risks and bring him down. Nothing else counts."

Chapter 22

Windhag, to guide them through the mountains. Kain is a former workmate of Engleitner's and is familiar with his objection to military service.

The scout patrol searches several huts and lodges in the neighborhood of the Schwarzensee. Guessing that Engleitner has gone into hiding in the Meistereben hut, Franz Kain tries to keep the Nazis away from it. Thick fog moves in as the group reaches Breitenberg Mountain, dangerously close to where Engleitner is hiding. On a hill only a few yards away from the hut, the leader stops. He examines his hand-drawn map and says, "There must be another hut down there!" Franz Kain, fearing that his friend Poidl could indeed be hiding there, tries to dissuade him, but the Nazi says decisively, "Let's pay it a visit," and starts to make his way down to the hut...

7. Franz Kain, circa 1950

Franz Kain (possibly Conrad Kain's cousin) was a former work-mate of Leopold Engleitner's and was familiar with his faith and his objection to military service.

"A patrol, consisting of three Nazis, forced a

local mountain guide, Franz Kain, to aid

them in their search."

A Kain Saves a Friend

March 12, 1938 was a sunny spring afternoon when Leopold Engleitner rode his bicycle to one of the gatherings of the International Bible Students (now known as Jehovah's Witnesses) in Bad Ischal, Austria. Upon his return at around ten o'clock he heard the ominous sound of heavy footfalls marching in a rhythmic cadence.

"That can't be Hitler's troops already, can it?" he wondered nervously to himself.

But as he rounded the corner, his worst fears were confirmed—a seemingly endless column of German soldiers goose-stepped past him in the direction of Bad Ischal from where he had just come.

According to the book, *Unbroken Will*, that day German troops advanced across the border and began their occupation of Austria—the infamous Anschluss was underway. Much to Leopold's dismay, hundreds if not thousands of Austrians lined the streets, cheering Hitler's troops. Within a matter of days the Nazi Gestapo had arrested 90,000 people (an estimated two per cent of the Austrian adult population). Communists, Social Democrats, Christian Socialists, Jehovah's Witnesses and Jews were either thrown into prison or deposed to concentration camps.

Over the next few weeks Leopold Engleitner followed the developments concerning Hitler's reign of terror closely, wondering in the back of his own mind what it would mean to him. The Fuehrer instituted a new greeting—Heil Hilter—a phrase synonymous with a cult of personality, which to Leopold was tantamount to an act of worship and something his political neutrality would not allow him to participate in.

Within a year Leopold Engleitner found himself at a penal company, his hair shaved off, wearing a striped prisoner's uniform. He had been reduced to a number—6678. He was given two purple triangles and told to sew them on his uniform, so that everyone in the prison would see that he was a hated Bible Student.

Despite their small numbers, Hitler raged against the small religious group, stating publicly, "They will be exterminated in Germany!" Leopold was the first Bible Student from Austria to be interned in Buchenwald. He was soon swinging a heavy sledgehammer from dawn to dusk in a nearby limestone quarry—in unimaginable conditions.

On March 7, 1941, Engleitner and the others of his faith were forced into cattle trucks wrapped in barbed wire and taken from Buchenwald to Niederhagen concentration camp near Paderborn. His humiliation continued there for two more years.

From May to August 1942, the internees in Niederhagen suffered a drastic reduction in food rations. The midday meal consisted of nettle soup and the longer his imprisonment wore on, the thinner and weaker Leopold became.

In the spring of 1943, Engleitner was on the move again. He was transferred to the notorious Ravensbruck concentration camp and his number was changed to 3523. The deplorable conditions at Ravensbruck made cleanliness a near impossibility, made worse by an infestation of lice and parasites.

In the afternoon of July 15, 1943, two SS men arrived at the subcamp Comthurey in a truck. They quickly located Leopold Engleitner and said, "Come on! We've got to take you to the main camp for the release formalities."

The releasing secretary gave Leopold a piece of paper containing the last order he was instructed to carry out. It read, "Report to the office of the Gestapo in Linz, Langgasse 13, Room 13, at 1600 hours on July 16th, 1943."

An SS guard then led him out of the camp. "You can count yourself lucky that you've escaped from this hell," sneered the officer, slamming the iron gate behind him.

It was Tuesday, April 17, 1945, and though World War II raged on, the people of Upper Austria sensed that this horrific slaughter was near to drawing to a close.

It was already late in the afternoon and farmers were still working hard in the fields. Franziska Unterberger had been left to care for the family farm when her husband had been wounded in the battle of Normandy. For several months now she had been working side by side with the former concentration camp internee, Leopold Engleitner, who was now a forced labourer on the farm.

From the field Leopold saw a postman approaching the house.

"Who are you looking for?" called Engleitner.

"You," came back the terse reply.

"Why—what is the matter?"

"I have brought your call-up papers," the postman replied.

Leopold felt nauseated and weak in the knees.

"What more must I endure?" he wondered.

Determined to avoid being re-captured, Leopold decided to hide out in the nearby mountains. The days passed slowly as Leopold divided his time between walking the high alpine trails and searching for secure places to hide.

A scout patrol searched for him relentlessly after being tipped off by a Nazi sympathizer. A patrol, consisting of three Nazis, forced a local mountain guide, Franz Kain, to aid them in their search. Franz Kain (possibly Conrad Kain's distant cousin) was a former workmate of Leopold Engleitner's and was familiar with his faith and his objection to military service.

The book *Unbroken Will* describes the chase: "The scout patrol searches several huts and lodges in the neighbourhood of the Schwarzensee. Guessing that Engleitner has gone into hiding in the Meistereben hut, Franz Kain tries to keep the Nazis away from it. Thick fog moves in as the group reaches Breitenberg Mountain, dangerously close to where Engleitner is hiding.

"On a hill only a few yards away from the hut, the leader stops. He examines his map and says: 'There must be another hut down there!' Franz Kain, fearing that his friend Leopold could indeed be hiding there, tries to dissuade him, but the Nazi says decisively, 'Let's pay it a visit,' and starts to make his way down to the hut.

"The noose was around Engleitner's neck. Have all his efforts to avoid detection been in vain? After the adventures of his flight from the military authorities and the nightmare of the last few years, was he destined to be caught and executed after all?"

Franz Kain saw only one possibility to prevent his friend Leopold Engleitner from being found and executed. He planted himself firmly in the way of the leader of the Nazi patrol and objected, "I'm not going down to that hut in this fog! It's much too dangerous."

The leader of the patrol was taken in by his guide's ruse and said, "Well, if it's too risky, we'll have a look at it some other time."

It was a close call for Engleitner. Franz Kain's quick thinking had saved Engleitner's life, because this was the last search.

Within days, World War II came to an end and Leopold Engleitner returned home a free man.

Chapter 23

A patient is delivered to the St. Eugene Hospital in Cranbrook in 1933, the same year Hetta Kain died from an intestinal obstruction at the hospital.

"Dear Mr. Thorington, I had the misfortune
to lose my wife. She died in the hospital at
Cranbrook, B.C....I miss her very much."

Hetta's Pain | February 1933

Due in large part to a large land syndicate called Columbia Valley Irrigated Fruit Lands Ltd., many pioneer families were attracted to the benchlands, which hung above the Columbia River sloughs and provided a panoramic view of the Rocky Mountains to the east.

At the heart and centre of this area was the little town of Wilmer, fuelled by nearby mining camps—including the famed Paradise Mine to the west—and Wilmer's strategic steamboat dock on the Columbia River. However, as World War I broke out across Europe, Wilmer had more than this far-away conflict to worry about. To the chagrin of many, there was suddenly a wholesale exodus to the upstart communities of Athalmer and Invermere. The death knell came when the Canadian Imperial Bank of Commerce announced that it would move—lock, stock and barrel—from Wilmer to Athalmer, following on the heels of the recent departure of the offices of the Columbia Valley Irrigated Fruit Lands company.

Local outrage filled the coffeeshops and waterholes of Wilmer as the new town of Invermere began to build a new hospital which was destined to replace the long-time hospital that had called Wilmer home for many years.

———————————

"Hetta, what is it?" said Conrad, stirring, rubbing his eyes and sitting up in bed.

"The pain, I can't stand the pain," she said, clutching her abdomen, her face drawn in excruciating agony.

"Have you been suffering all night?"

"Yes, I've been pacing the floor in the kitchen since 2:00 this morning. I can't stop vomiting for the pain."

"Why didn't you wake me?"

"I thought it would pass but it just keeps getting worse and worse."

"Hetta, I'll get a hot-water bottle for you. Here, just lie down again. I'll go across the street and get your brother to take us to the hospital in Invermere."

"Conrad, it's too early. I can wait till morning."

"No, put this against your stomach and see if eases the pain," he said, handing her the freshly prepared hot-water bottle.

"Something's wrong inside, Conrad," she gasped, as another sharp spasm swept through her body.

"I'll be back in just a few minutes once I wake your sister-in-law," he said, propping her up with a couple of pillows.

Conrad pulled on his old mountaineering jacket and worn boots. Still feeling groggy he rushed out into the frigid winter air.

"Conrad, Conrad, what's the matter? You don't have to break our door down," said the sleepy-looking sister-in-law.

"Who is it? Did the cattle break the fence again?" shouted her husband and Conrad's brother-in-law, John, from the small bedroom in the back of the house.

"No, no. It's Hetta, she's in terrible pain. She's all bent over. Something's wrong. She's been up all night. Can you take us to the hospital in Invermere?" rambled Conrad almost incoherently as he shivered in the early morning cold.

"Come on, John. It's Hetta, she's suffering from those pains in her stomach again."

"It's real bad this time. She's as white as a ghost, been vomiting all night and she's sweating like a racehorse," said Conrad anxiously.

"Give us a minute to get dressed and we'll be right over."

Conrad pushed the frozen door shut and scurried back up the street to his farmhouse about a quarter of a mile away. His quaint little clapboard house looked ghostly in the early morning light as the massive old poplar tree next to it, frozen stiff, creaked and popped in the light breeze blowing up from the river below.

"Conrad, Conrad, help me. I think I am going to die. I can't take this pain," Hetta shrieked, as he stamped his snowy boots off in the porch before heading for the bedroom where his stricken wife lay curled up in a tight ball.

"Your brother and sister-in-law are on the way and they are going to take you to hospital."

After rushing Hetta to the Invermere Hospital, Conrad and his relatives were left alone in the cramped waiting room near the main entrance. Minutes turned into hours and it was starting to wear on everyone's nerves. A man with a gash in his leg was brought in—a wood-splitting casualty, he said. A young girl with a heavy, hacking cough and bright-red nose was ushered into the hospital.

A few minutes before 9:30 a tired-looking doctor dressed in a white jacket entered the far end of the long, narrow, high-ceilinged hallway leading toward the waiting room.

"Mr. Kain, is there a Mr. Kain here?" he asked, surveying the room quickly.

Conrad jumped to his feet and thrust his arm into the air to identify himself.

"That would be me, Doctor. What can you tell me about Hetta? Is she still suffering?" he stammered.

"Mr. Kain, I must say her situation looks very grave," said the doctor, drawing him away to the privacy of one corner.

"Grave? What do you mean grave?"

"Serious, her condition is very serious," said the doctor, realizing Conrad was struggling to understand him.

"Is there anything you can do to help her?"

"I am afraid it is beyond the capabilities we have here at the Invermere Hospital. I believe she is suffering from some obstruction of the inner intestine or bowel."

"What do you suggest?" asked John Granito, Hetta's brother, as he moved forward to join the discussion.

"The doctor says there is nothing they can do here," said Conrad, panic rising in his voice.

"You must get your wife to the St. Eugene Hospital in Cranbrook as soon as possible," said the young doctor in no uncertain terms. "It is possible they can operate right away and relieve the blockage."

"We can take the train tomorrow?" suggested Conrad.

"No, I would recommend you drive her by car as soon as possible. She needs immediate attention," the doctor urged.

The ninety-mile drive south to Cranbrook was a slow and arduous trip at the best of times, but in the middle of a winter cold snap it became even more precarious. The narrow two-lane gravel road wound its way down the west side of Windermere Lake, along the base of a ridge of towering clay hoodoos, across a narrow one-lane bridge which spanned the rushing waters of Dutch Creek before heading up the steep hill above Columbia Lake.

With every bump and pothole, Hetta moaned in excruciating pain, her face moist with a feverish flush.

"Conrad, tell him to slow down. I can't stand this rough ride," Hetta begged.

"Hetta, Hetta, it's okay. Here, put your head on my knee and try to rest," said Conrad, gathering an extra quilt around her shivering body, as she lay across the back seat of the old car.

The driver of the old Ford, John Granito, spun the steering wheel back and forth as he struggled to keep the car on the rough, rutted road. They spun and swerved wildly along the frozen track. As they rounded the last corner before heading down the sharp incline of Thunderbird Hill, a heavy, blinding blizzard blew across the road.

"My Gawd, are we going make it?" asked Conrad from his backseat perch.

"Hard to say, but it's going to slow us up," said John, easing off the throttle.

The next twenty miles seemed to take forever as the little car crept through the whiteout, its windows coated with a heavy blanket of snow and frost. Every few miles the car would shudder to a stop. Conrad would clamber out and scrape the snow and ice away so the driver could see again.

"It looks like the storm is passing," said John, his knuckles white from his tight grip on the wheel, as he noticed the wind dying down.

The car coughed and sputtered as it turned to start the steep descent to the Kootenay River crossing at Skookumchuck. They climbed out of the river bottom and onto the Skookumchuck prairie where they could see the late afternoon sun shining brightly on the snow-encased Rocky Mountains to the east.

The almost six-hour drive was nearing completion as they chugged by the Wasa Lake Hotel and along the main road to Fort Steele and back across the Kootenay River.

"We're almost there, Hetta," Conrad said. "Another ten miles and we'll have you at the hospital."

Dr. Green stood at the stainless steel wash basin scrubbing his soapy hands several times in the steamy hot water before reaching across to grab one of the freshly cleaned towels hanging above his head.

"Seems like a classic case of intestinal obstruction to me," he said to the young doctor beside him. "Go to the medical library and grab a copy of the July 1930 Canadian Medical Association Journal. If I remember right it had a whole article about what we're dealing with."

"Yes, sir. I'll be right back," said the young doctor, quickly wheeling around to head for the hospital's reference room.

"Did you find it?" asked Dr. Green, ten minutes later as the intern returned to the room.

Yes, you're right, a ten-page writeup on intestinal obstructions."

"What does it say?"

The young doctor began to read brief excerpts from the article . . .

"There is a considerable amount of confusion in the use of the term intestinal obstruction, because in the minds of many students and practitioners the paramount conception is that some mechanical agent is always the cause of the obstruction. It is true that a mechanical primary cause frequently exists, e.g., in strangulated hernia, tumour growth or intussusception, but it is essential to know that the most insidious and most fatal form of obstruction is often present in the absence of any mechanical etiological factor.

"Acute intestinal obstruction is the term applied to a sudden and complete development of obstruction constituting a surgical emergency demanding immediate operation for its relief . . . Acute obstruction, in spite of improved technique based on a more intelligent conception of its etiology, still possesses a very high mortality . . . in a recent study of 343 surgical cases . . . it reported 209 deaths, a mortality of 60.9 per cent."

"Sounds like exactly what we are dealing with with Mrs. Kain, wouldn't you say?" said Dr. Green, standing with his arms crossed and staring out the tall, narrow window in the general direction of the snow-covered Steeples Range.

"Listen to this," the young doctor continued to read.

"Pain is one of the earliest symptoms, usually paroxysmal in type, sudden seizures of a colicky character and increasing in severity. The bowels fail to move and the patient vomits first gastric contents and, later, those of the duodenum containing bile and pancreatic juice . . . If the obstruction is unrelieved a further stage is developed, in which we have distension, more severe pains, with continued vomiting and, possibly, visible peristalsis with growing depression . . . the abdomen remains distended, the patient is extremely toxic, the extremities cold and clammy, the pulse becomes rapid and compressible, the blood pressure falls, and the patient is well-nigh moribund. The rapidity of development of these stages varies in individual cases, but twelve hours after the occurrence of initial symptoms the patient's condition may be practically hopeless. Shock is a feature in certain cases, more particularly where the circulation is interfered with in the segment of bowel affected."

"How long did it take the Kains to get here?" asked Dr. Green.

"They were in the car for over six hours. They evidently checked into the Invermere Hospital around 5:30 or 6:00 o'clock this morning. It's going on twelve hours as we speak," said the young doctor, glancing over his shoulder at the big clock on the wall.

Here's how the article concludes . . .

"Operation is the sole method of relief. Let me advocate a very long abdominal incision, permitting the distended bowel to escape freely from the abdominal cavity. The object of this is to avoid unnecessary traumatism to the intestines by attempting to seek for the cause of the obstruction; if there be severe traumatism one may induce post-operative acute paralytic obstruction, which must be avoided if possible."

The young doctor's reading was interrupted by a piercing scream from the patient in the next room.

"That's enough," waved Dr. Green, indicating the young doctor should close the journal. "We've no choice but to operate. Scrub up again. I'll notify the surgery ward and the head nurse."

"Dear Mr. Thorington," wrote Conrad, on February 13th, 1933. "I had the misfortune to lose my wife. She died in the hospital at Cranbrook, B.C. We had been happily married for 16 years. I miss her very much, but I have the satisfaction of knowing that I did all I could for her while she was alive. The death of my wife was a terrible shock to her 71-year-old mother. When her mother has recovered and my mind is settled I will write."

Chapter 24

The #473 train steams out of the Cranbrook CPR station heading east to the Crowsnest Pass and beyond.

"Despite the early hour and cold rain, the
station buzzed with anticipation of the
arrival of the 8:30 a.m. eastbound passenger
train."

Raising Kain

The weather had turned wet and cold overnight as the two German grave robbers readied themselves for their return journey home. They were up by 6:30 a.m. and after an early breakfast at the hotel's diner, they made their way to the Cranbrook Railway Station, located adjacent to Van Horne Street. Gone were the silvery moonbeams and spectacular view of the Rockies to the east, replaced by a heavy, grey blanket of moisture-laden clouds. A steady drizzle turned into a drenching downpour as they lugged their heavy bags across the street to the train station. The pelting rain left the station's busy platform slick and glistening.

Despite the early hour and cold rain, the station buzzed with anticipation of the arrival of the 8:30 a.m. eastbound passenger train. Cars of all types arrived, one after another, disgorging a variety of passengers, porters scurried around arranging luggage and freight, the stationmaster prowled up and down the platform checking his CPR-issue stopwatch at regular intervals and a lone newspaper boy stood at one end of the platform hawking copies of the *Cranbrook Herald*.

The growing tension of war in Europe was beginning to spill over into North America, even trickling into small towns like Cranbrook in the southeast corner of British Columbia.

"So what do we have here?" asked the portly stationmaster, as he approached the two Germans struggling to get their heavy bags across the platform and through the station's large wooden doors.

"We are Austrian scientists and mountaineers. We have spent a number of weeks in the Canadian Rockies gathering artifacts for the anthropology department of the University of Vienna," explained the short, heavy-set German.

"Okay, what's in those bags?" replied the stationmaster somewhat suspiciously. "I'll need to see your passport and train ticket," he added.

"Here are our passports and tickets," said the taller of the two Germans, stepping forward to help his travelling companion.

"As you can see from the official Canadian tags on our bags, we have been given permission by your government to transport these valuable items," added the short man, pointing to the official-looking documents.

"Sir, can you just open the bags. I would like to see what is inside," demanded the stationmaster, impatiently.

"As you can see from these Canadian government documents, once these artifacts have been sealed inside the bags they cannot be opened," explained the heavy-set German, while producing another official-looking document verifying that the sealed bags were not to be opened.

"Okay, okay. I can hear the train coming from Moyie. We don't have time to look anyway," said the stationmaster, turning to the ticket agent behind the counter.

He shouted over the din, "Let these men through and get their bags onto the baggage cart."

The two Germans completed their boarding passes as quickly as possible. The ticket agent stamped all their paperwork, three times with different colours of ink.

Just as they turned to head out onto the platform to await the arriving train, a young police constable pushed his way through the crowded platform. He stopped and surveyed the crowd. Then he spotted the Germans and strode determinedly toward them.

The two men glanced nervously at one another as they saw the constable heading in their direction.

"Now what?" said the tall, thin man under his breath.

"Excuse me gentlemen, would you step over here for a moment," demanded the constable in a no-nonsense tone, while pointing toward a small empty room just off the lobby.

"Yes sir, what is it you need from us?" asked the tall, thin man, in a suddenly heavy German accent.

"We have received a report of suspicious activity up by the cemetery last night," explained the police officer. "And we traced muddy footprints back to the hotel where you two were staying."

"We do not understand. We are sorry but our English is not very good," one of the German men said.

"Did you stay at the Cranbrook Hotel last night?"

"Yes, but there were many guests besides us at the hotel. In fact, it was such a beautiful night many were out walking if I am not mistaken," explained the short German.

"True, but looking at all the mud still on your boots makes me wonder," said the constable.

"We are mountaineers. Didn't you see our equipment piled high on the platform?" said one of the German men, pointing to several coils of rope woven around two ice-axes.

"So why all the mud on your boots?" the constable said suspiciously.

"To stay in shape we must hike every day. In fact, this morning we arose early and hiked through the nearby forest in the rain. It was very muddy and I guess our boots got a little dirty," explained the tall German.

"Surely, officer, you won't arrest us for having mud on our boots, will you?" laughed the heavy-set man.

Their conversation was interrupted by two loud blasts of the train's whistle. This was followed by the conductor crying out, "All aboard!" as the train started to gather up a head of steam.

The young constable then gave the two German men one long, last hard stare and waved them out the door.

"You better get going or you'll miss your train," he said.

The two German men clambered onto the train and hastily found their coach and assigned seats. They flopped down and, simultaneously pulling out large white handkerchiefs, began to mop the beads of moisture from their sweating brows. The train slowly chugged away from the station and headed toward the Crowsnest Pass. It would then take them on to Medicine Hat and right across Canada to Montreal.

In a little over five days they arrived in the port city of Montreal. They cleared customs without any additional problems and were soon on board the Empress of Ireland heading back across the Atlantic to Germany. Leaving Cranbrook had proven to be their most difficult challenge.

Upon their arrival back in Germany the two men were whisked directly to the forensic lab at Nazi headquarters. There they deposited their two heavy bags— still tagged with the official-looking tags that read, DO NOT OPEN - SCIENTIFIC SPECIMENS.

A balding, bespectacled man who looked like he was in his sixties greeted them and identified himself as the head of the forensic department. He thanked them for their delivery and said he was sure the Füehrer would be most pleased with their work. However, he warned them not to expect a forensic report any time soon, as his department was seriously backlogged. Though important, their shipment was not on any immediate priority list.

Three years later to the day, the telephone rang in the house of each of the German men, almost simultaneously. Both men were at home with their families on leave after six months of active duty.

"This is the forensic lab at headquarters calling. Was it you who obtained the 'scientific specimens' from Cranbrook, British Columbia, in Canada?" enquired an official-sounding voice.

"Yes, that was our assignment," they both said from their separate locations.

"I regret to inform you that there is a problem," said the deadpan voice from headquarters.

"What kind of problem?" they both asked.

"I am not at liberty to discuss any details with you at this time. However, what I can tell you is that the Füehrer is greatly displeased. He has demanded your presence at headquarters, one week from today at 10:00 a.m," said the official. "Is that clear?" he added sharply.

"Of course, I will be there," they both replied from their home telephones.

Within days of their meeting with the Füehrer the two German men were en route to the Russian front where the German army was bogged down in the heavy snow and even heavier Russian resistance.

The Füehrer had raged at them for more than an hour, his beady eyes flashing with anger and his moustache twitching with malice. He told them that their shoddy work was a disgrace to the Nazi motherland and how they had let down the entire German/Austrian nation. How it would be impossible now for the Füehrer to memorialize the bones of one of Austria's finest and most-respected climbers. How the Austrian people needed a hero to unite behind and now that would be impossible. How could they be so careless and bring back the wrong bones from Canada?

The two men had tried to explain that their research clearly indicated that the Austrian climber was buried next to his predeceased wife. That it was night when they dug the bones up. That they had great difficulty transporting the bones, undetected, across Canada, and the Atlantic—it was an extremely dangerous assignment. How were they expected to verify the authenticity of the bones out in the field?

The Füehrer would hear none of it. He jumped up screaming, his contorted face white with rage. "You will serve the rest of the war on the Russian front—maybe that will teach you a lesson about dangerous assignments!"

The two German soldiers sat huddled in a hastily dug trench, almost buried in mud and dirty melting snow. The pungent odour of dead or dying soldiers and horses hung in the air, coupled with the stink of diesel fuel and rocket propellant.

"Es wäre besser gewesen wenn uns der Füehrer standrechtlich erschossen hätte."

"It would have been better if the Füehrer had shot us on the spot," moaned the heavy-set man as he rubbed his cold, stiff hands together.

"Das ist wahrscheinlich richtig. Das ganze Battalion ist fest gefahren in dieser Hölle."

"You are probably right," agreed the tall thin man, trying to repress a heavy, hacking cough. "The whole battalion is mired down in this hell-hole."

"Wenn ich religiös währe, würde ich anfangen zu beten, den bei dem näherkommenden Lärm der russischen Panzer zu beurteilen haben wir nicht mehr lange zu leben."

"If I was a religious man, I would suggest we start praying right now because by the sound of the advancing Russian war machines we may not have too long to live," said the tall man, as the roar of the approaching tanks shook the ground around them.

"Wir haben doch nur versucht unsere Aufgabe zu tun?"

"All this for trying to do our job?" whined the other man, wringing his hands.

"Ja, und wer hätte gedacht wir wärden hier her kommen, nur weil wir die falschen Knochen zurück brachten? Woher solten wir es wissen?"

"Yes, who would have thought we would end up here, simply because we brought back the wrong bones? How were we to know?" he said, struggling through another heavy coughing fit.

He stood up to survey their dire situation and found himself staring up through the icy fog into the face of a Russian soldier, who had his menacing Kalashnikov rifle trained on them both.

"Ja, all das um Kain zu erheben!"

"Yes, all this for raising Kain!" the tall German soldier groaned, slowly putting his hands up in surrender.

THE DEATH OF AMELIA | 1945

According to the firsthand account by author Walter B. Maass in his book *Country Without a Name*, Austria was transformed into a Nazi regime almost overnight. He writes: "In the months after the Anschluss, an avalanche of laws and regulations descended on the bewildered Austrians, and Hitler, who was already planning his next act of aggression against Czechoslovakia, gave them no respite. Austrian currency, taxes, banking regulations, traffic laws—everything changed. A flood of German entrepreneurs appeared to acquire Austrian factories at bargain prices. This was indeed easy, because all business enterprises belonging to Jews were available. Major firms were often simply confiscated by the Gestapo and transferred to 'Aryans,' particularly those with good connections to high party circles. In all other cases, the owner was forced to sell at a ridiculously low price . . . The situation in Austria differed from that of other European countries that were later occupied by the Germans. In the first place, it took the Nazis a comparatively short time to establish themselves. There was no language problem, and German officials could be placed in responsible positions without encountering too much difficulty.

"One of the first consequences of the Anschluss (and the subsequent war) was an elaborate and extensive food rationing program. At the start some types of foods like canned fish and chocolate were still not rationed, but in the further course of the war, not only were all foodstuffs severely restricted, but also shoes, textiles, fuel and other goods were subject to controlled distribution. Food coupons became a necessity of life. A person without a ration card would starve unless he or she had enough money to buy food on the black market . . . The population of Austria obtained 2,700 calories per person during the first years of World War II and the per capita consumption never fell below 1,600 calories."

It was under these dire circumstances that Amelia Malek found herself during the occupation of Austria. She had heard all the rumours: if the Brownshirts didn't get you then the Blackshirts would, trust no one for the Gestapo was lurking everywhere, the British were coming, the Americans were coming, and most distressing of all—the ruthless Russians were set to overrun the country. With the dawn of each day a new set of rumours churned through the neighbourhoods and surrounding farmlands of Reichenau, Amelia Malek's hometown.

However, there was one persistent rumour that ran up and down the mountainous valleys—from Nasswald to Reichenau and all points in between—that bothered her more than any others. She had heard from numerous sources that Hitler had had the bones of her friend Konrad Kain exhumed and repatriated back to Austria. Though often told in hushed tones, the storyline was always similar. It went something like this—because of Hilter's Austrian roots (he was born in the city of Linz) and his unfading love of the mountains it had spurred him in some perverse way to turn the likes of Konrad Kain into a German/Austrian folk hero.

From the very start, Amelia had found the idea repugnant. She had actively and adamantly worked to oppose the idea, though no Nazi official would confirm or deny that such a scheme even existed. However, her opposition was loud enough that she soon was attracting the attention of the secret police and the ultra-zealous Blackshirts. She became a magnet for as much scrutiny as her Jewish neighbours living down the street.

"Konrad hated every minute of his compulsory military service," she argued. "He travelled to Canada and New Zealand in part to avoid any involvement in World War I and yet Hitler is trying to turn his legacy into a rallying point for his own war efforts and political means," she would tell anyone who would listen.

"Amelia, Konrad is gone. Why don't you just give it up? Is it worth ending up in prison defending someone who has been dead for over 10 years?" pleaded her aged mother and younger sister.

"The dead have rights too," she replied, undaunted in her dogged determination.

"Amelia, look at yourself. You are skin and bones and you've been in and out of prison," said her mother despairingly. "And now you have been summoned to appear before the magistrate again."

"Mama, you worry too much. I can look after myself," she replied.

Early the next morning Amelia Malek once again made her way to the local courthouse, a large stone building which dominated the main street of Reichenau. As she pushed her way through the heavy wooden doors, she could sense the beady eyes of the local magistrate upon her. He was known to be a staunch Nazi sympathizer.

"Miss Malek, I regret to see you here before the court once again. However, I keep hearing reports of your anti-social behaviour," said the magistrate forcefully.

"Defending the reputation of a friend can hardly be deemed as anti-social behaviour, can it?" she retorted, looking him straight in the eye.

"I have warned you before, Miss Malek, to keep your wild ideas and theories to yourself. The Führer himself is not taking kindly to your constant questions and criticism," he explained.

"Well, if the Fuehrer is complaining then at least I am making some headway."

"I ask you again, as I have in the past, are you willing to drop these wild allegations about your friend Konrad Kain?" he asked, adjusting and re-adjusting his eyeglasses.

"They are not allegations. Everyone is talking about Hilter's plan to lionize the memory of my friend. I simply do not believe it is right."

"What proof do you have?"

"It is true that I have little actual proof, but I have reliable sources who have spoken directly with one of the German spies who smuggled Konrad's bones back from Canada. I have no basis on which to doubt their claim."

"Hearsay is actually all you have, isn't it, Miss Malek. Even if it is true, don't you think the Fuehrer has the right to make a hero out of one of our own?"

"Konrad is dead and cannot defend himself. He would never approve of having his legacy become a rallying point for the Nazi party," Amelia said in a barely audible whisper.

"Speak up, Miss Malek."

"I said, Konrad Kain would never approve of Hitler's grand scheme!" Amelia shouted, mustering as much strength as possible.

"Miss Malek, I once again order you to keep your wild ideas to yourself," the magistrate said. "I have no option but to order you back to prison on the charge of subversion."

"You cannot suppress the true story of Konrad Kain. I have turned over his letters and writings to the American climber and writer, Mr. Roy Thorington. He already published his autobiography five years ago. The world will not be fooled by your ploy," said Amelia.

"Miss Malek, I think we've heard enough from you today. Bailiff, please remove her from the court and cut her rations by half," stated the magistrate.

"But, your honour, my mother and sister are already worried about my health. They say I look like a waif. I cannot possibly survive on less rations," she implored, trying to shake off the bailiff's tight grip.

"My point exactly," the magistrate grumbled under his breath. "If you die here it would save me the trouble of sending you to Mauthausen."

"I appeal to your sense of fairness and justice," Amelia screamed over her shoulder as she was forcibly pushed out of the courtroom.

"Miss Malek, it is your choice. Drop your campaign of complaints and you will be released. Continue on and I will have you sent directly to Mauthausen," he shouted after her.

"What's the difference? You are starving me to death as it is."

"Just remember there is still hope for you if you remain in this local cell, but I guarantee you that you will never get out of Mauthausen alive," the magistrate muttered quietly, closing his leather portfolio and pulling out a large white handkerchief to mop his brow.

It would be a week before the magistrate would return to his courtroom. It was early in the morning and the courtroom sat empty and silent. It was the magistrate's favourite time of day—a brief reprieve before the onslaught of the court's business was thrust upon him, with an endless stream of Jews, Gypsies, Bible Students, homosexuals, and other so-called dissidents of all types.

His comfortable silence was abruptly interrupted when the rotund bailiff banged his way through the heavy wooden doors.

"Sorry to disturb you, your honour," said the bailiff.

"Then why did you?"

"I have two important notes for you. I am sure you would want to hear about these two developments."

"They better be important! What are they?" the magistrate said, glaring over his half glasses.

The bailiff handed him the first note, which was printed on yellow teletype paper. It read:

THE GERMAN ARMY IN ITALY HAS SURRENDERED. HITLER HAS COMMITTED SUICIDE. MUSSOLINI HAS BEEN CAUGHT AND EXECUTED. THE 7TH U.S. ARMY HAS STARTED TO MOVE FROM THE NORTH.

The magistrate slowly reread the message, then he opened his leather folder and placed the note inside.

"Bailiff, instruct the staff that court has been cancelled for the day," he said sternly. "What is the other note?"

The bailiff pushed a newspaper clipping across his desk. The barely discernible print on the wrinkled scrap of paper read:

The Russians have released a German prisoner of war. The prisoner claims to be the one who smuggled back the bones of Konrad Kain to Germany. He now claims, with Hitler dead, that the bones, in fact, were not Kain's, that he and his partner mistakenly exhumed the wrong remains. As a result of their error they were sent to the Russian front as punishment and his partner died in the trenches.

"Bailiff, go release Miss Amelia Malek," instructed the magistrate. "Tell her that her fight to clear Konrad Kain's name is over, though from what this note says, it was clearly all in vain. Tell her that her friend's bones still lie buried somewhere in the wilderness of Canada."

"I regret to inform you, your honour, but Miss Malek was found dead in her cell this morning. Looks like she starved to death," the bailiff said hesitantly.

"Serves her right," said the magistrate, mumbling under his breath.

As the bailiff hustled out of the courtroom, the magistrate pulled open the deep bottom drawer of his desk, and despite the early morning hour, poured himself a full glass of vodka. He couldn't help but think it would be only a matter of months before he himself would be arraigned in his own courtroom. He quickly poured himself another drink and sat brooding in the silence of the empty court.

Chapter 25

The historic Payerbach "bahnhof" or train station—the last stop before the village of Nass-wald, a 30-kilometre bus ride through the Rax Mountains.

"Dear Doc, thanks for the letters and

pictures. I have been sick for over six weeks

and feeling not too good right now."

Death by Sleep

Last year I was out on Jumbo Creek with my cayuses (horses). A long bridge is rotten und the horse I am riding fell through. I hit my head und am knocked senseless. I do not know how long I am lying there, but when I come to, the back of my head is all blood. Und old Nelly is close beside, stuck in the logs. Say! If dot old horse of mine had not stayed still all dot time, I would have been kicked to death.

"I had wounded a grizzly on the far side of a swollen river and darkness compelled the crossing to be delayed till next morning, and then we decided to go over on the horses," wrote J.C. Dun Waters, mountaineer and once proprietor of the *Glasgow Herald*. "In negotiating a gulch, Conrad's pony stumbled and they both landed on the floor together, Conrad cutting his head. If a bear or elephant had done it, Conrad would have strangled either on the spot, but because it was a horse, and a horse was an unknown quantity, he lay there like a limp Victorian maiden while I poured water on his face and tried to reassure him."

J.C. Dun Waters further wrote: "I took Conrad to Alaska with me once, because I wanted someone with me on whom I could bank. We sailed on a cannery steamer from Bellingham one evening. Next morning Conrad's temperature was 104 degrees and he was in great pain. I called the Norwegian skipper and the purser into consultation, and we prescribed castor oil—a bottle at a time. If that failed, the only alternative was to take Conrad home—if he still lived—and to abandon the trip and all that it entailed, including the schooner and outfit which had been chartered and awaited us at Dutch Harbour. In the morning I found him sitting up, smoking his pipe, and when I took his temperature it was normal. I took it three times and then sent for another thermometer, as I thought mine must have boiled over and burst the night before. The new instrument proclaimed the little devil normal—as he usually was. So the trip was saved and Conrad, as ever, proved invaluable."

Conrad Kain and J.C. Dun Waters spent a windy, wet six weeks in Alaska and endured a blizzard that lasted two days. The wind drove snow through the new tents as through cheesecloth; it was like hell frozen over. With teeth chattering Conrad learned the following Alaskan ditty . . .

Damn Alaska,
Damn the Shack,
Damn the journey there and back,
Damn the flies,
Damn the weather,
Damn Alaska altogether.

In October of 1933, Conrad began to experience severe, blinding headaches. He was told by his local doctor to go to Calgary for diagnosis; the doctors there found nothing seriously wrong and merely extracted a bothersome tooth. But clearly they were wrong.

Conrad's niece, Vera (Hurst) Wikman, recalled that after he returned to Wilmer from seeing the doctors in Calgary, "Uncle began to frighten us (children). He would suddenly get up and wander around talking to himself. He became delirious and rambled on about who was going to take care of his horses."

On November 11, 1933, Conrad wrote his final letter to his friend and climbing partner J.M. Thorington. "Dear Doc, thanks for the letters and pictures. I have been sick for over six weeks and feeling not too good right now."

In the spring of 2004 a scientific paper was published with very little fanfare, in an obscure medical journal in the United Kingdom, but the contents of the paper were astonishing. In it was a potential solution to what has been called the biggest medical mystery of all time.

Two young British doctors had tracked down the probable cause of one of the world's most baffling epidemics of the 20th century—a disease called Encephalitis Lethargica.

Encephalitis Lethargica was a devastating illness that swept the globe in the 1920s. It attacked the brain, leaving victims like a living statue, speechless and motionless. During the outbreak, nearly a million died, and millions more were left frozen inside useless bodies—housed away in institutions.

For virologist Professor John Oxford, the disease was not just a disease of the past. As an expert on the condition, he was convinced that it could and would reappear.

"I certainly do think that whatever caused it could strike again. And until we know what caused it we won't be able to prevent it happening again."

Oxford remembers that in 1993, it seemed like his fears were being realized. Becky Howells was 23 years old when she suddenly became very ill. She started shaking, becoming feverish and hallucinating. Within hours she had become critically ill and was rushed to hospital. Doctors had no idea what was wrong. They knew her brain was dangerously inflamed, but had no idea what was causing it.

Her doctor, Stavia Blunt, said, "I was shocked by her appearance, stunned. She had these very bizarre clawing movements of her arms. It was weird."

Her father Tom prepared himself for the worst. "I said goodbye, I said goodbye at the resuscitation unit, because I didn't think I'd see her again," he said.

As the doctors battled to save her life they were forced to an incredible conclusion. Becky Howells was suffering from Encephalitis Lethargica—a disease that had last appeared over 70 years before. And it was just as baffling in 1993 as it was in the 1920s.

Professor Oxford was convinced that the solution lay in the past. He tracked down brain tissue samples from the original 1920 victims and tested them, looking for traces of a virus that could have been responsible for the outbreak all those years ago. At the time, an unusually severe strain of influenza, Spanish flu, had swept the world, and it seemed possible that both epidemics were linked. But despite exhaustive testing with molecular probes, there was no evidence of any virus—flu or anything else. Becky gradually recovered, but it was two years before she could restart her life again.

And Becky Howells was not an isolated case. Since then more and more patients were being discovered, all suffering from the same bizarre symptoms. At Great Ormond Street Hospital, a young doctor, Dr. Russell Dale, was becoming increasingly alarmed that the disease was more common than had previously been believed. He started tracking down other similar cases. Word got around the medical community and colleagues began referring their own cases to him. Gradually he built up a caseload of over 20 patients—all with Encephalitis Lethargica.

Dr. Dale and a colleague, Dr. Andrew Church, began analyzing all their patients to see if they had anything in common. The first clue was that many of the patients had had a sore throat before they were struck down with the illness. So the two doctors started looking for evidence of bacterial infection— and particularly streptococcus bacteria, which is a common cause of sore throats.

"It was amazing really and very exciting, when the first results came back," said Dr. Church. "We got first one, then two, then ten . . . then all the patients had the same result. So we realized we must be on to something."

Doctors Church and Dale had discovered evidence of a rare form of streptococcus bacteria in all their patients. The bacteria that can cause a simple sore throat had mutated into a much more severe form and triggered the attacks of Encephalitis Lethargica. It seems that in some people the body has a massive immune reaction to the streptococcus bacteria and then turns on the body itself, attacking the brain and destroying it.

Dr. Dale went back to the original medical records of the 1920s and pored over the reports, discovering two very telling pieces of evidence. First, many of the original victims had also presented with sore throats, and secondly, there was a reference to a particular bacteria—diplococcus. Diplococcus is a form of streptococcus bacteria.

It was astonishing that there in the medical records was a description of a bacterial infection very similar to the one causing the modern cases of Encephalitis Lethargica. The two doctors had cracked an 80-year-old medical mystery.

"I very much regret to inform you that our friend Conrad Kain passed to the great beyond on February 22nd, and I am reasonably certain that the cause of death was Encephalitis Lethargica. Evidently Conrad was a man well known, not only locally, but was renowned among mountain climbers. He was buried at Cranbrook with his wife, who died here a year or so ago."
—Dr. F.W. Green to J.M. Thorington, February 15th, 1934.

J.M. Thorington immediately dashed off a letter to Amelia Malek, informing her of Conrad's untimely death. He asked her to inform his mother and family in person, if possible. It was a cold, snowy winter's day in late February 1934, when the old, rusty brown and tan bus, which plied the Payerbach to Nasswald route, shuddered to a stop at the bus station in Reichenau to pick up Amelia.

"What are you doing travelling to Nasswald on a day like this?" asked the bus driver.

"I have sad news for the family of Conrad Kain," she said, rubbing her hands together to chase away the chill. The old bus had only one small heater which didn't begin to warm its cavernous interior, let alone start to melt the heavily frosted side windows.

"Sad news? Has Conrad slipped and broken a limb or two in the Rockies again?" the driver asked, as he struggled to keep the old bus moving forward through the blinding snow.

"Much more serious than that. Conrad has died."

"Died? Dead? He's younger than me."

"Yes, it is a tragedy. I am on my way to tell his family."

"How is that possible?"

"Evidently, he contracted what the doctor called 'sleeping sickness' and was hospitalized for five or six weeks before passing away in early February," she explained.

"Didn't his wife die, just last year?"

"Yes, Conrad and Hetta were such a happy couple. Her death left him a lonely man," Amelia said. "He couldn't have found a better woman than Hetta in the whole world."

"I sort of expected to see Conrad come back to Austria one of these days," added the driver. "At least to see his mother—she's getting up in years, you know."

"Yes, I believe he was saving to make the trip. May they both rest in God's peace and eternal love."

"Give my condolences to his poor old mother and his family," the driver said.

The gears of the ancient bus ground mercilessly as the driver shifted them back and forth as they crept up the last steep incline toward the Wirthaus Zum Raxko-ing—the local inn and pub.

"Sorry, this is as far as the bus can take you today, Amelia. Hinternasswald, where the Kain family home is, is another three or four kilometres up the road but this old bus won't make it any farther," the driver said, killing the engine and swinging open the creaky metal doors.

"I know. I have been there many times," she said.

It took Amelia well over an hour to hike up through the narrow valley that leads to Hinternasswald. The aquifer from which the City of Vienna receives all its water paralleled the winding road. The normally gurgling stream had been reduced to a trickle amongst big frozen blocks of ice.

Even with such sad news to deliver, Amelia couldn't help but admire the lovely spot where the Kain family home was located at the foot of the Raxalpe. Soon she found herself standing on the doorstep of the little Bavarian-style home. She raised one of her cold hands and firmly rapped on the door.

"Is anyone home?" she shouted, not sensing any movement after her first knock.

"Yes, who is it?" enquired Franziska Kain, Conrad's grey-haired mother, as she peered through a small crack, opening the door ever so slightly.

"Franziska, it's me, Amelia."

"My, my, my. Girl, what brings you to Nasswald on a day like this?" she said, throwing the door wide open. "Do come in and warm up."

"Thank you, Franziska. I come to share some terrible news with you," Amelia said, as she settled in a large chair near the kitchen stove. She hesitated as if wondering when would be the right moment to share such news.

"Terrible news? What could be so terrible to have you brave a storm like this?"

"I am afraid I must tell you of Conrad's death."

"My dear son, Conrad, is dead? That is not possible, first his wife and now him?"

"Yes, I'm so sorry to bring such news to you but I have been asked by Mr. Thorington, a friend of Conrad's, to deliver the news to you in person."

"Tell me, what happened? Was it a climbing accident?"

"No, evidently he has been suffering from what his doctor, a Doctor Green, called 'sleeping sickness.' He succumbed on February 2nd in the St. Eugene Hospital in Cranbrook, which is not too far from his home in Wilmer."

"I cannot believe it. I just cannot believe it," the elderly woman moaned, as she buried her weathered face in her apron and wept bitterly.

It was heartbreaking for Amelia to see the misery of a loving mother and hear her terrible lamenting. She reached out and took Franzsika's slight frame in her arms and tried her very best to console Conrad's grieving mother.

"I loved Conrad. He was such a good son," she sobbed.

"Yes, we all loved Conrad. So did his wife Hetta and all his friends in Canada. We will all miss him so much."

Amelia later wrote back to J.M. Thorington, "Conrad's younger brother, John, and his wife arrived after about an hour. We were all crying, while the children were wondering and staring at the sad group. I shall never forget the tragedy of that day, informing poor Mrs. Kain of the death of her dearest son."

Was it the blows to his head that contributed to Conrad's untimely death? Was his raging fever on the way to Alaska a precursor to what was to come? Was his misdiagnosis in Calgary really the first signs of streptococcus bacteria taking over? Did he somehow catch Encephalitis Lethargica or 'sleeping sickness' from being bitten by one of the fur-bearing mink or martens they raised on the little farm in Wilmer? Or did one of his half dozen cayuses give him a deadly bite? What exactly killed a relatively young Conrad Kain—at just 50 years of age—is a mystery that may never be fully solved.

IN SEARCH OF ANSWERS: JAKE RENSHAW

Jake Renshaw sat at the end of a long wooden table, flipping through page after page of old, discoloured *Cranbrook Courier* newspapers looking for clues about the death of Henriquita Kain and, a year later, her husband Conrad Kain. His white archival gloves became blacker with each page he turned of the heavily inked aging newsprint collection.

The Cranbrook Archives collection is situated in a dreary second-storey room above the City's landmark railway museum. It houses reams of old documents, files and newspapers. The room had become somewhat of a second home of late to the young newspaper reporter.

Finally, after much searching and digging, Jake Renshaw flipped open the front page of the *Cranbrook Courier* dated Tuesday, February 8th, 1934, and came across exactly what he was looking for. The short front-page article read . . .

WELL KNOWN GUIDE BURIED SATURDAY

Remains of Conrad Kain Interred Beside Wife. Brought Out Body of Professor Stone From Selkirks—Many Daring Exploits To His Credit.

After being a patient in St. Eugene Hospital for the past five weeks Conrad Kain, well known Hungarian guide, passed away Friday morning last, the funeral taking place here at 2:30 p.m. Saturday from the mortuary chapel with Rev. J.F. Bell, pastor of the Knox Presbyterian Church, performing the last sad rites. The funeral was attended by Miss Enid Hurst, niece of deceased, and friends from Wilmer, where the deceased had made his home.

The deceased was one of the first guides to be brought to this country by the Canadian Pacific Railway company working in and about Banff and the Selkirk

Range. *The deceased figured prominently in the rescue of Mrs. Stone, lost in the Selkirks for eight days, when her husband, Professor Stone, was killed in a fall from a ledge, Kain bringing the body out to civilization for burial. He had many daring exploits to his credit. He was a member of the party that scaled Mt. Louis and other peaks in the mountains.*

His wife predeceased him about a year ago, being interred in the Cranbrook cemetery. It was the expressed wish of the deceased that his remains be buried beside that of his late life partner.

"I must have missed the notice about Henriquita," Jake Renshaw thought to himself as he frantically flipped back through the pages of the *Courier*. Sure enough, in the issue of Tuesday, February 14th, 1933, he found the following short blurb . . .

FUNERAL FOR MRS. KAIN HELD LAST FRIDAY MORNING

The funeral of the late Mrs. Conrad Kain was held last Friday morning from St. Mary's Church here. Mrs. Kain was a resident of Wilmer, where she and her husband conducted a fur farm. Before locating to Wilmer Mr. Kain followed the occupation of guide, and was the first of the Swiss guides brought to this country by the Alpine Club of Canada. The late Mrs. Kain is survived by her husband, her mother, a married daughter at Port Angeles, Washington, and two brothers.

Returning to the original article he had found, Jake read and re-read it several times. He continued to scan several other pages in the same newspaper and was surprised to come across another mention of Kain. It read . . .

LAKE WINDERMERE (From Our Own Correspondent)

Invermere, Feb 2nd – News has just been received of the death of Conrad Kain in the Cranbrook hospital. Conrad Kain was one of the first Alpine guides to be brought over by the C.P.R. and had a number of memorable climbs to the tops of virgin peaks to his credit. Amongst them was the successful first and only ascent of Mt. Farnham in the Selkirks. He accompanied Captain MacCarthy's expedition in preparing the route and the climb of Mt. Logan in the north. He also located Mrs. Stone when she and her husband, Professor Stone, were lost climbing in the Selkirks, and assisted in bringing Mrs. Stone to safety after her eight days of clinging to a narrow ledge, afterwards helping to bring Professor Stone's body out for burial. He celebrated his 50th birthday this last summer in guiding a party to the top of Mt. Louis, a difficult feat and one never before accomplished. His wife predeceased him last May, leaving no family. He resided on his fur farm at Wilmer near here, and went to Cranbrook for medical treatment in December. His only near relative in this area is a nephew, Isadore Kain; he leaves an aged mother in Hungary. Since his wife's death her niece, Miss Enid Hurst, has been keeping house for Conrad Kain at Wilmer, and a number of his wife's relatives are living in Wilmer. Conrad's genial face and his campfire tales will be greatly missed at all the gatherings of Alpinists, and many memories of his unbounded confidence given to climbers and his cheerfulness under all conditions will long remain in the hearts of those he guided to successful ascents. He was buried beside his wife in the Cranbrook cemetery.

PAPER TRAIL SUMMER 2005

In the summer of 2005 a nondescript rental car drove into the parking lot of the Whyte Museum of the Canadian Rockies in downtown Banff. A tall, lean Austrian man opened the car door, unfolded his long legs and briskly stepped out into the bright morning sunlight.

Five years earlier the same man had been travelling through the Canadian Rockies and happened to recognize a photo of Conrad Kain displayed in a photo gallery on the main street of Banff.

Hardly believing his eyes, Gerhart Pistor quickly put two and two together, realizing this was the Conrad Kain his father, Dr. Erich Pistor, had helped sponsor to come to Canada in 1908.

"Welcome to the Whyte Museum," said the heavy-set curator, as Gerhart Pistor settled into a standard-issue office chair, across from a desk heaped with an unruly pile of papers. "What brings you to Banff, today?"

"I am here to donate my father's records," said Gerhart.

"And who is your father, may I ask?"

"Doctor Erich Pistor."

"Pistor, you say? Doesn't ring a bell with me," said the curator, a puzzled expression on his face.

"Does the name Conrad Kain mean anything to you?"

"Well, of course. We all know of Conrad Kain here at the Museum, legendary mountaineer that he was!"

"My father, Erich Pistor, met Conrad Kain in 1904 when he hired Kain as a guide. Then he hired Kain again in 1905 as a guide on my father's honeymoon trip."

"So your father knew Conrad Kain."

"Not only did he know him, in 1908 Conrad moved to Vienna and studied English with my father's first wife, Sara. Then my father contacted the CPR and the Alpine Club of Canada, which was based right here in Banff, to secure summer employment for Kain as a guide with the ACC," he further explained.

"Interesting," the curator mused.

"My father's first wife, Sara, as I said, was a British citizen with whom he had three children. Two of them died in World War II in Stalingrad and Sara died in 1930."

"Tell me more," said the curator, his interest piqued.

"My father remarried in 1932 and I was born in 1938. Because of the war, my father took his family and fled Vienna during the bombing of the city. We lived in

Prein/Rax, then in Reichenau, close to where Conrad is from in Nasswald."

He took out a large white handkerchief and dabbed his sweating forehead.

"When my father fled Vienna in 1944 for Prein, on the Rax Mountains, many of his books and records from their Vienna home were destroyed by occupying army personnel—both Russian and American. But before fleeing Vienna, my mother managed to store some records in the cellar of some friends."

"What happened to these records?" asked the curator.

"In 1999, I was relaxing at my home, and the telephone rang. It was a woman who had found two boxes belonging to the Pistor family in her basement and was about to toss them out. I said, 'No, don't do that,' I would come over to pick them up as soon as possible."

"Tell me what were in those boxes?"

"That is why I am here today. Those two boxes contained papers and photographs pertaining to Conrad Kain, including a draft manuscript of his autobiography, which the American climber Thorington used to compile *Where The Clouds Can Go*. Plus related correspondence, notes, drafts of articles, published articles and photographs."

"You have these boxes with you?"

"Yes, but best of all they contain 142 letters between Amelia Malek, Kain's friend; correspondence between my father and Kain, Thorington and others. So my question is, if the Whyte Museum would like to have these records, I would be happy to donate them to you," said Gerhart Pistor.

"Mr. Pistor, we would be more than happy to retain your records. Kain is an important pioneer here in the Canadian Rockies. We already have quite an extensive collection about him. This would only add to our library."

"These records mean a great deal to me but I can imagine they will mean that much more to you and your patrons."

"Yes, thank you," said the curator, leaning across his desk to shake Gerhart Pistor's sweaty hand. "So, tell me more about your father."

"Well, my father was born in 1873 in Graz, Austria. He studied History of Art and Law and eventually earned a Doctor of Law degree in 1898. He worked for the Chamber of Commerce in Graz and attended the 1899 International Congress in Philadelphia and was then appointed to the Chamber of Commerce in Vienna."

"So, he had been to North America?"

"Yes, he probably told Conrad Kain about the opportunities North America offered," Pistor said, pausing to reflect for a moment.

"Go on," the curator urged.

"He published his first book called *Der Exportforderungsdienst des Handelsmuseum in Philadelphia* in 1900. In 1901 and 1902 he travelled the world extensively, through Siberia, Japan, Australia and New Zealand, all on behalf of the

Chamber of Commerce," said Gerhart Pistor. "He wrote another business book in 1903 and organized many exhibitions for the Chamber of Commerce within Europe and in Buenos Aires, Argentina, as well as in Toronto, here in Canada."

"Maybe that's why he recommended Canada to Conrad Kain?"

"Could be. He eventually became the director of the Chamber of Commerce, vice-president of the Austria-British Committee, and president of the Austrian-Greek Society. My father spoke twelve languages."

"Fascinating, absolutely fascinating," said the curator, jumping off his chair to grasp Gerhart Pistor's hand again.

"I always remember one thing my father told me about Conrad Kain."

"What was that?"

"My father said he heard this from Conrad, 'Take life as it comes and make the best of it, and always be your own advisor in small matters.' So in this small matter, I am entrusting you to look after the papers and records of Conrad Kain on behalf of the Pistor family of Vienna, Austria."

"Thank you, Mr. Pistor. Let me reassure you that the Whyte Museum is up to the task."

Jake Renshaw sat drumming the eraser end of his pencil on the hard wooden surface of the long conference table inside the Cranbrook Archives. "So much for old-time newspaper men going for the facts and nothing but the facts," he thought. He recognized several inaccuracies in the two newspaper items laying on the table in front of him.

Jake knew the CPR didn't bring Conrad Kain to Canada; he wasn't a Swiss or Hungarian guide but rather from Austria; he knew Professor Stone died on Mt. Eon in the Rocky Mountains, not the Selkirks; he understood that Hetta died in February, not May; and it especially puzzled him as to why both articles stated that Conrad was buried beside his wife in the Cranbrook Cemetery.

"I'll have to ask Reggie Wilson back at the office about them being buried side by side. Maybe he knows the story," thought Jack as he pondered over the two obituaries for a few more minutes.

"Hey, Reggie. I found the obituaries for Conrad Kain and his wife in some old *Cranbrook Couriers*," said Jake excitedly as he rushed into the crammed newsroom of the *Cranbrook Daily Townsman*.

"You still obsessing over Kain's story?" grunted Reggie Wilson, hardly looking up from his computer monitor.

"When you have a minute, I need you to help me figure something out about where they are buried."

"That's easy, in the ground," retorted Reggie.

"Don't be funny. Look at these writeups about Kain's death. Both of them say they were buried side by side in the Cranbrook cemetery but I know for a fact that's not true. I've visited both plots and they are hundreds of yards apart."

"Let me see the clippings," said Reggie, reaching across his desk to snatch the two pieces of paper out of Jake's hand.

Reggie Wilson read both items carefully and then set them aside. "Let me think about it for a bit," he said, going back to typing on his keyboard.

It was almost a week before Reggie Wilson brought up the obituaries of Conrad and Henriquita Kain.

"I read the two obits again last night, and I think I've figured it out," said Reggie, just as Jake Renshaw was gathering his things together to head home for the day.

"Okay, why the discrepancy?"

"Actually, its pretty easy to figure out, if you read the clippings carefully,"

"I did read them carefully. I've read them both a dozen times," replied Jake, somewhat annoyed.

"Well, tell me, where was Conrad's wife's funeral held?"

"At the St. Mary's Church."

"And what kind of church would that be?"

"It's the Catholic Church on 10th Avenue, right?"

"Yes, and where was Conrad's funeral held?"

"It says the Knox Presbyterian Church, and the service was conducted by a Reverend Bell."

"So there's your answer," said Reggie Wilson, matter-of-factly.

"What do you mean, there's the answer?"

"It's simple. In 1933/34 the Catholic Church wasn't about to let a Presbyterian or non-Catholic be buried in their section of the cemetery. Even if it meant splitting up a husband and wife, and burying them in separate parts of the cemetery."

"Reggie, you're right. It's so obvious now but I can't believe they wouldn't let them be buried side by side."

"Probably wouldn't have been problem if Conrad had died first. He would have been buried in the main part of the cemetery and his wife could have been laid to rest beside him. But since she was buried first in the Catholic section, that sort of left old Conrad out in the cold," Reggie chuckled.

A large granite stone and memorial plaque, erected by his climbing friends and the Alpine Club of Canada, stands in the Cranbrook cemetery where Conrad Kain is buried—it simply states, "A Guide of Great Spirit—Mt. Robson 1913."

"Looking for… Nasswald—a village so small

that it hardly ever appears on maps of Aus-

tria."

Epilogue

When we pulled back the curtains covering the hotel's 18th floor windows, the entire City of Vienna was still cloaked in darkness. Off in the distance lights from several tall office buildings twinkled in the pre-dawn blackness. A subway train glowed like a snaking centipede as it left an above-ground station, before it plunged back underground to continue its trip across the historic city. In the near distance, lights flickered on and off as early risers in the adjacent apartment building began to stir and ready themselves for the day. We scurried downstairs to the hotel's restaurant, only to find that we had beat the kitchen staff there and the promised breakfast buffet was yet to be set out.

We had spent the three previous days touring the sights of Vienna and breathing in as much history and culture of the Austrian capital as we could. The Schönbrunn Palace, the famed Vienna Opera House, the restaurants of the Grinzig district, the Imperial Palace and the apartments of Emperor Franz Joseph and his beloved wife Sisi, the Austrian National Library—they had all been on our must-see list.

The day had started out early because we knew we needed to catch the 7:20 a.m. train to Payerbach, some 50 minutes west of the city. This would allow us to interline with the only bus to Nasswald—hometown of Conrad Kain.

What happened next was a comedy of errors, which saw us first taking the wrong subway, then going back and forth as we tried to find the right train station. We finally stopped to ask for directions from a young Austrian woman who clearly didn't understand us or didn't know the way either, and once again we found ourselves on a subway heading in the wrong direction. When we finally did arrive on the right station platform, our westbound train had left five minutes earlier—reminding us once again that everything in Germany and Austria runs annoyingly and precisely on time. A quick visit to the ticket office assured us that another train would be heading west within the hour, so not all was lost.

There was still the dilemma of how we would find our way from Payerbach to Nasswald, having missed our bus connection as well. Taking a deep breath, I convinced my somewhat skeptical wife, Linda, that we should still go and see what transportation options we could find at the other end. Once aboard, we relaxed and watched the suburbs of Vienna flash by and the Rax Mountains start to come into view. We passed vineyard after vineyard as we travelled beyond the city limits—only later did I read that Vienna has the most vineyards within its city limits of any city in the world.

After numerous stops in small towns and villages, picking up or disembarking gaggles of noisy school children, we came to the end of the line in the town of Payerbach. The historic train station was virtually abandoned, except for a train crew waiting to return to Vienna—no info desk and no one to ask about the next leg of the trip. We made our way across the parking lot to a small, cramped, smoke-filled diner, which basically consisted of a couple of tables, six chairs and a lunch counter.

The proprietor was a matronly woman dressed in a large, floral apron with her hair tightly pulled back. She didn't speak a word of English, we didn't speak a word of German, so we struggled to explain through a series of hand gestures that we were looking for a way to get to Nasswald—a village so small that it hardly ever appears on maps of Austria. About all we could glean was that we had definitely missed the only bus of the day and there were few other options to consider.

We decided to follow a winding path down a long hill to the downtown area of Payerbach in hopes of finding some other transportation options. Halfway down the steep pathway, we met Ewald Stiglitz, a printer by trade, coming up the path toward the train station.

"Grüss Gott," he said, using the traditional Austrian greeting and looking at us with a definite "what are you doing here?" expression.

"Hello, do you speak English?" I asked.

"Yes, I do," he replied, much to our relief. "You look lost."

"We're not really lost. We are just trying to make our way to Nasswald, after missing the day's only bus," I explained.

"Nasswald, you say. That's another 45 or 50 kilometres up the road. You can take a taxi," he replied.

"But isn't it very expensive?"

"Come with me, I'll phone the taxi company and negotiate a good price for you."

Within 20 minutes we were speeding along a narrow stretch of winding highway, along the banks of a clear blue river and up into the Raxalpe Mountains, finally on our way to Nasswald.

Nasswald turned out to be less of an actual village and more of a collection of loosely scattered Bavarian-style homes and small acreages. Our taxi skidded to a stop in front of the local inn, called the Wirtshaus Zum Raxkönig, leaving us standing across from the village church and next to a rough-sawn building, which housed a small museum.

We swung open the heavy wooden doors of the Wirtshaus Zum Raxkönig and walked into the tavern. The air hung heavy with blue clouds of cigarette smoke and the noisy chatter of some twenty or more hunters dressed in camouflage and bright orange vests—all planning their day's chamois hunting strategy. (A chamois appeared to me to be a cross between a North American mule deer and an elk—judging by the the one I saw later in the day, complete with a sprig of pine needles in its mouth, laying dead in the back of one successful hunter's truck.)

The lounge, appropriately called the Konrad Kain Room, went silent as we entered. The hunters set down their drinks, looked at each other and all turned in unison to stare at us. The young Russian wife of one of two elderly twin brothers who owned the inn hurried over to seat us, welcome us to the Wirtshaus Zum Raxkönig and take our order.

After bringing us our order of coffee and a light lunch, she disappeared, as the hunters quaffed their last mouthful of beer and headed for the door—off to a day of hunting chamois in the Rax.

The waitress returned with the inn's accountant in tow. She introduced us to English-speaking Robert Grollnigg, who was making his weekly visit to do the bookkeeping for the enterprise. Robert Grollnigg was also the son-in-law of one of the owners.

"Welcome to Nasswald," Robert said, shaking our hands enthusiastically. "What brings you to this little village at this time of year? We don't see too many visitors in the fall."

I explained I was writing a historical novel about Konrad Kain, the famed Austrian mountaineer, who was born in Nasswald.

"Would you know of any family or family friends who might still live in the area?" I asked.

"No, evidently the family home burnt down many year ago, but there might be some information in the museum across the street."

"It is closed and locked up tight," I said, having already checked it out.

"It might be possible to get a key and open it up for you to look through," Robert suggested.

This turned out not to be possible, as the person who kept the key had gone away for the day.

"I will ask some of the patrons if they know anything about Konrad Kain, and when my father-in-law returns I will ask him as well," said Robert.

It turned out the Wirtshaus Zum Raxkönig was one of the village's most historic buildings and each room was named after a noteworthy individual. There was the Konrad Kain Room, in which we were seated; the Daniel Innthaler Room named after another well-known climber from Nasswald and mentor to Konrad Kain; the Sepp Pehofer Room; and the Georg Hubmer Room, so named for the original woodcutter and settler in Nasswald.

Robert returned, chuckling, half an hour later.

"My father-in-law asked, 'Do you know why Konrad Kain left Austria?'" Robert asked.

I explained how he immigrated to Canada to guide tourists through the Rockies and how he obtained a job with the Alpine Club of Canada.

"This may be true, but my father-in-law says legend has it that Konrad Kain had an affair with Countess Hoyos, whose family was the major landowner of the day in these parts."

"I hadn't heard that in all the research I've done on him."

"Rumour has it that Konrad was paid a sum of money and told never to return to Nasswald," said Robert, with a twinkle in his eye.

"I understand there is a plaque, installed by the American Alpine Club, commemorating Konrad Kain somewhere nearby," I said.

After another lengthy consultation with the patrons and his father-in-law, Sepp Hagszan, Robert returned once again to our table.

"The plaque is located another 4.5 to 5 kilometres up the road past Hinternasswald. It is near my father-in-law's hunting cabin," he said.

"Is there a way to get up there?"

"I will drive you in my father-in-law's truck, when you have finished your lunch," he said.

Thus we found ourselves standing looking up at the Raxalpe Mountains. If we didn't know better, it was as if someone had dropped us off in a typical mountain meadow of the Canadian Rockies. Seeing this scene, it quickly became obvious why Conrad Kain felt so at home in the Canadian Rockies and particularly in the small Village of Wilmer in the Columbia Valley—the similarities of the two regions were strikingly obvious.

The simple bronze plaque, provided jointly by the American Alpine Club and the Alpine Club of Canada, simply stated:

Dem Lieben Bergfreund
KONRAD KAIN
Nasswald 1883 – Cranbrook, B.C. 1934
DEM GENIALEM FEHRER DURCH
DIE WUNDERWELT DER BERGE
ERSTERSTEIGER IN KORSIKA, KANADA,
NEUSEELAND
Errichtet von seinen freunden in der heimat und ubersee – 1936

The Dear Mountain Friend
KONRAD KAIN
Nasswald 1883 - Cranbrook, B.C. 1934
THE GENIUS OF GUIDES
THE WONDER OF THE WORLD OF MOUNTAINS
FIRST IN CORSICA, CANADA, NEW ZEALAND
Erected by his friends at home and overseas - 1936

It reminded me of a note J.M. Thorington had published in the American Alpine Journal: "It may be noted that the sale of *Where the Clouds Can Go* has yielded a profit to date of approximately $350, most of which has been sent on an installment basis to Kain's mother. Foreign editions of the book are expected, an agreement having been made whereby a part of any profits will be turned over to Mrs. Kain (Conrad's mother). A small sum has been reserved and will be used in connection with several foreign subscriptions to secure and place a suitable bronze memorial on the Raxalpe, near Kain's old home. It is expected that Sektion Reichenau will assist in a brief ceremony to be held in the autumn of this year."

We lingered there for close to an hour before deciding to hike back to Nasswald, along the winding mountain road. Robert, the accountant, had left earlier to return to some pressing business. It was a beautiful fall day with a distinct crispness in the air, the autumn leaves in radiant hues of red and yellow and the sharp peaks of the Rax towering above us. The narrow track paralleled the subterranean aqueduct which is the source of the fresh water for the city of Vienna—the quarrying of which Konrad Kain had been employed at, on and off, before leaving for Canada.

As we returned to the Wirtshaus Zum Raxkönig to await our return bus ride, we sat down and ordered a stein of beer and a bratwurst. The heavy tavern door swung open and in streamed the returning hunters, all flushed with victory—a large chamois draped over the back of one of their pickup trucks.

Amongst the hunters was a young man dressed in a traditional olive-green climbing outfit complete with floppy felt hat, who had just returned from guiding a group of women hikers through the Rax. It was as if Konrad Kain himself had returned to grace our presence. A cold shiver ran down my back.

Conrad Kain's name is attached to a finger-like peak in the Robson area, the Kain Finger, which he so selected himself; Nasswald Peak, in the Assiniboine Group, was climbed and named by him for his old home; Birthday Peak, in the Purcells, was climbed on his date of birth; Pigeon Spire in the Bugaboos was renamed Mt. Conrad; and in the Southern Alps in New Zealand, another Mt. Conrad in the Murchison district also honours him.

Appropriately, a large stone of granite marks his grave in the Cranbrook, British Columbia, cemetery, placed there by his admiring mountaineering friends and the climbing fraternity. "He will be much missed, for he was a kind, honest man," said his neighbours in the Columbia Valley.

Possibly the finest tribute of all came from his old packer friend, Jimmy Simpson, who spoke eloquently of Conrad Kain, "He would die for you if need be quicker than most men think of living. No matter what his creed, his colour or his nationality he was measured by a man's yardstick, no other. We shall all miss him ... He was perhaps the best guide that has ever been in the country for any length of time."

His short but extraordinary life echoed the words that his dying Father had whispered in young Konrad's ear, so many years before, back in his Austrian hometown of Nasswald. "Konrad, listen. The flood of things that come and pass...Beckon, and shine and fade away."

As his biographer, J.M. Thorington, wrote, "A candle burned at both ends—a brave soul gone too soon. Let it be remembered that some of us would have given our right hand to delay Time's turning down of Conrad's glass."

"Mountains, and all hills, fruitful trees and all cedars...
Let them praise the name of the Lord."
Psalms 148: 9, 13
—King James Version

Author's Note

Those who actually met and knew Austrian/Canadian climber Conrad Kain often mentioned that he was a man keenly aware of the world—a very nice man in every way.

In this historical novel about one of the greatest mountaineers ever to grace the Canadian Rockies, I have endeavoured to retell the story of Conrad Kain's life in a fresh and entertaining way, though it could be argued that his colourful life in itself does an adequate job.

While most accounts in this book are firmly based on documented events and occurrences, other parts are purely fictional and have been added to move the storytelling along.

For example, I have created the chance meeting of Adolph Hitler and Conrad Kain in Vienna's Mannerheim. Though both men were in Vienna in 1908 and both frequented "public" or soup kitchens, history does not indicate if they ever met. Likewise the use of the grave robbers is a fictional element of the story, though we do know Conrad Kain is buried in the "commoner" section of the Cranbrook Cemetery. A stroll through the cemetery clearly shows that his beloved wife Hetta was buried in the Catholic section some 300 feet away. And because of the shortage of burial plots, one Dorothy Breakwell was later buried on top of Conrad Kain's original gravesite.

The fictional debate plays out the two sides of the real-life debate among mountaineers over who should actually be given credit for the official first ascent of Mount Robson, the tallest peak in the Canadian Rockies—Reverend George Kinney and Curly Phillips or Conrad Kain, Albert MacCarthy and William Foster. The debate continues to rage to this day.

Whether Franz Kain was actually a relative of Conrad's the historical record does not show; however, it was Franz's deft mountaineering skills that saved the life of Leopold Engleitner from Nazi tyranny.

The only historical reference to Amelia Malek's death by starvation is made in a footnote in Phil Dowling's book *The Mountaineers*. Exactly how she starved is not known for sure, though severe food shortages were commonplace in Austria during World War II.

I have tried to capture the essence of Conrad Kain's life and his personality in the pages of this book. He was truly one of the Canadian Rockies' most colourful characters and I believe it is appropriate that we should remember and appreciate his extraordinary legacy.

In recent years much has been done to revive and remember the legacy of Conrad Kain, thanks in large part to the Columbia Valley-based Conrad Kain Centennial Society, led by notable mountaineer, Patrick Morrow. He and a dedicated group of volunteers have spearheaded a number of legacy initiatives including the building of a rock cairn—made of stones gleaned from many of the peaks he climbed—in Conrad's hometown of Wilmer. For more of the group's activities or if you would like to contribute to the Kain legacy, visit the society's website at www.conradkain.com.

It is my hope that you have discovered a number of colourful characters of the Canadian Rockies, in addition to Conrad Kain, through these pages and that you have enjoyed reading their accounts as much as I have in writing about them. I welcome your comments and feedback at keithp57@gmail.com.

Special Thanks

Special thanks for their research, assistance and contributions:

Ursula Brigl and staff at the Cranbrook Public Library, Cranbrook, British Columbia

The archive staff of the Whyte Museum of the Canadian Rockies, Banff, Alberta

The photo archive staff of the Glenbow Museum, Calgary, Alberta

Derryll White and staff at the Columbia Basin Institute, Cranbrook, British Columbia

Dorothy Blunden, Curator, Windermere District Historical Society, Invermere, British Columbia

The photo archive staff of McCord Museum, Montreal, Quebec

Robert Grollnigg, accountant, Wirtshaus Zum Raxkönig, Nasswald, Austria

Ewald Stiglitz, printer by trade and helpful guide, Payerbach, Austria

Brian Clarkson and Alan Maudie, photographers, Cranbrook and Calgary

Koocanusa Publications Inc., management and staff

Kerry Shellborn, creative director and cover design

Murray Shellborn, operations manager

Dianne Lorincz, layout and composition

Sandra Albers, copy editor and proofreader

Josh Lorincz, designer and Bugaboo guide

Linda Powell, photography, project research and travel guide

Bibliography

Anschluss: The Rape of Austria (Gordon Brook-Shepherd, Macmillan & Co. Ltd. 1963)

A Passion for Mountains: The Lives of Don and Phyllis Munday (Kathryn Bridge, Rocky Mountain Books 2006)

Canadian Alpine Journal: CD and numerous issues

Canadian Summits: The Canadian Alpine Journal 1907 to 1994 (R.W. Sandford and Geoff Powter, Alpine Club of Canada 1994)

Carving the Western Path (R.G. Harvey, Heritage House 1998)

Climbing in North America (Chris Jones, University of California Press 1976)

Country Without a Name: Austria Under Nazi Rule 1938-1945 (Walter Maass, Frederick Ungar Publishing Co. 1979)

Diamond Hitch: The Early Outfitters and Guides of Banff and Jasper (E.J. Hart, Summerthought Publishing 1979)

Ever Upward: A Century of Canadian Alpine Journals 1907 to 2007 (CD) (The Alpine Club of Canada 2008) (Various references)

Germany and Austria (Rick Steves, Avalon Travel 2006)

Guyana and Belize: Country Studies (Federal Research Division of the Library of Congress 1993)

Guyana: Politics and Development in an Emergent Socialist State (Kempe R. Hope, Mosaic Press 1985)

Jimmy Simpson, Legend of the Rockies (E.J. Hart, Rocky Mountain Books 1991)

Lords of the Line (David Cruise and Alison Griffiths, Viking 1988)

Mapper of Mountains: M.P. Bridgeland in the Canadian Rockies (I. S. MacLaren, University of Alberta Press 2005)

Made to Measure: A History of Land Surveying in British Columbia (Katherine Gordon, Sono Nis Press 2006)

Myth and the Mountains (Sound Heritage, Volume V, Number 3)

Powder Pioneers: Ski Stories from the Canadian Rockies and Columbia Mountains (Chic Scott, Rocky Mountain Books 2005)

Pushing the Limits: The Story of Canadian Mountaineering (Chic Scott, Rocky Mountain Books 2000)

Rocky Mountain Madness (Edward Cavell and Jon Whyte, Altitude Publishing Ltd. 2001)

The Canadian Rockies: Early Travels and Explorations (Esther Fraser, Hurtig Publishers 1969)

The Columbia River (Stewart H. Holbrook, Rinehart and Co. Inc. 1956)

The Glittering Mountains of Canada (J. Monroe Thorington, John W. Lea Publishing 1925)

The Great Glacier and Its House (William Lowell Putman, The American Alpine Club 1982)

The Guiding Spirit (Andrew J. Kauffman and William L. Putnam, Footprint Publishing 1986)

The Last Spike (Pierre Berton, Random House 1971)

The Mountaineers: Famous Climbers in Canada (Phil Dowling, Hurtig Publishers 1979)

The Rise and Fall of the Third Reich: A History of Nazi Germany (William L. Shirer, Simon and Schuster 1959)

The Reluctant Empress: A Biography of Empress Elisabeth of Austria (Brigitte Hamann, Ullstein-IP 1982)

The Selling of Canada: The CPR and the Beginnings of Canadian Tourism (E.J. Hart, Altitude Publishing Ltd. 1983)

Thunder at Twilight: Vienna 1913/1914 (Frederic Morton, Da Capo Press 1989)

Unbroken Will: The Extraordinary Courage of an Ordinary Man (Bernhard Rammerstorfer, Grammaton Press 2004)

Van Horne's Road: The Building of the Canadian Pacific Railway (Omer Lavallee, Railfare Books 1974)

Wheeler (Esther Fraser, Summerthought Publishing 1978)

Where the Clouds Can Go (Conrad Kain, The American Alpine Club 1935)

A young fresh-faced Conrad Kain, dressed in his traditional Austrian alpine guide clothing, poses for his official Alpine Club of Canada portrait.

A relaxed Conrad Kain stands on the banks of a Rocky Mountain stream with his tradenark pipe in his mouth. Kain made first ascents of the highest peaks in both the Canadian Rockies and the Purcell Range.

Conrad Kain was known as one of the best big game guides in the Rockies—with grizzly bear and mountain goats his specialty. Here he poses with a trophy mountain goat.

Conrad Kain balances precariously on a downed tree while trying to cross the Grand Fork River. Kain eventually fell into the freezing water and nearly drowned.

J. Monroe Thorington, Conrad Kain's fellow climber and eventual autobiographer, survey a rock cairn atop Trapper Peak in the Wapta Icefield in the summer of 1933.

The group of founders of the Alpine Club of Canada (ACC) gather outside a meeting hall in 1906 in Winnipeg. A.O. Wheeler, the first president, stands in the back row third from the left next to outfitter Tom Wilson, to his right.

CONRAD KAIN **233**

William Cornelius Van Horne (centre) surveys the construction of the CPR mainline near Glacier House in the Canadian Rockies. Albert B. Rogers, namesake of the Rogers Pass, stands to the far right.

William Van Horne ran the entire empire of the CPR from this rolltop desk in his office at Windsor Station in Montreal. It was his vision to capitalize on the scenic beauty and alpine potential of the Canadian Rockies.

The once robust health of Conrad Kain looks to be in decline in this American Alpine Journal photo published in 1930. The picture was taken at a mountain campout on Findlay Creek.

A memorial plaque was installed in 1936, before a large crowd, by the American Alpine Club and the Alpine Club of Canada on a rock face near one of Conrad Kain's favourite climbing areas in the Raxalpe Mountains near his home village of Hinternasswald, Austria.

The same memorial plaque commemorating Conrad Kain's mountaineering feats still stands today in the Rax Mountains near Nasswald, Austria. This picture was taken in the fall of 2010 in the shadow of the soaring Raxalpe.

The historic Wirtshaus Zum Raxkönig, or the Inn of the Rax King, stands in the centre of the village of Nasswald, Austria. One of its rooms is named after Conrad Kain.

Welcome to Nasswald, Austria. The home village of Conrad Kain lies about 90 kilometres from Vienna in the heart of the Rax Mountains.

Living in the Shadow of
Fisher Peak

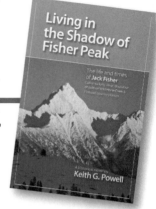

Living in
the Shadow of
Fisher Peak

The life and times of Jack Fisher

This engaging historical novel tells a story of the riveting adventures had by Jack Fisher, the prospector for whom Fisher Peak was named.

Gold rushes have played an important and significant role in the development of modern-day British Columbia and Montana. Much is known about the Fraser River and Cariboo gold rushes, but the Wild Horse Creek gold rush in the East Kootenay, and the Montana gold rush in Libby, are in many ways the "forgotten" gold rushes of the West.

Buried in the Conrad Memorial Cemetery in Kalispell, Flathead pioneer and prospector Jack Fisher has long been forgotten. That is until now because a new historical novel *Living in the Shadow of Fisher Peak* by Keith G. Powell, explores the Kootenay (and Montana) gold rush of 1864, which spurred the extension of the Dewdney Trail beyond Hope through the West Kootenay to the banks of Wild Horse Creek near Fort Steele.

After this discovery, Jack Fisher spent most of his life in and around the Flathead Lake region. He is buried in an unmarked grave in Kalispell's Conrad Memorial Cemetery.

The book, *Living in the Shadow of Fisher Peak*, tells the true-to-life life story of Jack Fisher, who was one of the West's most colourful (and long forgotten) characters. The story of his adventurous life is captured and brought to life in this historical novel. The book is 176 pages and contains over twenty historical photos. | $21.95

For more information or to order a copy email keithp57@gmail.com.

LINDA POWELL PHOTO

About the Author:

Keith G. Powell (pictured with his black Lab, Coal) is a life-long resident of the Kootenays and is the publisher of Koocanusa Publications Inc. in Cranbrook. He has a keen interest in local history and the lives of the many colourful characters who at one time or another called the Kootenays home. He is the founder of *Kootenay Business* magazine and publisher of one of the largest independent publishing companies in Western Canada. This is his first historical novel. www.wildhorsecreekpress.com